Volcanoes of Southern Italy

Earth in View

Dedicated to the memory of

Sir William Hamilton

who started it all

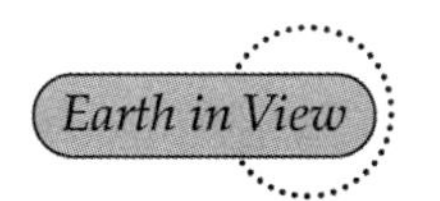

Volcanoes of Southern Italy

John E. Guest
Paul D. Cole
Angus M. Duncan
David K. Chester

2003
Published by
The Geological Society
London

THE GEOLOGICAL SOCIETY

The Geological Society of London (GSL) was founded in 1807. It is the oldest national geological society in the world and the largest in Europe. It was incorporated under Royal Charter in 1825 and is Registered Charity 210161.

The Society is the UK national learned and professional society for geology with a worldwide Fellowship (FGS) of 9000. The Society has the power to confer Chartered status on suitably qualified Fellows, and about 2000 of the Fellowship carry the title (CGeol). Chartered Geologists may also obtain the equivalent European title, European Geologist (EurGeol). One fifth of the Society's fellowship resides outside the UK. To find out more about the Society, log on to www.geolsoc.org.uk.

The Geological Society Publishing House (Bath, UK) produces the Society's international journals and books, and acts as European distributor for selected publications of the American Association of Petroleum Geologists (AAPG), the American Geological Institute (AGI), the Indonesian Petroleum Association (IPA), the Geological Society of America (GSA), the Society for Sedimentary Geology (SEPM) and the Geologists' Association (GA). Joint marketing agreements ensure that GSL Fellows may purchase these societies' publications at a discount. The Society's online bookshop (accessible from www.geolsoc.org.uk) offers secure book purchasing with your credit or debit card.

To find out about joining the Society and benefiting from substantial discounts on publications of GSL and other societies worldwide, consult www.geolsoc.org.uk, or contact the Fellowship Department at: The Geological Society, Burlington House, Piccadilly, London W1J 0BG: Tel. +44 (0)20 7434 9944; Fax +44 (0)20 7439 8975; E-mail: enquiries@geolsoc.org.uk.

For information about the Society's meetings, consult *Events* on www.geolsoc.org.uk. To find out more about the Society's Corporate Affiliates Scheme, write to enquiries@geolsoc.org.uk.

Published by The Geological Society from:
The Geological Society Publishing House
Unit 7, Brassmill Enterprise Centre
Brassmill Lane
Bath BA1 3JN, UK

(*Orders*: Tel. +44 (0)1225 445046
Fax +44 (0)1225 442836)
Online bookshop: http://bookshop.geolsoc.org.uk

British Library Cataloguing in Publication Data
A catalogue record for this book is available from the British Library.

ISBN 1-86239-138-6

Typeset by Type Study, Scarborough
Printed by Antony Rowe, Chippenham, UK.

Distributors

USA
AAPG Bookstore
PO Box 979
Tulsa
OK 74101-0979
USA
Orders: Tel. + 1 918 584-2555
Fax +1 918 560-2652
E-mail bookstore@aapg.org

India
Affiliated East-West Press PVT Ltd
G-1/16 Ansari Road, Daryaganj,
New Delhi 110 002
India
Orders: Tel. +91 11 327-9113
Fax +91 11 326-0538
E-mail affiliat@nda.vsnl.net.in

Japan
Kanda Book Trading Co.
Cityhouse Tama 204
Tsurumaki 1-3-10
Tama-shi
Tokyo 206–0034
Japan
Orders: Tel. +81 (0)423 57-7650
Fax +81 (0)423 57-7651

Contents

Preface

The volcanoes of southern Italy are instructive in two specific ways. First, there is a wide diversity in the type of volcanic activity from one volcano to another. In consequence, the products and the resulting landforms illustrate most of the known volcanic phenomena, all within a small geographical area. Second, as the area was the centre of western civilization in classical times, there is a longer, more continuous record of observed volcanism than in virtually any other part of the world. As a result of these two factors, studies of volcanoes in southern Italy have played an important role in the development of ideas in earth science; and because areas on and around the volcanoes have become densely populated in recent decades, an understanding of the hazard they present is important for future developments.

Many professional geologists, and, more specifically, volcanologists, from all over the world visit this region to see the volcanoes. Tourists with a keen interest in geology and archaeology also visit and, indeed, volcanoes such as Vesuvius, Etna, Stromboli and Vulcano are in themselves tourist attractions. Visitors, whether professional or amateur, are also interested in the long history of civilization, made evident by the archaeological sites, the architecture and other artefacts of human endeavour. In many places this history is intimately entwined with volcanic activity, which has influenced the lives of the people. We briefly describe the history of human habitation on each of the volcanoes.

The area is a popular one for student field trips in both geology and geography because it is such an excellent training ground in physical volcanic process and volcanic environments. In view of the large number of visitors who are about to embark on new research or on field trips to the area, there appears to be a need for a suitable book to provide a wide background to the understanding of the volcanoes and their environmental impact through time. This aim we hope to achieve.

What are our credentials to take on this task? J.E.G. first visited the area in 1966 when he and his wife took a holiday in Sicily. Although 'holiday' was the main purpose, a significant incentive was to witness the summit flows and explosions on Etna, an experience recommended by George Walker who had been there earlier in the year. From this visit it was clear that there was much scope for work on a volcano that was in a state of activity most of the time, and three years later J.E.G. started a programme of research, initially to study the persistent summit activity. In this the logistical support of Haroun Tazieff and his French team was of great value. The eminent Alfred Rittmann was the foremost volcanologist in Catania at the time. He was determined that an up-to-date geological map of Etna be prepared, and in 1972 invited J.E.G. to collaborate with Romolo Romano, one of his ex-students, in setting up a team to accomplish this task. In the UK, the Natural Environment Research Council (NERC) agreed to sponsor three postgraduates to take part in the project; A.M.D. was one of the students chosen.

Impressed by the success of the Hawaiian studies of ground deformation, J.E.G. set up an NERC-sponsored study of ground deformation of Etna in the mid-1970s, and also started work on flow field development and the role of lava tubes with Ronald Greeley.

On completion of his PhD in 1976, A.M.D. teamed up with D.K.C. to study the evolution of river terraces round the volcano and their relation to the eruptive history. This work was followed by a reconstruction of the history of the whole volcano using stratigraphy and geomorphology by J.E.G., A.M.D. and D.K.C. At this point we decided to spread our interests to other Italian volcanoes. Vulture and Roccamonfina were chosen after reconnaissance visits to the other volcanoes of southern Italy. P.D.C. joined the team as a postgraduate for the Roccamonfina study. On completing his PhD in 1990, P.D.C. worked at the University of Naples for two years studying Campi Flegrei and Lipari. We can claim experience of all of the volcanoes in this book, except Linosa and Pantelleria, where we have to rely on the published works of others.

As well as our own field observations, this publication owes much to research by other volcanologists. Rather than putting our sources in the text, we direct our readers to our sources in a 'Notes' section at the end of each chapter. It is our intent that this will not only acknowledge the input to our text by others, but also provide a lead into the whole bibliography on the volcanoes of southern Italy. We also use the 'Notes' to give additional information where inclusion in the main text would impede the flow of expression. This includes discussion of debates, where we have given what is mainly our own interpretations in the text, but need to guide the reader to views of other authors. This is especially true of the stratigraphy of each volcano. For many of the volcanoes there is no consensus between workers about the details of the stratigraphy. We have presented our own considered views; but in the 'Notes' we have attempted to provide our readers with leads to all alternative interpretations.

A Glossary is provided for those who are not familiar with all the geological terms used. There is also an Appendix that provides a table of typical chemical compositions for rocks of each of the volcanoes. The pictures and photographs are all by the authors except where indicated. Historical dates are indicated by BC or AD; the lack of such an indicator implies an AD date.

Acknowledgements

We owe so much to so many during our studies in Italy over more than three decades. We must start with two pioneers: Alfred Rittmann, who was wonderfully encouraging to us and others working on Italian volcanoes, and George Walker, who was a great inspiration to our early work.

Others we have worked with, received help from, or been provided with hospitality by, include Chris Argent, Remo Bianchi, Sonia Calvari, Ruggero Casacchia, Renato Cristofolini, Donnatella De Rita, the Di Bella family and all at the Rifugio Sapienza, Jayne Dunn, the Etna Guides, John Foster, Giovanni Frazzetta, Renato Funicello, Ronald Greeley, Tom Huntingdon, Jörg Keller, Guy Kieffer, Christopher Kilburn, Wendy Kirk, Gigi La Volpe, Fan Fan Le Guern, Rosaly Lopes, Giuseppe Luongo, Bill McGuire, John Murray, Annamaria Perrotta, Harry Pinkerton, Romolo Romano, Roberto

Scandone, Claudio Scarpati, Stuart Scott, Tony Seaton, Ellen Stofan, Haroun Tazieff and his team, Jim Underwood, Letero Villari, Claudio Vita-Finzi and Michael and Janet Worstall. They all deserve our unreserved thanks.

Constructive and positive reviews of the manuscript were provided by Peter Cattermole, Guido Giordano, Wes Hildreth, Jörg Keller, Joe McCall, Harry Pinkerton, Claudio Scarpati and Lionel Wilson.

We are indebted to Sandra Mather, who researched and drafted the maps in this volume, collating information on topography, communications and other data. Suzanne Yee also helped with drafting of figures and Sean Gammon scanned most of the photographs. Ben Guest helped with picture editing.

Angharad Hills of the Geological Society Publishing House is specially thanked for her help and patience.

John E. Guest[1]
Paul D. Cole[2, 4]
Angus M. Duncan[2]
David K. Chester[3]

[1] Department of Earth Science, University College London, UK
[2] Centre for Volcanic Studies, University of Luton, UK
[3] Department of Geography, University of Liverpool, UK
[4] Present address: Department of Geography, University of Coventry, UK

Chapter 1. **Birthplace of volcanology**

Southern Europe has a rich selection of volcanoes representing almost every type of known volcanic activity. In addition, because there is a long written history for the region going back over 2000 years, we have a unique temporal framework in which to investigate observed phenomena. Within the southern European area there are 11 volcanoes that are known to have erupted in historical time; nine of these are in southern Italy. From a scientific point of view, this area is an excellent place to study active volcanoes: the way they work, and the effects that might be expected when they do erupt.

Amongst the active volcanoes are well-known ones such as Vesuvius, Etna, Vulcano and Stromboli, but there are others including Campi Flegrei, Ischia, Lipari and Pantelleria (Fig. 1.1). Also there are volcanoes that do not appear to be active, but are young enough

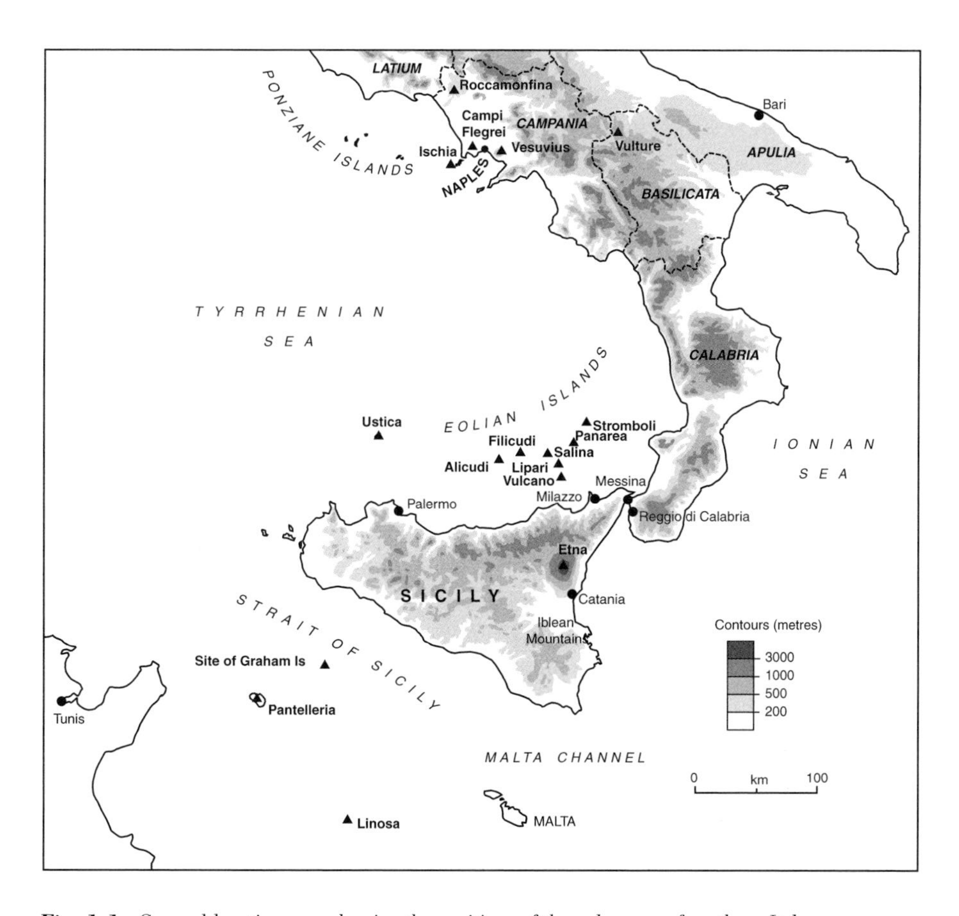

Fig. 1.1. General location map showing the positions of the volcanoes of southern Italy.

that they cannot be completely ignored as possible sites of future activity. These are Vulture, Roccamonfina, several of the Eolian Islands and Linosa (Fig. 1.1). There is also the remote possibility of a new eruptive centre opening up. This has occurred in the Mediterranean Sea during historical time with the formation of the albeit temporary Graham Island, and it could happen on land in the future.

The other side to this is that the south of Italy is a target for future damaging eruptions. Most of the historically active volcanoes here have produced significantly violent activity, and in some cases eruptions of extremely large magnitude. There are volcanoes that could erupt, but have not done so within historical time. Experience tells us that it is these volcanoes that could reap the most damage when they unexpectedly burst into activity. We do not know which or any of these currently dormant volcanoes will erupt again in a violent way, but we do know that when one of them does, the effects could be catastrophic: on Italy disastrous, and on Europe, from an economic point of view, profound.

Concern about natural hazards in general increased in the 1980s, leading to a *United Nations International Decade for Natural Disaster Reduction* (IDNDR) during the last decade of the twentieth century. Volcanoes identified for special study during this decade included Vesuvius. At about the same time, the European Science Foundation identified six European volcanoes for detailed study within the European Union, with special emphasis on hazard implications. These are titled *European Laboratory Volcanoes*, and Mount Etna is one of them.

Geography

The southern part of Italy with which we are concerned is made up of five administrative regions: Campania, Basilicata, Puglia, Calabria and Sicily. Of these only Puglia and Calabria are volcanically barren. The Apennine Mountains form the majestic spine of Italy, swinging to the west through the toe of the peninsula and along the north coast of Sicily (Fig. 1.2).

The floor of the Mediterranean also has considerable topographic relief. To the north of Sicily is the Tyrrhenian Sea, whose floor plunges from the Sicilian shore to a deep basin that is, in places, over 3500 m below sea level. The slope from the peninsula coastline is more gentle. To the east is the Ionian Sea, which deepens gently from the peninsula shore off the toe of Italy, but drops steeply to over 3000 m off the eastern coast of Sicily. Between Sicily and the African continent is the Strait of Sicily, where the seas are generally shallow and the submarine topography is marked by a series of NW-trending troughs (Fig. 1.2).

Although the volcanic regions tend to have rich fertile soils, much of southern Italy has limited agricultural potential and is subject to rapid erosion during heavy winter storms. This situation has not been helped by poor land management and extensive deforestation from the Classical period onwards.

Compared with the north, southern Italy has been traditionally a poor rural society, with little industry. This is now much changed as a result of aid from both central

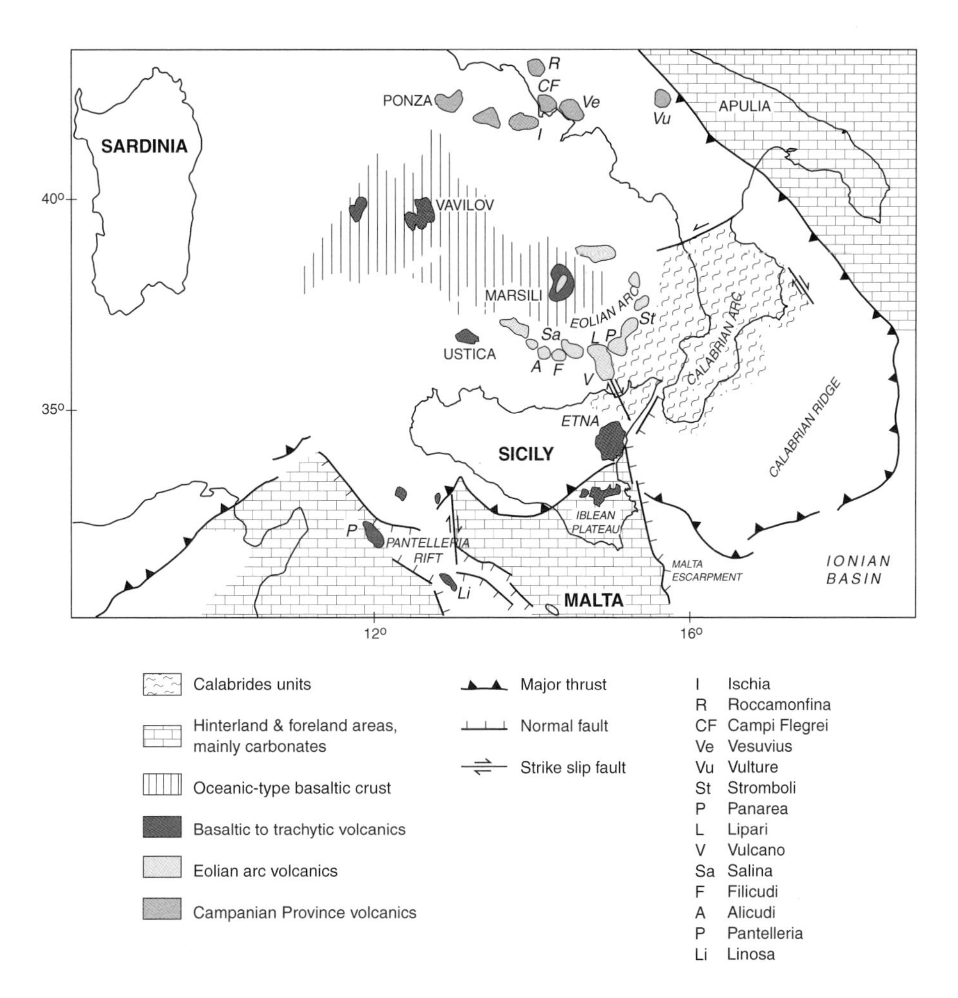

Fig. 1.2. Tectonic map of southern Italy (adapted from Ferrari & Manetti 1993).

government and the European Union. Industrial developments in cities such as Naples, Melfi and Catania have created jobs and more wealth. An accelerating rise in the standard of living has been evident since the late 1970s: at first this was patchy, some areas developing faster than others, but has now become almost universal.

The main features of the climate of this part of Italy are hot, dry summers and generally mild, but wet, windy winters. The highest temperatures are normally in August, but July is also a hot month. Temperature in summer ranges from 24° to 27 °C and in winter ranges to below 10 °C. Weather is affected by altitude, and, for example, conditions on Mount Etna near the summit at over 3000 m may be dramatically different from those at the coast. Weather is susceptible to wind direction in the Mediterranean, and there are four main winds that bring distinctive conditions. The *scirocco* comes from the Sahara and is hot; when it reaches southern Italy it is also very humid, having picked up water vapour from its crossing of the Strait of Sicily. The *greco* and *tramontana* from the European north bring cold, dry weather from the interior of

Europe through the Alpine passes. The latter rarely reaches as far south as Sicily, but the former can give cold wet spells. The *libeccio* from the west brings wet and blustery weather.

Travel to and around the region is generally good. There are regular international scheduled and charter flights to Rome, Naples, Catania and Palermo as well as local flights between them. Naples is linked to Rome by an autostrada (motorway/freeway), and the Autostrada del Sol links Naples with Reggio Calabria where a car/train ferry crosses the Straits to Messina on Sicily. From here there is an autostrada to Catania and beyond to Palermo. All these cities are also linked by railways. Of the island volcanoes, only Pantelleria has an air service, but all are served by sea.

General geology

The complex structural geology of southern Italy (Fig. 1.2) is largely governed by the fact that it sits astride the east–west boundary between the African and European plates. Since Mesozoic times, tectonism in the Mediterranean area has been controlled by this interaction between the two plates, but, in addition, the evolution of the region has been strongly influenced by the opening and spreading of the Atlantic Ocean. The consequence is a complex tectonic picture with an evolving mosaic of subsiding continental margins, thrust belts, subduction zones and marginal basins. It is not surprising, therefore, that some geological students of the Mediterranean area were highly sceptical of the theory of plate tectonics when it was first proposed.

During the Triassic, the Tethys Ocean opened between what is now Europe and Africa as a consequence of continental rifting. Ocean-floor spreading dominated through the Jurassic, with the ocean widening at a greater rate to the east. An eventual closure of Tethys began towards the end of the Jurassic. The Cretaceous was dominated by consumption of oceanic lithosphere followed by continental collision, which occurred in the Tertiary to give the Alpine orogeny.

The Apennine–Maghrebian chain, the mountain belt that formed as a result of the Tertiary continent–continent collision, runs down the spine of Italy as the Apennines, through Calabria and along northern Sicily to North Africa. The marked curvature of the Apennine mountain chain as it sweeps round the Alps through Italy and westwards into North Africa has caused difficulty in terms of a straightforward plate tectonics model. The deep northward embayment into the mountain chain running up the eastern side of Italy has been explained by the action of the rigid continental Adriatic block, which has been considered as either a promontory of the African plate or as a microplate in its own right. The region has been further complicated by the opening up of young oceanic basins such as the Balearic and Tyrrhenian seas.

Throughout much of the Tertiary there was NW subduction of oceanic lithosphere beneath Sardinia, giving rise to calc-alkaline magmatism. In Sicily the major earth movements had climaxed by the mid-Miocene, with the Apennine–Maghrebian nappes being emplaced to the south. At the top of this thrust complex is the Calabride Complex, consisting of crystalline Hercynian basement and Mesozoic carbonates. Below this are the highly deformed shales of the Sicilide Complex, which in turn are thrust over carbonate nappes of the Panormide Complex. In front of the advancing thrust sheets, flysch sediments accumulated in developing basins on the foreland.

The stable foreland in Sicily is represented by the Triassic to Miocene carbonates of the Iblean Mountains, which are a northern continuation of the Saharan Platform, part of the African plate. The Apennine–Maghrebian chain, representing the southern margin of the European plate, stretches from Italy through northern Sicily under the sea to Tunisia. This belt is characterized by underthrusting of the Adriatic and Ionian continental crust. But the Iblean platform does not appear to underthrust the Apennine–Magherebian chain, but abuts against it, causing curvature in the arc in the position of Etna (Fig. 1.3). Subduction stopped or was greatly reduced where the Iblean platform collided with the Apennine–Maghrebian arc.

The Tyrrhenian Sea, to the north of Sicily, is generally accepted as being a back-arc basin. The southern and eastern part of the Tyrrhenian basin has a 7–10 km thick crust and a seismic velocity profile typical of basaltic oceanic crust. The absence of linear

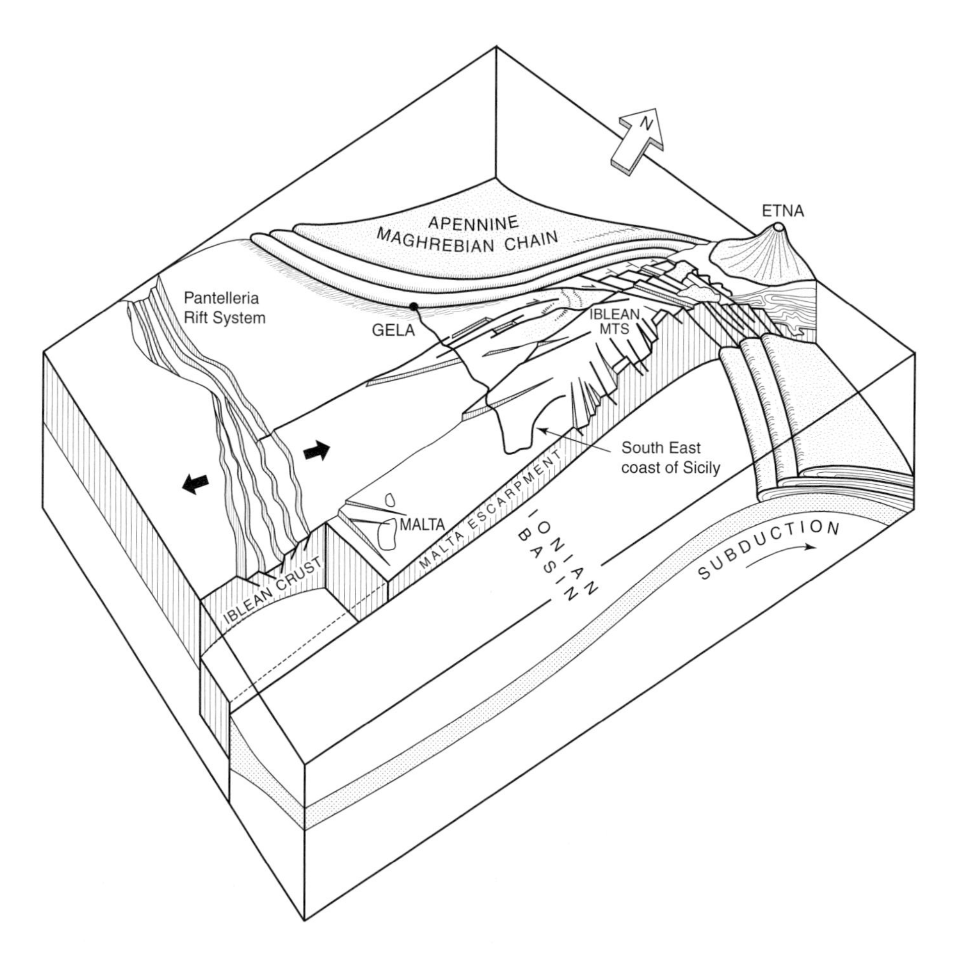

Fig. 1.3. Block diagram showing relations between Etna, Apennine–Maghrebian mountain chain, the Iblean Mountains, Strait of Sicily and the Ionian Sea (after Ben-Avraham & Grasso 1990).

magnetic anomalies implies that the sea-floor spreading was diffuse and not associated with a simple ridge system. Extension began in the late Miocene, about 7 Ma, and continued to the Pliocene. This back-arc extension is too old to be related to the Eolian Islands volcanic arc off the northern coast of Sicily; this is predominantly less than 1 Ma in age. It is argued that the Tyrrhenian Sea formed as a result of extension initiated by the sinking of the lithospheric slab that followed the cessation of calc-alkaline magmatism of Sardinia about 13 Ma ago. This sinking of the slab led to a SE migration of the arc and crustal extension as a consequence of 'roll-back' of the subduction zone.

Occasional more voluminous magmatism from specific centres in the Tyrrhenian Sea built up seamounts such as Magnaghi, Vavilov and Marsili within the Tyrrhenian basin (Fig. 1.2). These volcanoes typically have intra-plate petrological characteristics; both Magnaghi and Vavilov have tholeiitic and alkali ocean island basalt types. Marsili is the largest seamount, rising 2600 m from the sea floor, and has the oldest recorded products, consisting of basalts with intra-plate characteristics, which date back to the mid-Pleistocene. Younger material from the summit of the seamount has been dated at 0.1–0.2 Ma, and is of calc-alkaline affinity similar to that of the Eolian Islands.

In the southwestern part of the Tyrrhenian Sea, ocean island type basaltic magmatism (<1 Ma) formed the island of Ustica with mildly alkaline lavas ranging from hawaiitic to mugearitic composition. Ustica is built on continental crust in the transitional zone between extension in the Tyrrhenian Sea and the Apennine–Maghrebian chain. The Tyrrhenian basin, though no longer opening, has a high heat flow of 200 mW m^{-2}. The basin is underlain by the subducted slab from the Ionian Sea. The lack of shallow seismicity associated with this Benioff Zone suggests that subduction may have ceased; however, deep earthquakes do occur, and may indicate movement of a detached slab.

With such a complex tectonic configuration and the range of contrasted structural environments, it is not surprising that there is wide diversity in the magmatism of southern Italy. On the mainland, the volcanoes of Roccamonfina, Vulture, Campi Flegrei, Vesuvius and Ischia are all members of the Campanian Province. They are characterized by potassic magmas, which belong to two series: the High-K Series (HKS), comprising tephrites, leucite phonolites and leucite trachytes; and the less potassic K Series (LKS), containing trachyandesites and trachytes. The potassic nature of these magmas has been attributed to the mantle source regions being metasomatized through interaction with fluids derived from subduction slabs formed by previous episodes of lithospheric consumption. The potassic magmatism is associated with distensive tectonics and graben formation along the western margin of Italy. For example, Naples is situated on a graben structure with Campi Flegrei on its western side and Vesuvius astride the eastern margin.

Vulture volcano also belongs to the Campanian Province, but is unique in that it is located on the east side of the Apennines where the crust has been thickened by subduction of the Adriatic crust underneath the Tyrrhenian crust.

The Eolian Islands are considered to be an island arc formed by magmas generated by the NW subduction of Ionian Sea oceanic crust. Stromboli, Panarea, Lipari, Vulcano, Salina, Alicudi and Filicudi are all Quaternary in age, and the products are mainly either calc-alkaline or shoshonitic in affinity.

Etna volcano in Sicily sits on, or near, the junction between the African and European plates. This large, mainly alkali basaltic edifice, has built up on top of thickened continental crust (27 km), where the crust of the African foreland has been overridden by the nappes of the Apennine–Maghrebian chain. It is amazing that from the top of Etna, a volcano with many of the petrological characteristics of a within-plate ocean island basaltic volcano, it is possible to see the Eolian Islands, representing an active island arc. This enigma will be discussed further in Chapter 8.

Volcanism has also occurred on the foreland of the African plate. In the Iblean Mountains to the south of the Plain of Catania, both submarine and subaerial fissure eruptions produced tholeiitic and alkali basalts. The earliest of these are well-developed pillow lavas and hyaloclastites of Pliocene age; the eruptive activity ended here in Early Pleistocene time.

In the Strait of Sicily the carbonates of the Saharan platform have been fractured by the Pantelleria rift system. There are three graben: the Malta, Pantelleria and Linosa basins, which formed as en echelon ‘pull-apart’ structures associated with a east–west right lateral wrench fault system. To the east, the Malta Escarpment represents a large vertical offset separating the continental crust of the Strait of Sicily from the oceanic crust of the deep Ionian Basin. The magmatism associated with the continental rifting in the Strait of Sicily is alkalic in character. Linosa and the submarine volcano that produced Graham Island are characterized by alkali basaltic volcanism, whereas Pantelleria has also erupted trachytes, and peralkaline rhyolites known as pantellerites.

The volcanoes and types of volcanic activity

Volcanoes emit four types of product: lavas, tephra (pyroclastic materials), volatiles and sublimates. In addition there are secondary deposits produced by reworking either during an eruption or after; these include lahars, alluvial materials and products of major slope failure. It is the relative frequency of the processes that generate these products that determines the form of the volcano.

Each of the volcanoes of southern Italy is distinctly different in history and geomorphology irrespective of the magma composition. For each type of volcanic process at least one of these volcanoes provides insight into understanding the nature of the phenomenon by means of studies of the products, landforms, geophysics and observations of active volcanism.

Mount Etna, with its frequent effusive eruptions provides the opportunity for observing active lava flows, which, together with studies of historical flows, well documented by records, has contributed greatly to the understanding of *aa* and some types of *pahoehoe* flow fields. Studies of Etnean flows have shed light, not only on how lava flow fields develop, but also on the rheology of lava; that is, the physical nature of the material and the way it responds to applied stresses. Lava flows have also played an important role in the history of Vesuvius, and in the last eruption of 1944 lava destroyed a town on the flank of the volcano.

Volcanic domes formed of material more evolved than basalt are found on many of the volcanoes in the region. Roccamonfina has one of the largest dome complexes in Europe. The obsidian flows from the eruption in Roman times on Lipari are thick blocky flows, and had they formed on a level surface are likely to have produced domes.

A wide range of styles of explosive activity has occurred in southern Italy from major ignimbrite-forming eruptions to small phreatic events in which no fresh magma was ejected. Ignimbrites are formed from dense flows of tephra and gas. These are called pyroclastic flows and are driven, at least in part, by gravity; they are formed from explosive columns that collapse because they are too dense to continue rising, or by collapsing dome margins. The largest of this type of eruption in southern Italy produced the Campanian Ignimbrite, which covers an area of over 30 000 km^2 around the Naples region and was erupted some 35 ka ago. The most likely source of this ignimbrite is the area that was to become Campi Flegrei. Another large eruptive event from Campi Flegrei some 12 ka ago produced the thick and complex sequence of tephra deposits known as the Neapolitan Yellow Tuff. As well as ignimbrites and fall materials, this unit contains fine examples of pyroclastic surge deposits. Intermediate volume ignimbrites on Roccamonfina provide examples of internal structures of these deposits including well-developed lithic breccias of various types. Most ignimbrites in the region are non-welded or incipiently welded. The origin of welded tuffs on the island of Pantelleria has, however, been the focus of debate owing to different interpretations of their internal structures.

Pyroclastic surges are similar to ignimbrite-forming flows, but have a lower particle density. The products show a variety of textural characteristics including sandwaves. Examples on Lipari display a comprehensive range of textures and provide the opportunity to compare those formed from magma–water interactions (wet and cold) with those from purely magmatic explosive events (hot). In the caldera of Roccamonfina there are also excellent examples of surge deposits. Young surge deposits from the Fossa volcano on the adjacent island of Vulcano are also instructive. The deposits of the Fossa eruption at Vulcano in 1888 gave its name to vulcanian explosive activity, a style consisting of discrete explosions of viscous magma typically producing breadcrust bombs. Ironically, this is not the normal type of eruption from the Fossa volcano.

Studies of Vesuvian eruptions have made major contributions to understanding explosive activity and the resulting deposits. The typical major explosive eruption on this volcano consists of a sustained jet of ejected material, rather than a discrete explosion, above which rises a convective column of tephra-laden hot gas. Such events can last for days. The height of the column is proportional to the mass flux rate, and heights can be tens of kilometres. Such explosive events are termed plinian after Pliny the Younger, who both observed and decribed the AD 79 eruption of Vesuvius, and his Uncle, Pliny the Elder, who died during the eruption. A further (arbitrary) refinement in nomenclature, sub-plinian eruption, refers to those eruptions that produce columns of heights less than *c.* 20 km. It is not always possible to determine column heights from the deposits or contemporary records for many eruptions, and we use sub-plinian here only for eruptions of this type with known eruption column heights. All such eruptions are extremely hazardous, not only from thick accumulations of tephra fall, but from pyroclastic flows and surges formed by collapse of the eruption column.

Plinian eruptions played an important part in the history of Vulture, as shown by the thick and extensive accumulations of bedded tephra round the volcano. But Vulture provides us with another important dimension to some explosive eruptions: the remobilization of tephra deposits by water, either during or shortly after an eruption. Water-laden tephra, especially on steeper slopes, can form lahars (volcanic debris flows). Vulture has different types of lahar deposits, which provide fine examples for studying the mechanisms of emplacement.

A much less violent form of explosive activity is known as strombolian after the island volcano where it has been the dominant form of activity probably for several thousand years. Any visit to this volcano is almost guaranteed (nothing is completely reliable on an active volcano) to provide a view of this spectacular phenomenon. The explosions are discrete and eject relatively fluid lava bombs. This type of activity is also common from the summit craters of Etna, giving spectacular displays and good opportunities to observe and investigate this form of volcanism.

Another form of basaltic explosive activity is fire fountaining. This is common on Hawaii, but relatively rare on the currently active volcanoes in Italy. It can occur, however, on Etna and has done so more frequently in the period 1998–2001. Cinder cones on many of the volcanoes in southern Italy testify to strombolian and fire fountaining eruptive events in the past

Water–magma interaction is illustrated by many of the volcanoes of southern Italy. Hydromagmatic activity where explosive activity has been generated by magma interacting with ground water or crater lakes is illustrated by volcanoes such as Roccamonfina (surge deposits in the main caldera), Campi Flegrei, Vulcano and Lipari. On Etna one of the older exposed volcanic centres, known as Triffoglietto, also testifies to major hydromagmatic eruptions.

Submarine eruptions also involve water–magma interaction. Graham Island was a nineteenth-century emergent tuff cone in the Strait of Sicily, formed by a type of hydromagmatic activity known as surtseyan; it was washed away within months of forming. The classic pillow lavas and hyaloclastite (highly comminuted and altered lava deposits) exposed on the coast of Etna are also important examples. Here we see also the results of high-level injection of magma into wet submarine sediments. The uplifted coast of the island of Ustica also shows good examples of the products of submarine basaltic volcanism.

Nearly all the volcanoes discussed in this book have suffered either caldera or sector collapse, or both. The cliffs formed by such collapses often provide good exposures deep into the volcano. The most spectacular caldera in the area is the relatively fresh Fossa caldera on the island of Vulcano with the active Fossa cone sitting within it. The Somma caldera of Vesuvius is also impressive. The so-called caldera of Campi Flegrei is less obvious on the ground, but is clear from space, and consists of a complex of calderas of different ages. Etna also has had caldera collapses now largely buried by younger products, but still preserved by the geomorphology. On a smaller scale, collapse of pits is a normal part of summit activity of Etna. Typical pits reach several hundred metres in diameter and depth. One pit in particular, the Bocca Nuova (New Mouth), has been instructive because its life has been continuously monitored since it first opened in 1968.

The 1 km deep amphitheatre-shaped Valle del Bove on the eastern flank of Etna is a scar formed by gravity sector collapse on the seaward side of the volcano. The high bounding cliffs provide exposures that have played an important role in unravelling the history of the volcano. In addition, there are large, active fault scarps with seaward downthrows on the volcano's eastern flank. Seaward sliding of the volcano has played a significant part in near-surface controls of volcanic activity.

Ustica provides an example of how an island volcano can be substantially reduced in size by, often fault-controlled, collapse into the sea of a large part of the subaerial portion of the volcano.

Ground deformation is common on volcanoes and can often provide valuable information about the movement and storage of magma, especially at high levels in the construct. Archaeological studies in the vicinity of the Bay of Naples, including underwater exploration by scuba diving, have shown a complex pattern of vertical movements in historical time. In one area a Roman town is now submerged, whereas in other parts uplift has taken place. Campi Flegrei provides clear evidence of this, with the Roman columns of Serapis in Pozzuoli showing evidence of submergence and uplift since they were built. The piers built in the port nearby in the 1980s are at a lower level than the old ones and were constructed to accommodate a short period of rapid uplift occurring at that time.

The most dramatic uplift is illustrated by the volcano of Ischia in the Bay of Naples. Here, sea-floor material dated at 33 ka BP now stands at least 800 m above sea level. The coastal region of Etna also shows net uplift during the Holocene at rates of at least 1.5 mm a^{-1}.

Etna and Vesuvius, the two most active volcanoes, provide us with the best evidence for the nature of volcano 'internal plumbing'. Ideas about the plumbing of Vesuvius developed during the twentieth century and are based on observations of activity and petrological considerations. For Etna, on the other hand, we have geophysical observations that indicate there is currently no major high-level storage of magma; but petrology suggests that at times in the past there was.

Scientists, controversies and ideas

To select scientists who have made important contributions to our understanding of these volcanoes is no easy task; there are so many. Here we will look at those who have used their observations of Italian volcanoes to bring them to a wider global audience. The following chapters, which discuss individual volcanoes, will attempt to recognize the work of those who have made more specific studies.

Scientific ideas about the Earth started to ferment in Europe during the late eighteenth and the nineteenth centuries, and modern geology began to develop. Inevitably the volcanoes of southern Italy played a crucial part in the development of ideas. There were many questions and controversies. Was basalt formed from volcanoes, or was it a marine precipitate? Were volcanic mountains pushed up from below, or were they constructed by build-up of volcanic products? What drove volcanic action? What were the volcanic processes and how did they relate to the deposits?

An important student of the Earth in the seventeenth century was the German Jesuit, Athanasius Kircher (1602–1680). He had a lively interest in many things, but his 1000-page, three-volume *Mundus Subterraneus*, published in 1664 (and in English in 1669) is probably his crowning glory. It was an attempt to explain the internal working of the globe. His ideas were based on the observation that temperature in mines rose with depth and thus, by extrapolation, the interior of the Earth is very hot. The book provoked considerable interest amongst his contemporaries. He hypothesized that there was a great fire at the centre of the Earth; this was connected by a network of tubes to smaller bodies of fire nearer the surface, and these in turn fuelled volcanoes at the surface. Kircher's knowledge of volcanoes was not theoretical. He travelled extensively amongst the volcanoes of southern Italy and observed eruptions on Vesuvius, Stromboli and Etna at close quarters. He likened the crater of Vesuvius to 'Hell without the demons'. The cause of volcanic activity for him was the inflammable mixture of sulphur (which he could smell), salt, nitre and bitumen. The volcanic craters also allowed air to enter the depths to fuel the fires that drove the whole system. To illustrate his observations of volcanic activity, he presented engravings of Vesuvius and Etna in eruption, but with cut-aways to show the volcanoes' interiors (Fig. 1.4).

Fig. 1.4. Sketch of Vesuvius and its interior as envisaged by Athanasius Kircher (1669), showing the 'internal burning fires'.

Kircher's observations were a step beyond the ideas of the ancients in that they were based on observation, but fell short of understanding what the products of an eruption were. In 1669, Mount Etna had its largest eruption in historical time, resulting in a large, destructive lava flow. The eruption gave the Sicilian scholar from Syracuse, Francesco d'Arezzo, the opportunity to test the contemporary idea that lavas were a burning mixture of sulphur and bitumen. He already knew about burning sulphur as he and friends had set light to vessels of it in Palermo. The stench was intolerable, and produced an outcry from the local inhabitants. On Etna, d'Arezzo reasoned, the lava flow of 1669 should have produced an odour far greater than his small experiment with sulphur; it did not. In addition, the consistency of the lava was not what would be expected of sulphur when he pushed a stick into it. This was probably the first rheological observation of active lava. He also showed that lava had a much higher melting temperature than either sulphur or bitumen. His conclusion was that lava was vitrified rock and that flowing lava was liquid glass. His revolutionary ideas were largely ignored.

It was the eminent US volcanologist, Gordon Macdonald, who claimed Sir William Hamilton (Fig. 1.5a) as author of the first text in modern volcanology. Sir William had a colourful and exciting life entwined not just in volcanology, but in politics, art and love. He glorified under the title of 'His Britannic Majesty's Envoy Extraordinary, and Plenipotentiary at the Court of Naples'. Hamilton and his ailing wife, Catherine, arrived in Naples late in 1764 when he was 34. Official duties at that time were not great and he was able to indulge in his hobbies of hunting, collecting works of art, music and his new-found pleasure in volcanology. He became one of the first to seriously document the activity of Vesuvius and, importantly, to present these observations to the whole scientific community. His studies were published in an extensive memoir, produced by the Royal Society of London. The volume was entitled *Campi Phlegraei* (Hamilton 1776), and is beautifully illustrated with commissioned paintings by the artist Pietro Fabris (Plate 1). Without the aid of photography, geologists who had never witnessed an eruption could see the phenomenon clearly in his pictures. The monograph describes in detail his observations, not only of Vesuvius, but also of other active volcanoes of southern Italy including Etna. Hamilton had a number of narrow escapes during his observations of Vesuvian activity.

Sir William took a great interest in the excavations of Pompeii and Herculaneum. He acquired an extensive collection of Greek and Roman vases and other artefacts, which he later sold to the British Museum, where they became the basis for the Greek and Roman Collections. His second collection, also destined for the same museum, went down with the *Colossus* off the Isles of Scilly in a storm. However, he was a meticulous recorder and had all his collection documented so that most of the lost items were at least carefully recorded by commissioned artists.

Hamilton's first wife died in 1782 when he was 52. His marriage with Catherine had been a quiet one. She was a fine musician and they spent much of their leisure time playing music together and holding musical parties. His second wife to be, Emma, was quite different. She was the no longer wanted, extremely beautiful mistress of his nephew Charles Greville, shipped off to Naples from London with her mother to be looked after by Sir William. Now 56, with his eye as a collector of classical art, Hamilton enjoyed her classical beauty; he educated her in the art of singing as well as encouraging

Fig. 1.5. Sketches of (**a**) Sir William Hamilton; and (**b**) Lady Emma Hamilton (both from Gamlin 1891).

and showing her off in what she called her 'attitudes' (Fig. 1.5b). In these she posed in ways to illustrate different moods and ideas, again in the classical style. So good was she that famous painters, especially Romney and Reynolds, for whom she had modelled in London, have left us a superb record of her skill. In Naples she entranced visitors on the Grand Tour, many of whom, for example the German poet Goethe, wrote ecstatically about her.

William and Emma became lovers. Emma had become a confidante of Queen Maria Carolina, and courtly duties required that the liaison between her and William was respectable. They went to London and were married in 1791; he was 61, she just 26. They had a happy few years enjoying the life of the Court of Naples, until the spectre of Napoleon invaded their lives.

The Hamiltons' lives were severely disrupted by the Napoleonic Wars in a number of ways. Admiral Horatio Nelson arrived in the Mediterranean with his fleet of Royal Navy ships, and during his official visits to Naples stayed at the Hamilton residence where he got to know Emma. The situation in Naples became unstable and Nelson was persuaded to evacuate the Royal Household to Palermo in Sicily. The Hamiltons went as well and one of the best-known love stories began between Emma and Nelson. Eventually they were able to return to Naples, but Hamilton was withdrawn to London. William, Emma and Horatio travelled together by land, being fêted in every capital they passed through. Once in London, they eventually set up house together, but sadly not all ended happily for the *ménage à trois*: Hamilton died a sad man in 1803; Nelson, as we all know, was killed in the naval battle of Trafalgar in 1805; and Emma died in 1815 an alcoholic pauper tended by her daughter, Horatia, who had been sired by Nelson.

Hamilton's contribution to volcanology was considerable. First, he saw the value of observation both of active volcanism and of older rocks. He left a comprehensive record of the activity of Vesuvius over some 35 years. He not only recognized that lava was liquid rock, but that basalt, even in now volcanically non-active areas, such as those at the Giant's Causeway in Ireland, represented lavas that formed in the past. He observed that lavas, although sometimes scoriaceous at the top and bottom, had massive interiors, and recognized that vesicles were caused by expanding gases that had exsolved from the lava as it cooled. He described the formation of lava crusts and recognized the two types, later termed pahoehoe and aa. The former he called 'petrified cables', or ropy lava as we now call it; and the latter he likened to the surface of the River Thames in winter with a broken crust of ice and snow.

The Naples region has large amounts of pyroclastic rocks (known then as *tufa*) exposed in quarries where it is excavated as a building stone. Hamilton correctly interpreted this material as the product of explosive volcanism and became one of the first to identify both lavas and pyroclastic rocks as important products of volcanism. Comparing the rocks in the country round Rome led him to realize that major explosive volcanism had occurred near the city in the past, and that Rome was built on the products. He also suggested that interaction of magma with ground water could cause explosive volcanism. Further, he identified dykes as the feeders of lavas to vents at the surface.

Prediction and hazard mitigation were also in Hamilton's mind. He considered volcanism and earthquakes to be linked, and realized that in the case of Vesuvius earthquake swarms were a precursor to eruptions. He argued that lava flows could be diverted by embankments; he was later to learn that this had indeed been accomplished on Etna in 1669; and that clearing ash from roofs helped to prevent them collapsing under the weight. In many ways he was the prototype of a modern volcanologist.

Another colourful eighteenth-century geologist who studied the activity of volcanoes in southern Italy was the Frenchman, Déodat de Gratet de Dolomieu (1750–1801). He was professor at the Paris School of Mines, a Knight of Malta, and member of the French Academy of Sciences, and his name is remembered in the mineral dolomite named after him. His life was, to say the least, eventful. He was a well-known womanizer. When only 18 he killed an opponent in a duel, and was condemned to life imprisonment, later to be pardoned.

As with Hamilton, the French Revolution and the Napoleonic Wars greatly affected Dolomieu's life. Most of his family died under the guillotine, but he escaped. He travelled widely in southern Italy, including visits to observe Stromboli, Etna and Vesuvius erupting. In his visit to Vesuvius, Hamilton was his guide. He later took part, as an army officer, in Napoleon's Egyptian campaign, but on his return, his ship ran aground and he found himself again imprisoned, this time for nearly 2 years. Three people in particular strived in vain to obtain his release: his friends Sir William Hamilton, Admiral Nelson and Sir Joseph Banks, then President of the Royal Society. He became ill and depressed by his confinement under poor conditions. Despite this he had great courage and succeeded in writing a classification of minerals as well as preparing a will! He was eventually released as a result of French victories in Italy, and returned to France in 1800 to die, prematurely, only a year later.

Despite his short life, Dolomieu accomplished a lot. In common with many of his time, he, wrongly, considered that to obtain liquid lava a combustible substance such as sulphur was required. Nevertheless, he pioneered petrological studies of volcanic rocks. He made the distinction between vitreous rocks such as obsidian and crystalline ones such as basalt, recognizing that some melts were pure liquid, whereas others were a mixture of crystals and liquid. Like Hamilton, he saw expanding gases as important to the volcanic process and emphasized the importance of explosive phenomena. Correctly, he explained pumice as just obsidian that had been frothed up by expanding gas bubbles. He observed ash deposits preserved in marine sediments, and produced evidence for submarine eruptions in the form of lavas within sedimentary sequences.

The twin debates about basalt: was the lava fuelled by the presence of sulphur, and were basalts found in regions with no active volcanism the products of precipitation from water, were solved by two pioneers in experimental geology. Abbé Lazzaro Spallanzani (1729–1799), a natural historian from Pavia, took on the first of these questions. He travelled widely in Italy to study volcanoes and published his observations in a four-volume monograph. He conducted melting experiments with lava both in the presence and absence of sulphur, demonstrating that sulphur made no difference. He argued on this basis, and his observation that lavas did not emit flames, that lava was not the result of combustion, but was melted by some other source within the Earth. He was not so certain that all basalts formed in the same way, and conceded that some may be formed from aqueous solutions.

This second debate about basalt was resolved from experiments by Sir James Hall (1761–1832). Hall was a protégé of James Hutton, the Scottish physician who transformed geology. Here is not the place to review this stimulating phase in the development of the whole of geological thinking, only to say that Hutton refuted the idea that basalts were formed as precipitates on an ocean floor. The debate appears a silly one in view of the observations that were being made of active volcanoes producing basalts; but it was strongly held by, it must be said, those who had not witnessed active lavas. It should also be said that Hutton was none too keen on the experimental approach. How could one reproduce a geological process in a tiny crucible? He did not live to see the final results produced by Hall vindicating his geological arguments.

James Hall visited active volcanoes of southern Italy in 1785. He explored Vesuvius in the company of both Hamilton and Dolomieu, and collected rocks with Dolomieu in the Eolian Islands. The basalts collected in Italy were demonstrably rocks of volcanic origin. Hall compared these with basalts from non-volcanic regions and found them to be similar. He then melted both types of rock and found that with rapid cooling they all gave glass, and when slowly cooled, they produced the equivalent crystalline material. There appeared little doubt that ancient basalts were formed from volcanoes now extinct or dormant.

An aqueous origin for basalts was a part of the global geological philosophy of Abraham Gottlob Werner (1749–1817). An influential German mineralogist who lectured at the Academy of Mines at Freiberg, Werner erroneously saw the stratigraphic history of the Earth in terms of precipitates from an ocean, basalts included. He had many disciples. One such was Leopold von Buch (1774–1853), who travelled widely in Europe. His first visit to Vesuvius forced him to admit there was no difference between basaltic lava and basalts elsewhere; nevertheless, he would not give in and reject his Wernerian training. He argued that basaltic lavas were just melted aqueous basalts! Another visit to Vesuvius, travels round the basaltic sites of Europe and finally the columnar basalts of Staffa in Scotland and Giant's Causeway in Ireland eventually convinced him. That controversy concluded, he started another, the idea of 'craters of elevation'.

So much has been said about 'craters of elevation' in the past that we are reluctant to dwell on it here; but we must say something, because Italian volcanoes played a key part in the debate that followed von Buch's idea. Basically, he claimed that volcanoes were elevated by being pushed up from below, not by construction as successive lavas and tephra layers were emplaced on top of one another.

It is amazing that the 'craters of elevation' theory managed to generate so much debate in the early 19th century, but it did. Geologists searched the volcanoes of Europe and elsewhere for evidence to support their views. A vehement objector to the idea was the English volcanologist, George Poulett Scrope (1797–1876). Scrope had been fascinated with volcanoes from an early age, having spent family holidays in southern Italy. He later studied Etna, the Eolian Islands and eruptive activity on Vesuvius. As a result of his studies there and in southern France he published in his late twenties the influential book *Considerations on Volcanoes*. His studies convinced him of the error of the idea of 'craters of elevation'. He also recognized the importance of volcanic gases in assisting the rise of magma within a conduit. Sadly, once he was married to a wealthy heiress, his contribution to volcanology faded away.

Charles Lyell (1797–1875) was impressed by his friend Scrope's book; so much so that he made trips to Vesuvius and Etna to investigate for himself the question of 'craters of elevation'. As a result of his field observations, Lyell had no doubt that volcanoes were built up by accumulated lavas and beds of pyroclastic rocks, and not by elevation. Curiously, however, he did find evidence of uplift as well. He observed that Etna, although not formed by uplift, had been the subject of wholesale slow uplift exposing marine sediments at the foot of the volcano. On the island of Ischia he found evidence of large-scale uplift, and, of course, he was impressed by the evidence of Earth movements provided by the Roman columns of Serapis at Pozzuoli, an engraving of which became the symbol of his book *Principles of Geology*. Nevertheless, these movements were not those that gave the radiating dips of strata round the central crater, and 'craters of elevation' died a fairly rapid death.

The German, Baron Wolfgang Sartorius von Waltershausen (1809–1876), is a significant player in our story. His detailed volcanological map of Etna, surveyed between 1836 and 1843, is a landmark study, as is his accompanying, posthumously published monograph (1880), a compendium of knowledge about that volcano's eruptive history. The cones formed during the 1865 eruption were named Monte Sartorius in honour of him. During his time in Sicily he looked at the rocks of the Iblean Mountains to the south of Etna. Here he discovered a brown rock consisting of an iron- and water-rich mineral, which he named palagonite after the nearby town of Palagonia. He observed that this rock was associated with marine sediments, and proposed that it had formed as a result of eruptions of basalt under marine conditions. He was able to take this further when he studied palagonite deposits in Iceland. He found within the palagonite fragments of basaltic glass, which he named sideromelane, and correctly inferred that palagonite was the result of hot basaltic lava being modified on contact with water. The term palagonite is now restricted to the mineral, and the rock is called hyaloclastite.

The Italian volcanoes also played their part in the early work of collecting and analysing volcanic gases. French mineralogist Charles Sainte-Claire Deville (1814–1876) expanded his studies of gases from volcanoes on Atlantic islands and in the Caribbean to Vesuvius, where he took great risks in collecting gases throughout the eruption of 1855. The study of volcanic gases had begun.

Vesuvius has the distinction of being the site of the first volcanological observatory in the world (Fig. 1.6). It was built in 1841 by the Bourbon Ferdinand II, King of the Two Sicilies, with the aim of increasing knowledge of the volcano to protect the people of Naples and the surrounding region. Sited on a small hill about 300 m below the summit, the observatory commanded a fine view, and was protected from lavas and to some extent pyroclastic flows, but not from heavy ash falls. The King appointed Macedonio Melloni (1798–1854) as the first director, and he started the systematic daily observations required. Melloni was followed by Luigi Palmieri (1807–1896), who designed and equipped the observatory with seismographs to monitor activity. His careful observations started to show that there was a pattern to Vesuvian eruptive activity both long term and short term. He recognized cycles of eruptive activity in the years since 1631, as well as daily changes, which he ascribed to the effects of lunar tides. The presence of permanent equipment to measure earthquake activity provided an important tool to predict activity.

When Palmieri died, he was succeeded by Raffaele Matteucci, who became infatuated by Vesuvius, which he likened to a lover that he could not leave however much she may hurt him. He was indeed hurt in 1900 when he slipped and fell into fresh hot ashes, burning himself badly. This accident did not deter him, and he continued his observations, often camping close to the activity. He was joined by the US physicist Frank Perret (1856–1943), who became his Honorary Assistant. Perret had formally been an assistant to the famous Thomas Edison, but with deteriorating health he retired to Naples, where he developed an interest in the activity of Vesuvius. He was an ingenious inventor and developed new ways of making volcanological observations, such as gripping the bedstead with his teeth to test for tremors. He was also a fine photographer, and recorded his observations for posterity.

Matteucci and Perret, together with Giuseppe Mercalli (1850–1914), who gave us the earthquake intensity scale named after him, made a detailed observation of the paroxysmal eruption that ended a cycle of Vesuvian activity in 1906. Despite extremely dangerous conditions (the people of Naples and the surroundings were in a state of panic and many were killed) these brave scientists stayed the eruption out. Sadly, Matteucci died, his health probably not helped by the effects of the eruption, before he could prepare an account of their observations. The distinguished Mercalli, who succeeded him as director, also failed to leave a record, and it remained for Perret to document their important observations and ideas developed as a result of careful studies of this eruption, which much advanced our knowledge of how this volcano works. As well as Vesuvius, Perret made significant scientific observations on activity at Stromboli and Etna.

Fig. 1.6. The Royal Vesuvius Observatory, located 2 km west of the summit of the volcano. It is now open to the public as a museum.

One visitor to Vesuvius, who saw the results of the 1906 eruption, was Henry Johnston-Lavis (1856–1914), an English medical doctor who had developed a keen interest in volcanoes. Johnston-Lavis graduated in medicine at University College London, and continued a medical career throughout his life; but he ran a successful geological one in parallel. In 1879 he started a medical practice in Naples serving British and US expatriates. Although his work was exacting, especially during a cholera epidemic in Pozzouli, he found time to study Vesuvius. Important legacies of his work were a volcanological map in six sheets of Vesuvius at a scale of 1:10 000, and a bibliography of the volcanoes of southern Italy. He was an intrepid observer of activity, taking considerable risks, and was probably one of the first volcano epidemiologists. He died in France in a car accident.

The study of rocks in thin section began in the mid-nineteenth century. This new tool opened up the whole subject of petrology. Igneous rocks could be classified based on their mineralogy as well as their chemistry. The US petrologist and volcanologist, Henry Washington (1867–1934), collected volcanic rocks widely in southern Italy as well as observing volcanic phenomena. Based on this and collections from elsewhere, he was able to develop a new classification of igneous rocks.

Returning to the history of the Vesuvius Observatory, Giuseppe Imbo succeeded Mercalli as director, moving from Catania where he had been studying Etna. He assiduously monitored Vesuvius, which produced only minor activity for him until the eruption of 1944; this spectacular eruption occurred while the Second World War raged round it. Imbo recognized the precursory signs of an eruption and set up base at the Observatory where he slept. He advised the Allied Authorities of the dangers and when the eruption started he monitored it in detail, often at risk to his life.

No account of the scientists who have contributed to our understanding of Italian volcanoes would be complete without mention of Alfred Rittmann (1893–1981), the Swiss-born geologist who eventually made Italy his home (Fig. 1.7). He inspired many students of volcanology in Italy, and studied most of the volcanoes in southern Italy from his base in Catania. Originally he was a professor in the university, but he later established the International Institute of Volcanology (IIV) of which he was the first Director. He will be remembered as a strong-minded leader who habitually had a large cigar clenched between his teeth. Indeed, in later life he used to say: 'I am like a volcano. While I am smoking, I am still active.'

Rittmann contributed considerably to our knowledge of the chemistry of lavas in southern Italy, and their petrogenesis. Rittmann was not afraid to question established thinking on all aspects related to volcanoes and magmas. In consequence, many of his views were controversial, and a discussion with him was always stimulating and thought provoking. It was he who initiated, in the 1970s, the work by a joint Italian–British team to make a new geological map of Etna, finally published in 1979, 2 years before he died.

As shown by the above account, southern Italy has attracted students of volcanology from many countries. This continues today. Work amongst Italian volcanologists has largely been consolidated under the Gruppo Nazionale per la Vulcanologia spearheaded by Franco Barberi of Pisa University. Members of this group representing many institutions in Italy have contributed to further knowledge of these volcanoes, as well as taking part in monitoring and aiding in civil protection measures.

Human history

As we shall see, each of the volcanoes has played its part in the historical development of southern Italy. In many ways they have been a focus of attention for the potentially

Fig. 1.7. Alfred Rittmann on the steps of Paterno Castle, Etna, in 1975.

rich soils associated with volcanic products; they were lush places to live, and even better places to visit on vacation.

For each volcano in the following chapters we have given a brief history of human occupation of the area, and the way the volcano has influenced the life of the people. Generally speaking, the pattern of history has been the same for all of southern Italy with local variations. Early tribes were superseded by Greek and Roman colonization, followed by a succession of invasions and changes in power amongst the Royal Houses of Europe. This was brought to an end by the Unification of Italy in 1860, which was orchestrated by Garibaldi. During the Second World War southern Italy was brought to its knees by the Allied invasions, first of Sicily, and then the mainland. Many villages and small towns were severely damaged or even destroyed, and many people were left starving.

Aid from Rome in the 1950s and 1960s started to bring the south out of its generally poor conditions, and European Community support made considerable changes in the 1980s and 1990s. Globalization has changed much, at least of the external character, of southern Italy. The increase in wealth has also dramatically increased the risk from natural hazard associated with volcanoes. There has been massive development in new homes, and second homes, in areas extending high up volcanoes such as Vesuvius and Etna. Industry has expanded, as has the general population. The eruption of Vesuvius in 1631 took about 4000 lives and was half the magnitude of the eruption of AD 79, which buried Pompeii and Herculaneum. An eruption today similar to that of 1631 at Vesuvius would do massive damage and, unless there were an effective and timely evacuation, there would be considerable loss of life.

Hazard, risk and prediction

For each of the volcanoes in southern Italy we discuss the potential impact on the people who live in its environs. This involves the physical effects on humans, as well as effects such as destruction of personal property, agriculture, industry and communications. We shall see from the human history of each volcano that people have lived hand-in-hand with volcanism. Despite the heavy loss of life, at times, on Vesuvius, or of property on Etna, people continue to live there and the size of the vulnerable population is increasing.

Volcanologists recognize that they have serious responsibilities, through governments, to the communities that live in volcanically active areas. Civil defence authorities, in preparing for a potential eruption, need information on the likelihood of an eruption from a volcano, and the extent of damage it may cause. This information, broadly, can take two forms which are referred to as *general* and *specific prediction*. General prediction stems from an understanding of the history of a volcano, especially the frequency of different styles of eruption, and their magnitude and violence. This information can be derived from several approaches. Stratigraphical studies, together with radiometric dating, provide long-term statistics of different types of eruption that have occurred. Assuming the volcano will continue to act as it has in the past, we thus have a measure of what may happen in the future. Detailed examination of the products of individual eruptions also provides valuable information on what to expect from future eruptions, as do eye-witness reports from historical eruptions. From all such data hazard maps and eruption scenarios can be made, and from these it is possible to identify the risks; that is, potential injuries, fatalities and damage to land and property. Civil protection officers can develop plans for mitigation of the risk including, if necessary, wholesale evacuation of vulnerable populations. Hazard data can be, but usually are not, taken into account in land use planning.

Evacuation plans must also take into account other geological factors. Earthquakes, including precursory ones, can cause landslides that block roads and railways. Potential sites for such activity must be identified, and alternative routes included in the plan. Tsunamis can destroy harbours, and floods can bring down bridges. All these factors must be taken into account.

Specific prediction identifies more precisely when and where the next eruption will occur. This relies on routine monitoring of the volcano by geophysical techniques (e.g. seismic and ground deformation), geochemical techniques (e.g. composition of fumarole gases and hot spring waters), and general surveillance. We will discuss this more in the final chapter.

Notes

Geography and history

There are several good guides to southern Italy. We have used the *Blue Guide* (Blanchard 2000) for peninsular Italy and the *Rough Guide* (Andrews & Brown 1999) for Sicily. A dated, but useful source of information in English on Italy in general is the four-volume set that forms one of the *Geographical Handbook Series* prepared for the Naval Intelligence Division of the British Admiralty (Admiralty 1944, 1945). Russell King provides a more up-to-date text on the geography of the country (King 1987), again in English. For a concise history of Italy, Duggan (1994) is a good source for the English-speaking reader. The last two references include important non-English sources. Some volcanoes of southern Italy are covered in a general way in a book on European volcanoes by Scarth & Tanguy (2001). Kilburn & McGuire (2001) provide an excellent pocket-sized field guide to the more famous Italian volcanoes.

The website, *Cradle of Volcanology*, authored by Boris Behncke, contains useful information about Italian volcanoes (http://boris.vulcanoetna.com/Italiahome.html).

For advice on safety on volcanoes, see the website of the International Association of Volcanology and Chemistry of the Earth's Interior (http://www.iavcei.org).

General geology

McKenzie (1970, 1977) followed by Dewey *et al.* (1973) first attempted to provide a coherent reconstruction of the structural evolution of this complex region in terms of the then-new model of plate tectonics. Barberi *et al.* (1974) provided an early interpretation of the magmatism of the Eolian Islands and Etna within a plate tectonic context and considered the implications of the fact that continental collision did not occur simultaneously in the Calabria–Sicily area. In Sicily, collision took place in the Tertiary and in this region Africa and Eurasia have been locked since the late Miocene. To the east, however, subduction has continued NW beneath Calabria and the Eolian Islands until the present. Barberi and his colleagues consider that this explains the close association of the calc-alkaline magmatism of the subduction-related Eolian arc with the basaltic volcano of Mount Etna more typical of tensional tectonics.

Subsequent to this other groups have related the magmatism of southern Italy to a reconstruction of the tectonic configuration: the Tyrrhenian basin and Eolian arc (Keller 1981; Ellam *et al.* 1989; Serri 1990; Ferrari & Manetti 1993; Milano *et al.* 1994), the potassic volcanism of the Campanian Province (Beccaluva *et al.* 1991) and the magmatism associated with the Pantelleria Rift (Cello 1987; Esperança & Crisci 1995).

Following the pioneering work of McKenzie, Dewey, Barberi and colleagues the broad outlines of the tectonic configuration of the Mediterranean area were largely accepted. The detailed picture, however, presented more of a problem. Several workers have presented a synthesis of the palaeogeographical evolution of the Mediterranean area involving the opening and closure of Tethys since the Triassic (Biju-Duval *et al.* 1977; Robertson & Grasso 1995).

More detailed investigation of the spatial and temporal sequence of events has led to a fuller understanding of the role of lithosphere sinking (Malinverno & Ryan 1986) and plate detachment and roll-back in the evolution of the Eolian arc and surrounding region (Gvirtzman & Nur 1999*a*,*b*). It is considered that most of the potassic magmas of southern Italy and the Tyrrhenian region are derived from mantle sources enriched by metasomatism in K (Tamburelli *et al.* 2000). Subduction of lithosphere in the southern Apennines region ceased in the late Pliocene, yet magmatism in the Campanian Province is younger, restricted to the Quaternary. Indeed, the volcanism in the Campanian Province is considered to be associated with extensional tectonics. The time–space relationship between the magmatism and the subduction event, therefore, is not always straightforward. In a region with a complex tectonic evolution the mantle source regions are likely to be heterogeneous and mantle metasomatized by a previous subduction event may subsequently be the source for magmas associated with tensional tectonics yet bearing a signature of subduction-related magmatism.

A comprehensive bibliography up to the year 1914 on the volcanoes of southern Italy was compiled by Henry Johnston-Lavis and published posthumously (Johnston-Lavis 1918). His large collection of books, pictures and rocks was donated to University College London (Kirk *et al.* 2000). The Journal *Acta Volcanologica* is the independent organ of the Italian Volcanological Group and provides up-to-date reports on volcanic research in Italy.

Styles of activity

As a general introduction to volcanic activity, that by the late Gordon Macdonald is a superbly written classic (Macdonald 1972). A more modern, and equally readable volume, by the late Peter Francis, covers explosive volcanism more fully (Francis 1993). Fisher & Schmincke (1984) have written an authoritative book on the subject of pyroclastic rocks and explosive volcanism. For a weighty tome in every sense, the reader can do no better than the *Encyclopedia of Volcanoes* (Sigurdsson *et al.* 2000). At a more popular level is *Volcanoes* by Scarth (1994), a well-written description of volcanoes and their activity with examples from round the world.

Petrology

The Quaternary volcanic rocks of southern Italy show a remarkably diverse range. It is not surprising therefore that the history of petrological research in this region has thrown up a plethora of names and classification schemes. For the purposes of this book a uniform approach has been adopted to use the nomenclature recommended by the International Union of Geological Sciences Subcommission on the Systematics of Igneous Rocks (Le Maitre 1989). Early classic work on the petrology of rocks in this region was carried out by Washington (1906, 1913, 1914), Washington *et al.* (1926) and Rittmann (1962). Other important works are those by Appleton (1972) and Middlemost (1997).

People and ideas

The history of ideas on volcanism has been treated extensively by Sigurdsson in his book *Melting the Earth* (Sigurdsson 1999). The delightful book by Kraft charts the history of volcanology, and it is packed with information and fine pictures (Kraft 1993, English translation). The definitive, and only full biography on Sir William Hamilton is by Fothergill (1969), and an exhibition of his works held at the British Museum in London was accompanied by an excellent and lavishly illustrated book (Jenkins & Sloan 1996). *Volcanoes and History*, edited by Morello (1998), has a number of papers on the history of volcanology in Italy.

Hazard

A general text on volcanic hazard is that of Blong (1984). This covers in some depth the whole of this subject.

Chapter 2. **Vesuvius**

Geography

The famous cone of Vesuvius (or Vesuvio in Italian), rises majestically above the city of Naples (Plate 2): but thick industrial and motor-car-derived smog completely, or almost completely, obscures the volcano from view on most days. When the air *is* clear, normally following heavy rain, the sight of Vesuvius is one of the wonders of the natural world.

It consists of an almost symmetrical cone with a basal diameter of about 12 km rising from the Mediterranean coast to 1281 m. The summit cone sits in a 4 km diameter caldera, known as the Somma Caldera, which is open to the sea (Fig. 2.1). This structure

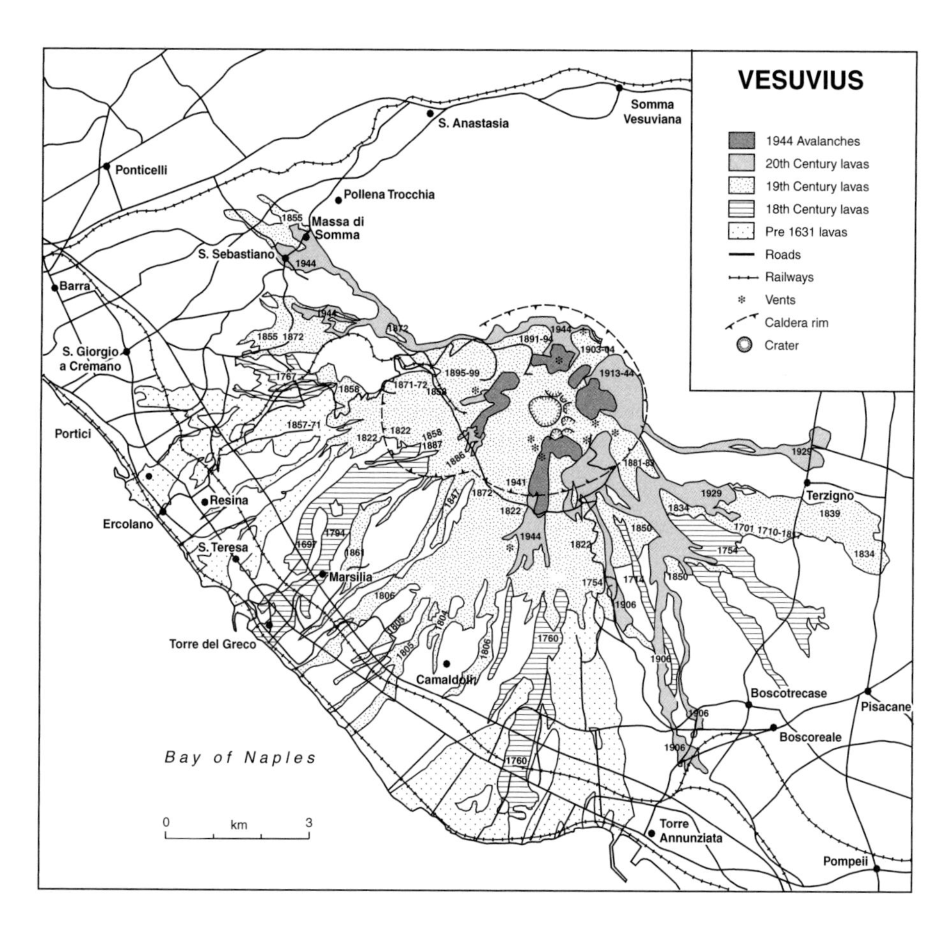

Fig. 2.1. General map of Vesuvius showing the distribution of historical lavas. (Adapted from Santacroce *et al.* 1987.)

truncates an older cone known as the Somma Volcano, which forms the main edifice. The Somma caldera has a high wall to the north, and the trough formed between it and the Vesuvius summit cone is known as the Atrio del Cavallo to the west and the Valle dell'Inferno to the north (Plate 3); the former name was coined because this was where visitors to the summit grazed their horses before the advent of the car. Nowadays one can park a vehicle on the cone and climb easily to the rim of the summit crater. This has rugged inner walls and is 450 m across and 330 m deep. Fumaroles within the crater and round the rim remind the visitor that this is still an active volcano. The summit area is virtually bare of vegetation, but at lower altitudes the slopes are progressively more vegetated, and nowadays increasingly covered by houses.

The terms Somma and Vesuvius can be confusing, especially when the whole volcano is variously referred to as Somma–Vesuvio or Vesuvius. We shall refer to the volcano in general as Vesuvius because it has had a continuous history over the same site since its inception. Nevertheless, we recognize a phase in its history that built up what is called the Somma part of Vesuvius and culminated in major summit collapse to give the arcuate cliffs that surround the present summit cone, Vesuvio.

Much of the activity of Vesuvius has been associated with the summit, with explosive activity from the summit crater and lava effusion from the base of the summit cone. Nevertheless, flank eruptions also occur, either forming lavas from fissures, or building cinder cones over effusive vents (Fig. 2.1).

Vesuvius sits at the southern end of the Campanian Plain, an area of subsiding late Tertiary and Quaternary sediments bounded by mountains made up of predominantly Mesozoic carbonates. The Campanian plain consists of a number of graben structures with the two main fault trends aligned NW–SE to NNW–SSE and NNE–SSW to NE–SW. There is an ENE–WSW-trending discontinuity that separates the Vesuvius sector of the Campanian Plain, with a crustal thickness of around 35 km, from the Campi Flegrei–Procida–Ischia sector, which has a thinner crust of 25 km. Recent detailed seismic investigations have revealed that Vesuvius is located at the intersection of two main faults, following NW–SE and NE–SW alignments.

The crustal structure beneath Vesuvius has been explored by seismic and gravity techniques. Modelling of the gravity data suggests that the limestone basement is about 2 km beneath Vesuvius and the carbonate sequence is around 11 km thick. This is corroborated by a borehole at Trecase (2 km north of Torre Annunziata at the foot of Vesuvius), which reached limestones at a depth of 1700 m b.s.l. (below sea level). Two-dimensional seismic tomography shows a reflector at 12–14 km depth, which is interpreted as the junction between the carbonate sequence and the underlying crystalline rocks of the lower crust.

Vesuvius is classified as a central composite volcano, because it is centred on a cylindrical conduit and has been built up by eruptions that in some cases were dominated by explosive activity and in others by the effusion of lava. It consists, therefore, of crudely alternating layers of tephra and lava.

For most people, Vesuvius conjures up the image of Pompeii and the drama of the eruption of AD 79. The burial by pumice and ashes from this eruption of whole communities, preserving their houses, goods and chattels, has provided a record of the Roman way of life at an instant in time nearly two thousand years ago. More of this later!

History

Greek and Roman times

Before AD 79 it was apparently not, at least widely, known that Vesuvius was a dangerous active volcano. It was probably not even thought of as a volcano by most inhabitants. The earliest settlers had no reason to be concerned, given that they had a pleasant climate, fertile soil and fine harbours. The origins of Naples are uncertain, but Neapolis means 'new city' and was probably founded by Greek colonists in the 6th century BC, near an existing small settlement called Parthenope or Palepolis that had been established by navigators from Rhodes three centuries earlier.

Neapolis (Fig. 2.2) soon became the main centre of the area, with new blood arriving from Athens and other parts of Greece. Then about 200 years after it was founded, the Samnites, a warlike people from the southern Apennines, conquered it and the surrounding area. In 326 BC, following a 3 year siege, the people of Naples surrendered to the Roman army. Even under Roman rule, the Hellenic culture was preserved and a dialect of Greek continued to be the most commonly used language. It developed as a major European centre of culture and learning highly developed in the arts, especially in poetry, music and rhetoric; Romans flocked there to learn. Rich Romans also came to build their villas, not just in Naples, but in the surrounding regions at the foot of Vesuvius. Many famous people made the area their home, for example Virgil, who wrote the *Georgics* and *Aeneid* here.

Not only was Naples rich from a cultural point of view, but the surrounding region of Campania was also an agricultural paradise. Under the mild Mediterranean climate, farmers were able to produce two harvests of durum wheat per year, and the fertile slopes of Vesuvius supported vines, olives, wheat and vegetables, as well as livestock. People could eat, simply or richly, but well, as they still do, and there were many wealthy landowners as a result. Small towns grew up before the Roman occupation, and then developed under Roman rule; in addition, sumptuous villas for rich Romans were built round the foot of Vesuvius.

One well-known story of the Roman era involving Vesuvius is that of Spartacus from Bulgaria (then called Thrace), who became a Roman soldier; he later deserted, but was captured and consigned to the life of a slave-gladiator. In 73 BC he led over 200 fellow slaves in a plot to overthrow their Roman masters. They were foiled in the attempt, but 78 of them escaped, stole arms, and hid in the crater or caldera of Vesuvius, which was at that time filled with a dense growth of vines. It was a well-protected site with only a narrow entrance, which would only allow a party to enter single file. Once the news of the hideout became known, many thousands of slaves joined Spartacus in the crater. The gladiators were, of course, highly trained in single combat and in these conditions the Roman army had little chance of breaking the hold of Spartacus and his men. The siege, however, could not last forever. Spartacus and his men climbed out of the crater using ladders made of vines and from behind drove the Romans out. Nevertheless, the rebels were eventually defeated by the might of Rome and Spartacus was killed.

The end of an era came first with the earthquake of AD 62, which caused great damage, and finally the cataclysmic eruption of AD 79. Apart from Naples itself, most of

Fig. 2.2. Maps showing the development of the city of Naples from Classical times (**a**) to recent years (**d**). In (**b**) sites of the Medieval and Roman city walls are shown in the context of the modern city. The growth of Naples from 1939 to modern time is shown in (**c**) and (**d**).

civilization round the flanks of Vesuvius was destroyed: but, ironically, preserved as a 'snapshot' in time below the ashes that buried everything. Whole communities and their effects were fossilized to be discovered by archaeologists, and plunderers, a millennium and a half later. Two towns, Pompeii and Herculaneum, were totally buried by the AD 79 eruption, but have since been excavated.

The most famous and largest is Pompeii (Fig. 2.3) on the lower SE flank of Vesuvius. The Oscans, a native people of this part of Italy, built the original village on the site of Pompeii. Then, in the sixth century BC, the Greeks settled to develop the town as a key maritime link. They introduced their own religion and built a Doric temple to Apollo. In the fifth century BC, following a short period when the Etruscans held the area, the Greeks progressively enlarged the town and fortified it with a substantial wall. However, this did not prevent the Samnites from taking Pompeii, as they did

Fig. 2.3. A street in excavated Pompeii showing rutted paving stones. Vesuvius looms over the city 12 km away.

Naples. Indeed, they spread over the coastal plain and became known as the Campani.

Eventually the Campani were subjugated by Rome, but Pompeii remained independent and an even more substantial wall was built to fortify it. Despite this, when the Campani rebelled against Rome in 90 BC, Pompeii was taken and became a Roman town. Under

Roman rule relatively few changes were made. A Forum was built as well as temples to Roman gods. The infrastructure of Roman administration was put into place and the town became largely self-governing: but the people were subject to Roman authority, which was little used.

What has been captured about everyday life of a Roman town, based on the buildings, paintings, writings and casts of bodies that have been recovered? Pompeii was a cosmopolitan town of about 20 000 inhabitants including some 8000 slaves. There was, it is claimed, no strife between social classes and, because food was relatively cheap in this fertile region, even the poorest did not starve. All could not, nevertheless, have been idyllic as there were street beggars, at least one depicted on a wall painting.

As a Roman town it had an elliptical shape (Fig. 2.4) just over a kilometre in length and half a kilometre wide: not large, but much was packed into it. In the surrounding wall there were eight gates. The main street was the Via di Stabia, which was intersected by the Via Nola and Via Abbondanza; the present-day names of the streets are derived from names on Roman street-corner drinking fountains. Between the main highways were numerous side streets, generally forming a grid pattern. During the Roman period, the streets were paved with polygonal lava blocks with regularly spaced rows of stepping stones for pedestrians. Deep ruts are visible today, reflecting the heavy use made of the roads by animal-drawn vehicles (Fig. 2.3).

Pompeii was essentially a residential town based on maritime trade. Houses were built to offer the best environment to accommodate the warm Mediterranean climate. A typical house had at its centre an open, airy atrium filled with plants and fountains, giving a fresh cool environment during hot summer afternoons. Walls were adorned with frescos, many of which depict mythical and religious scenes, as well as pictures of everyday life. Some are blatantly erotic, or depict priapic prowess.

There were numerous shops, often attached to houses, bars, inns and taverns, as might be expected in a port town. Also, not surprisingly, there were brothels decorated by pictures that indicate the services available. The Roman public buildings, from which the town was administered and law enforced, were centred by the Forum, the hub of the colony with its long axis pointing directly towards Vesuvius.

The Pompeiians were a religious people with many gods. They not only attended festivals in temples and shrines devoted to specific gods, but also worshiped in their own homes. Worship took place at regular hours marked by sundials and water clocks. Most important of the gods were the triad consisting of Hercules, the legendary founder of Herculaneum, Bacchus, the god of wine and orgy, and Venus, seen as the giver of luck and prosperity. A second triad, Jupiter, Juno and Minerva, also played an important part in religious life.

Being a port, sailors brought tales of gods from other lands, and these were assimilated into the religious repertoire. The most striking was that of Isis, which caught the imagination particularly of the wealthy, and almost became the official religion. Isis was the principal goddess of ancient Egypt where she typified the faithful wife and devoted mother; to the Romans she was a goddess of the natural world. But the god of gods was the Roman Emperor who, as time went on, took the supreme place above all other gods.

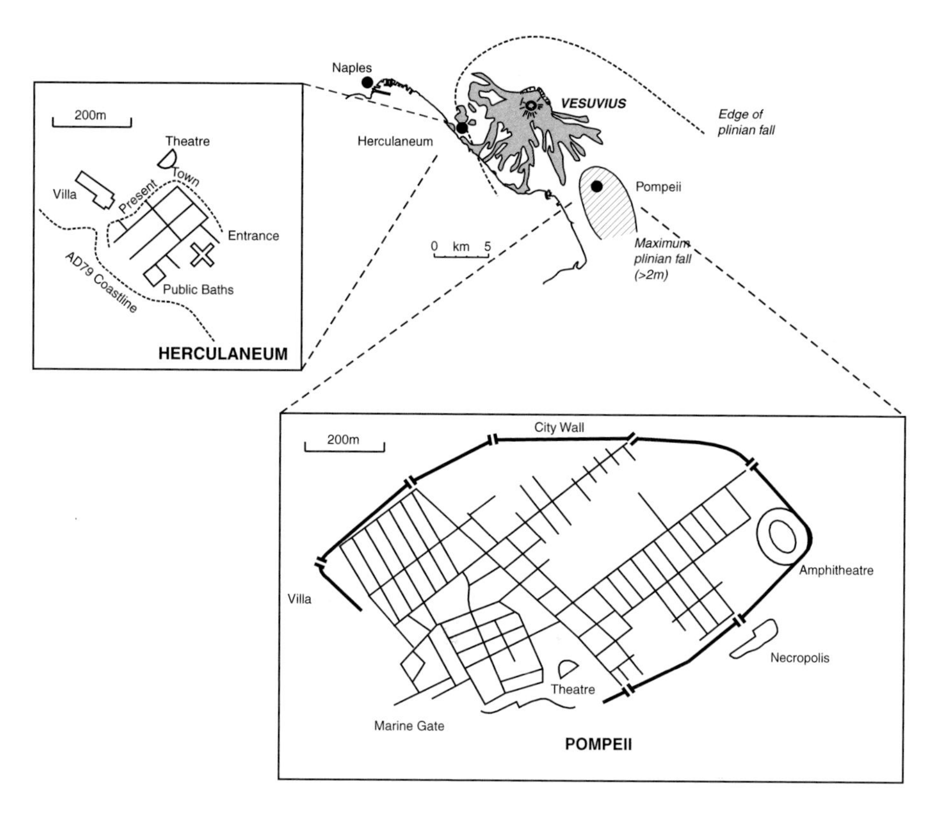

Fig. 2.4. Maps of the excavated portions of Pompeii and Herculaneum and their positions with respect to the main ash fall from the AD 79 eruption.

Fig. 2.5. The excavations at Herculaneum, with Vesuvius in the background 7 km away.

Fig. 2.6. The 1944 eruption plume of Vesuvius with a stone pine tree in the middle foreground.

What did the people of Pompeii do? Much the same as in any small rural town and port. Many worked in agriculture, toiling in the fields. Wine was a major industry, and wool from sheep provided the raw material for making cloth that was dyed in many colours. Bread making was an important industry, and metals such as bronze and silver were crafted into tools, instruments, ornaments and jewellery.

Pompeiians liked to be entertained. They had two theatres, one holding 5000 spectators, and an amphitheatre. Many sports were played in the amphitheatre, but most notorious were the activities of the gladiators, highly trained warriors who fought amongst themselves, often facing death, as well as with deadly animals such as lions. Social life extended to visits to the public baths. Pompeii sported three of these where men and women (separately) could get together to wash, relax and exchange gossip with their friends.

Herculaneum (Ercolano in Italian) was unlike Pompeii during Roman times in not being a commercial centre, but instead was a fishing town surrounded by the villas of wealthy Romans. It was named by the Greek settlers after the Greek deity Hercules (Figs 2.4 and 2.5). Like Pompeii it became dominated by Oscans and Samnites before being taken by the Romans in 89 BC. Much of Herculaneum remains unexcavated and the full size of the town is unknown. We do know that it was situated on a high bluff overlooking the sea, and in Roman times had a population of between 4500 and 5000. Some of its houses are similar to those of Pompeii, but some tended to be less open, and there were multi-storied tenement blocks for the poorer people of the town. There was a theatre, as well as public baths (the Suburban Thermae) on the sea front, together with wooden jetties used by the fishermen.

The Romans built fine villas, some in the country and others in towns. One of the villas that has been excavated, Oplontis, is now surrounded by the new town of Torre Annunziata; it is thought to have been the home of Poppaea Sabina, second wife of the Roman Emperor Nero. From what has been revealed, it was of extraordinary elegance with fine frescos and sculptures all typifying the fine style of rich Roman citizens. To the east of the volcano near Terzigno and Boscoreale other villas, known as *vilae rustico*, have been found in recent years, providing more information on the wine-growing estates on the volcano at this time.

There is not a great deal of evidence about how people coped with the effects of the AD 79 eruption. Naples remained intact and those inhabitants of the region closer to the volcano who survived started to rebuild the region with new villages. Thus were born many of the present towns such as San Sebastiano, Torre del Greco and Boscoreale. The Roman Emperor, Titus, sent relief to help cities such as Naples and Sorrento that were sheltering large numbers of refugees, and life went on.

Diocletian, Roman Emperor from AD 285 to 305, began persecuting the Christians, then a strong religious group in the region. Bishop Januariue, later to become a Saint, was, with two companions, brought to the amphitheatre to be eaten by beasts, but to everyone's surprise they would not touch the men. So their captors had to behead them instead! The skull of the Saint is kept in the Gothic Duomo (Cathederal) of San Gennaro in Naples, together with two vials of his blood. The annual miracle of liquefaction of the blood is said to take place, and his relics have since been seen as a protection against the evils of the volcano.

After the Romans

By the middle of the sixth century AD Roman rule was over and the south of Italy was chaotic, only to be stabilized by the Normans. Most of southern Italy fell quickly to these able Franco-Nordic fighters, but Naples withstood a 2 year siege that ended in 1078, and lost its independence only in 1139. The consequence was that the Norman capital of the Two Sicilies was established in Palermo not Naples. The Normans, with consummate skill in organization, brought order to the area once again.

But it was not to last, and the end of the twelfth century saw conflict between the Church and sectarian rulers. The area lost much of its previous glory. Order was again restored by Frederick II, and culture flourished once more at the start of the twelfth century. One of his important acts was to found the University of Naples. Conflict returned yet again between the various European Houses until the early 18th century, when the Bourbons took control of southern Italy and Sicily.

The first Bourbon ruler of the Two Sicilies was Charles III, who reigned between 1734 and 1759. He brought about social reform, began the famous royal palace at Caserta to the north of Naples, and was instrumental in starting, at the urging of his wife, systematic excavations at Herculaneum and Pompeii. Before then some excavation had taken place but mainly for the purpose of looting. Charles was followed by Ferdinand IV, who was crude and uncouth, and had little interest in government: his clever wife, the Habsburg Princess Maria Carolina, acted well in his place during a difficult time, which was to culminate in the conflict of the Napoleonic Wars.

The French army marched into Italy and took Rome; clearly Naples was in danger. Sir William Hamilton, as Britain's representative in Naples, persuaded the royal couple to sign a treaty of loyalty with Britain against the French, or at least to remain neutral. Britain, on her part, was to keep a fleet in the Mediterranean and would act to protect Naples. In 1793 Admiral Horatio Nelson arrived to show the flag and Hamilton provided him with hospitality at his villa; this was to be the start of his second problem, for then began the seeds of the famous love affair between Emma and Nelson as described in Chapter 1. Despite all the political turmoil and responsibilities that Hamilton had, he was still able to report in detail to the Royal Society in London on the major eruption of Vesuvius that occurred in 1794. The lava from that eruption entered the sea and Hamilton decided to visit the flow front by boat. He was forced to abort this plan when his boatman pointed out that the pitch on the hull was melting and the craft was starting to sink. They beached the boat nearby so that Sir William could continue his observations.

In the following turbulent years Nelson was to use his fleet to evacuate the royal family and the Hamiltons to the Sicilian capital of Palermo. Nelson himself was to be created Duke of Bronte, a small town on the NE flank of Mount Etna, for his services to the crown. The French were eventually defeated, Napoleon captured, and the Kingdom of the Two Sicilies restored as a corrupt despotism.

The Bourbon Dynasty in Naples was eventually overthrown in 1860 by Giuseppe Garibaldi as his army swept up Italy from Sicily to achieve the Unification of Italy under the rule of King Victor Emmanuel II. Following unification, Naples, and the south of Italy in general, became progressively poorer. Naples was particularly impoverished when captured by the Allied armies during the Second World War. Many lived in poor conditions and some starved.

Today

Since 1945, considerable state aid has served to improve the situation in the Naples region, although there is still high unemployment, crime and poverty. Agriculture has remained important, but there has been considerable growth in manufacturing industry. As a result of the latter, air pollution has become a serious matter in Naples and the surrounding towns. There has been a massive expansion in building, much of it illegal, although this is now largely under control. Nevertheless, the major expansion in urban zones has substantially increased the risk from eruptive activity, not only from Vesuvius, but also from the adjacent Campi Flegrei volcano.

The current population of the city of Naples is over two million with a 20% increase during the last 30 years. This increase is despite the fact that many have left the city for other places outside the region, or have moved to nearby towns and villages on the flanks of Vesuvius, thus increasing vulnerability. The estimated number of people living in the environs of Vesuvius (not including Naples) and at potential risk is over half a million. We will come back to this when we consider hazard and risk from Vesuvius.

Communications in the Vesuvian area range from very good to unbelievably dreadful. There are mainline train services to Rome and the north, to Sicily and the south, and also across the Apennines to Bari. In addition, there is a local train service that encircles Vesuvius, and another to towns in Campi Flegrei. The area is connected by good autostrada, and there are many country roads. Newcomers to the area, will, however, find Naples and other larger centres not easy to navigate, as the roads are often narrow and the local drivers opportunistic!

The AD 79 eruption

Let us go back to the eruption of AD 79, which has captured world imagination. Although it is pivotal to understanding Vesuvius, it is not the normal type of eruption from this volcano. Most of the eruptions since then have been much less violent. As we shall see, Vesuvius has cycles of activity each starting with an eruption of large magnitude; that of AD 79 marked the beginning of a cycle after a long period of repose.

Much of our understanding of what happened during this eruption comes from contemporary writings (mainly Pliny the Younger), excavations at buried towns and villas, and investigations of deposits from the eruption in outcrops at the archaeological sites and elsewhere.

Based on relatively modern studies, it is clear that three related volcanic processes took place during the eruption. The first was sustained plinian explosive activity in which there is a continuous jet of tephra and gas thrust out of the crater. This results from gas being exsolved from the magma below the surface, the bubbles rising, expanding and coalescing so as to fragment the magma into particles. The combined mixture exits at high velocity into the atmosphere and rises until all momentum is lost. During this uprush, the more massive fragments fall out on ballistic trajectories until only the smaller particles are left. These continue to rise as the column ascends by convection, the particles being carried up by the buoyant gas. Air is entrained as the column rises, thus cooling it, and eventually the material at the top of the column falls to ambient temperature and stalls shortly after. From then on the fine entrained ash falls either symmetrically round the source if there is no wind (a very rare situation), or is carried downwind and progressively finer particles fall out as the cloud moves away from the volcano. Such activity can be sustained for hours or days. The deposits consist in the near-vent region of pumice beds. Very proximal deposits have large pumice blocks tens of centimetres across with a relatively wide range of sizes; but down-wind the deposits become better sorted with lapilli becoming smaller, and finally finer ash is deposited.

The situation becomes more complicated if the convective phase cannot be sustained because the density of the eruptive column is too high. When this occurs, there is a sudden collapse of the column, and clouds of pumice, ash and gas fall from the column under gravity. Two types of fragmental flows are formed: those that are low density consisting of a turbulent cloud of ash and gas, and those that are of high-density clouds that, for the most part, deposit from laminar flow. The former are known as *pyroclastic surges*, and the latter as *pyroclastic flows*. Surges form deposits that are often thin and are not always preserved, but are nevertheless disastrous. When they are preserved they typically consist of thin planar beds, cross-bedded units and beds banked against obstacles in their path. Surges from plinian activity are normally hot (>200 °C). They can erode the surface that they travel over, ripping up vegetation and incorporating it into the flow sometimes as carbonized wood. Where surges entered towns during the AD 79 eruption, buildings were toppled, and roof tiles torn off and carried with the flow. Humans and other living creatures die by burning, or by asphyxiation as ash clogs the trachea.

The denser pyroclastic flows deposit a massive bed of poorly sorted material emplaced at high temperature. These ground-hugging flows can not only destroy, but also rapidly bury large areas. The dense part of pyroclastic flows is usually accompanied by a less dense, but hot surge cloud of hurricane proportions rising above it and, whereas the dense pyroclastic flow will normally follow the topography, the surge may not. Where a valley-following pyroclastic flow encounters a bend, it is possible for the denser flow to be retained in the valley, whereas the surge component may detach and leave the valley and continue in its original direction. This happened on Mont Pelée, Martinique, in 1902 when a detached surge destroyed the town of St. Pierre, killing some 27 000 people. Similar events of this type have occurred recently; for example, on Mt Unzen in Japan, killing 43 people including three volcanologists, at Merapi in Indonesia, where 64 were killed, and at Montserrat, where there were at least 19 fatalities.

With these thoughts in mind one can see the potential danger of eruptions at Vesuvius, especially those similar to that of AD 79, the largest in historical time. One of the most important reasons for studying past eruptions is to use what happened to predict what may happen again, first to recognize indications of an impending eruption, and second to predict the possible eruptive behaviour. With regard to the first, it is easy to be wise after the event.

Two phenomena have been seen as possible precursors of what happened in AD 79. The earthquake centred on Vesuvius in AD 62 did a fair amount of damage to towns around Naples. This was 17 years before the eruption. Whether it was directly concerned with what was to follow is debatable, but there is a strong possibility that this was an indication that Vesuvius was awakening. We have no idea if there were unfelt precursory swarms of quakes, but Pliny notes that earth tremors occurred just before the eruption, but were not taken seriously. There is also some evidence from excavations of the Roman beach at Herculaneum that there was uplift of the area some weeks or months before the eruption started. Some springs round the volcano also dried up, indicating a change in the water table.

Pliny the Younger, then 17 years old, gives us a graphic account in a letter to Tacitus of what happened. This was based on his observations from nearly 30 km away at Capo Miseno (see Chapter 3), where he lived with his mother. His uncle, Pliny the Elder, was

Admiral of the Roman fleet that was based in the Porto di Misenum. The account of the eruption by Pliny, probably the first of its kind, is marked by a lack of drama or fear, and shows an observant and amazingly calm approach to what must have been a most frightening event.

The story starts when Pliny's mother noticed a large cloud rising to the east. It quickly took on what was described as a pine tree shape. It should be noted that the pines of the area are stone pines (*Pinus pinea*), which have a tall trunk with a spreading foliage at the top (Fig. 2.6). Pliny's uncle climbed a hill to determine from where it was coming. The cloud was white with blotchy dark areas, which the young Pliny identified as owing to ashes and 'soil' being carried up in the cloud.

Once he had identified the source the uncle called for a boat to be made ready to visit the site. Initially this was to have been a fact-finding mission, but it rapidly became clear that people were in danger, and Pliny the Elder ordered the fleet to be launched. As he approached the coast hot ashes began to drop on the boats and they ran into rafts of floating pumice. He was forced to abandon his plan of rescuing Rectina, a friend who lived near Oplontis, because of the mass of floating pumice, and he turned south to land at Stabiae, where people were prepared to load their goods and be evacuated. The Admiral, however, took his time, insisting on a bath and dinner. His nephew attributes this to his desire to calm the people. That night they saw sheets of fire and were subjected to a steady rain of pumice. The buildings were shaking violently from earth tremors. They were in severe danger from toppling walls, and of being trapped in the buildings by the accumulation of pumice preventing doors from being opened. They left, venturing out with pillows tied to their heads to soften the blows of falling pumice and stones.

When daybreak came, it remained dark. Thick ash obscured the sun. The Admiral went down to the shore only to find that the wind was against them and the sea too rough for them to escape by boat. He was clearly exhausted, and lay down to rest. Not for long, because the party were overwhelmed by the smell of sulphur and 'approaching fire'. They tried to lift the Admiral, but he collapsed. Meanwhile others had fled. Almost certainly they were about to be overwhelmed by a pyroclastic surge, but it is probable that the Admiral died of a heart attack as a result of the stress. His nephew makes it clear that he was overweight and not in good health. We shall never know exactly what happened.

Meanwhile, Pliny the Younger sat in his home in Misenum writing with, apparently, little concern for what was going on. During the first night the earthquakes became increasingly violent and he and his mother left their beds and sat in the forecourt, Pliny absorbed in reading a volume of Livy. Buildings started tottering, and mother and son were forced to leave the town, followed by others. Once out of town, and out of danger of being crushed by falling roofs and walls, they planned an escape in carriages. However, ground movement was so violent that the carriages were thrown about. At that point the sea was sucked out, leaving sea creatures stranded, and they saw a 'fearful black cloud . . . rent by forked and quivering bursts of flame'. The cloud sank to the ground and covered the sea, spreading out to blot out Capri, and eventually passed close to them, obscuring the nearby peninsula and covering them with fine ash. What they observed was probably a pyroclastic surge that travelled across the Bay of Naples. By the time it reached Capo Miseno it had probably lost most of it energy through travelling over water and Pliny makes no mention of high temperatures. Pliny's mother implored him to leave her and escape, but he refused. Then a second dense black cloud was seen coming towards them 'spreading over the earth like a flood'. Conditions were so bad that Pliny and his mother left the road to avoid being trampled down by people in panic. Eventually the heavy showers of ash ceased and they saw a scene of devastation, everywhere covered with ash like snow drifted against the buildings. The earthquakes continued, but they were able to return to their home under a pale yellow sun.

This short, but succinct, description of the early part of the eruption serves to describe the effects on people distant from the eruption and upwind of it. It takes little imagination to understand the plight of those at the foot of the volcano, or downwind where metres of tephra were falling at an equivalent distance. We can interpret what happened there only by studies of the deposits that we see today, and the associated archaeological remains. The following is based largely on a careful geological and archaeological reconstruction by Haraldur Sigurdsson and his colleagues.

The eruption started with a mild phreatomagmatic explosion that produced a few centimetres thick bed of fine grey ash that has its largest extension to the east. The explosion cleared the central conduit, allowing the main eruption to begin. This ash layer is overlain by a thick pumice layer over 3 m thick at its maximum development. The tephra was deposited over a wide area, as far as the Ionian Sea. Maximum pumice sizes of over 30 cm are recorded, but at Pompeii directly downwind 10 km away, pumice was typically 1 cm across, although the largest found there is 20 cm. Lithic fragments of limestone and lava, representing rocks torn from the vent walls as the vesiculating magma was driven to the surface, are common in these deposits. They are probably the 'blackened stones' described as falling on Pliny the Elder's fleet together with the pumice. Isopachs for the pumice indicate that the wind was blowing in a consistent direction during this phase of the eruption and that the ash and pumice were borne to the SW, with little falling elsewhere. The total volume is estimated at 3.6 km^3 (dense rock equivalent), erupted during a period of at least 18 h.

The plinian fall deposit (Figs 2.7 and 2.8) forms two distinctive layers; the lower is white, the upper grey. The colour difference reflects an abrupt change in composition of the erupting magma, indicating partial evacuation of a chemically zoned magma reservoir. The grey pumice layer is more widely distributed than the white, has larger pumice and the percentage of lithic fragments increases from 12% to 20%. All these factors suggest that the grey pumice was ejected at the climax of the plinian phase late on the night of 24 August at the time when Pliny describes violent earth tremors at Misenum. None of the pumice is reported to have fallen in Capo Miseno, which was up-wind of the eruption. During this climactic phase, at least three surges occurred as a result of limited column collapse. These produced thin ash deposits interbedded with the grey ash. It is estimated that the height of the eruptive column was 27 km, rising to 33 km at the climax of the eruption.

Overlying the pumice fall materials are up to at least 20 m of pyroclastic flow and surge deposits (Fig. 2.7), as well as fine ash with accretionary lapilli. Because pyroclastic flows and surges are topograpically controlled and each one may have a restricted distribution, there are differences between rock sequences on different parts of the

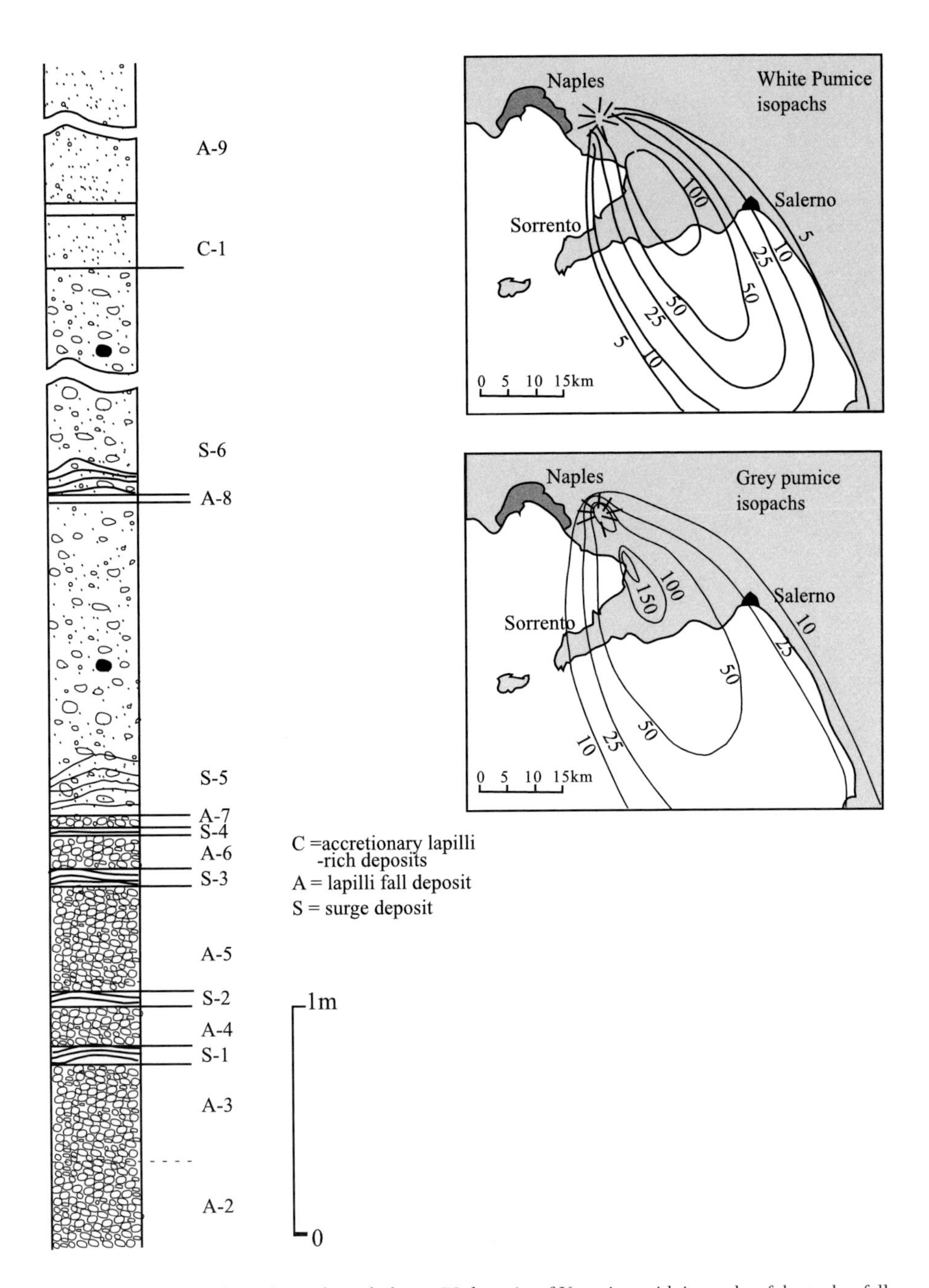

Fig. 2.7. Stratigraphic column through the AD 79 deposits of Vesuvius, with isopachs of the tephra fall materials (redrawn from Sigurdsson *et al.* 1985).

Fig. 2.8. Plaster cast of a tree excavated from the AD 79 deposits of Vesuvius at Villa Regina, Boscoreale. The lower part of the tree was initially buried by the lapilli fall of the plinian phase of the eruption; the upper part was then bent over by the pyroclastic surges and flows that followed. A section through the deposits is seen in the background.

mountain. Six thin pyroclastic surge deposits are present, intercalated with pyroclastic fall and flow deposits. The first surge (S1) probably took place at about 1 a.m. on 25 August, covering the south and west flank of the volcano, with only small lobes travelling over the Somma wall to the north. It formed a deposit which at Herculaneum is tens of centimetres thick and consists of silty grey ash. It is massive at the base, but cross-bedded in the upper parts. Directly above the surge deposit is a pyroclastic flow deposit (F1), a massive consolidated deposit less than 1.5 m thick. This is overlain by a layer of grey pumice representing continued eruption from a stable plinian column. The deposit is coarser than that of the first phase, indicating a higher eruption column and thus higher eruption rate.

A second surge deposit (S2), probably formed about an hour later, has some three times the volume of the S1 deposit and is much more widespread, extending well to the north and east of the volcano as well as reaching the sea to the west. The deposit is up to 24 cm thick and consists of relatively massive sand-grade material with faint stratification and some cross-bedded structures. To the south it is split by a thin pumice layer, indicating that the surge had two close-spaced pulses. Overlying it are pyroclastic flow deposits (F2) found at the coast north of Herculaneum and on the northern flank of the volcano towards Pollena and Santa Anastasia.

Fall deposits rich in lithic fragments follow, indicating erosion of the conduit walls and widening of the vent; this activity lasted for about 4 h. Overlying is material of the third surge (S3), which is more restricted in area than S2 and does not occur north and east of the Somma crest. At Herculaneum it is a sand-grade ash 10 cm thick. This may have been a smaller surge, but the pyroclastic flow deposit (F3) emplaced almost immediately after was large and extended the coastline at Herculaneum by 400 m. Here it is up to 10 m thick and is rich in both pumice and lithic fragments. Although its origin has been debated, some arguing that it is a lahar, it was clearly emplaced at high temperature because of the presence of carbonized wood (requiring temperatures of at least 250 °C and probably more like 400 °C) and palaeomagnetic measurements on lithic clasts that show evidence of being emplaced at a similar temperature.

Above the pyroclastic flow deposit is a darker and more lithic-rich pumice fall deposit that was formed over a period of about an hour. Column collapse occurred again to form the fourth surge deposit (S4). This deposit (Fig. 2.7) is found only to the west and south, and was the first to hit Pompeii. This surge deposit is directly overlain by a fifth surge deposit (S5), probably formed only a few minutes after the previous one. This is much more extensive and is found round the northern and western flanks of Vesuvius. At Pompeii it consists of up to 11 cm of cross-bedded ash. S4 and S5 in many exposures form a distinctive doublet, although in some outcrops there is a thin layer of pumice dividing them.

The next fall material is less coarse, indicating a diminishing height for the eruption column. The proportion of lithic fragments is also higher. Then came the sixth surge deposit (S6), the most extensive of the whole eruption. This material, up to 1 m thick, is found round the whole volcano and is interpreted as the deposit emplaced from the surge that overwhelmed Pliny the Elder and travelled across the water to the far western peninsula of Misenum 30 km away, where its arrival caused pandemonium as described by Pliny the Younger. Most of the inhabitants of Pompeii were probably killed by this surge. Near the volcano the deposit tends to be rich in sand-grade lithic particles. S6 grades up to a pyroclastic flow deposit.

The uppermost deposits from the AD 79 eruption were formed from a phreatomagmatic phase and consist of ashes with accretionary lapilli, and thin, fine-grained deposits from wet surges. There are about 20 units extending for at least 10 km radius from the volcano. This represented a phase when the eruption was waning and ground water was penetrating the system, as it might have done earlier but with only minor effect. How long this activity continued is unknown, as by then the whole area was deserted, and Pliny makes no mention of it.

Finally, using the timing provided by Pliny, and the evidence of the strata, let us look at what the archaeological sites can do to complete our picture of this incredible eruption, the major part of which lasted just 2 days. Let us start with Pompeii. It is likely the people here saw the first phreatomagmatic explosion, but the ash did not reach them as the wind was blowing from the west. The wind then moved round to blow directly from the volcano to Pompeii. They thus caught the brunt of the heavy fall of pumice throughout the eruption. In fact, Pompeii was located in an area of maximum accumulation of pumice on the volcano (Fig. 2.4). The people of Pompeii and the area surrounding were therefore at considerable risk for their lives, not only from falling projectiles, but also from collapse of roofs under the weight of tephra.

It appears likely that many people fled. The early surges did not reach the town, but S3 just reached the north side of the town in the early hours of second day, and must have added to the alarm of remaining citizens. The next pyroclastic surge at some time between 7 and 8 a.m. did hit Pompeii and was responsible for the majority of deaths in the city, probably some 2000, and possibly many outside. Death was not fast, as indicated by the agonized position of the bodies (Fig. 2.9); most apparently died by asphyxiation. At the time the surge hit, Pompeii was already half buried; the next surge and following pyroclastic flow not only buried the victims but toppled the upper parts of many buildings projecting above the pumice layer. There was no chance of anyone in this area surviving.

At Herculaneum events were very different. Although closer to the volcano than Pompeii (Figs 2.4 and 2.5), very little material fell during the first phase of the eruption. During the whole of 24 August the view from the town of Vesuvius spewing out material into a great cloud rising high into the sky, but being carried away from them by the wind,

Fig. 2.9. Cast of the body of a child killed at Pompeii by pyroclastic surges during the AD 79 eruption of Vesuvius.

must have been spectacular. Because no bodies were found in the early excavations, it was assumed that most of the people, scared by what they saw, had escaped during the early hours of the eruption. Only some ten skeletons had been found in the ruins. Excavations in 1982, and onwards, on the waterfront outside the wall of Herculaneum, throw a completely different light on the matter. Hundreds of skeletons have been discovered along the city wall, both on the beach and huddled in alcoves, the latter probably used to store boats and fishing gear. Only a small area has so far been excavated, allowing for the possibility that many more victims remain.

The story, although far from complete, that emerges from interpretations of the excavations at Herculaneum is that the city and its environs received only a light coating of ash during the first 12 h of activity. Although this was not life threatening, the view of Vesuvius only a few kilometres away with its tall, probably incandescent column rushing out of the crater and generating forks of lightning and thunderous bangs would have been an awesome sight. Many frightened people must have left their homes, fleeing north to Naples. For those few hundred people left in the town, the sight of the first surge in the early hours of the morning on the second day must have been beyond belief; a cloud of fire rushing towards them. We do not know if the majority of people who were killed had already moved to the beach in preparation for departure either by boat or on foot, or whether they had dashed there thinking the sea wall would protect them. The surge probably took no less than 4 minutes to reach them, and caught them as they sought to protect themselves. The surge hit, carrying roof tiles and other debris picked up as it swept through the town partly destroying buildings. Some people may have been killed by being hit by these flying objects, but most died instantly from the heat. The pyroclastic flow that followed just a short while later was mainly diverted by the town walls but swung round onto the beach and the deposits buried the newly dead. It also buried and carbonized an upturned boat. There may be other boats yet unexcavated, but on the basis of this one, the fact that it was not prepared for sea suggests there was no existing plan for a marine escape as the people rushed for the beach.

We can assume that when the second surge hit the town an hour later, all remaining inhabitants were dead, but the high velocity of this surge caused major destruction of buildings. The whole town was finally buried by the deposits of the third pyroclastic flow, leaving only the remains of the theatre poking up above the surface. Deposits from this flow extended the land for a nearly half a kilometre from the pre-eruption shoreline.

Thus, based on geological, archaeological and first-hand accounts, the course of this famous eruption and its effects on the population and their property is now remarkably well understood. Apart from making a major impact on volcanological knowledge, especially in providing input into theoretical models, it also provides a 'worst case' model for hazard and risk analysis.

History of excavations at Pompeii and Herculaneum

The ruins of Herculaneum and Pompeii lay buried and undiscovered for nearly 16 centuries. Covering Pompeii was a cultivated mound known as La Civita, the City, and Herculaneum was near the expanding town of Portici. The story of the excavation of these two Roman centres and other sites is a fascinating one and deserves further reading. The following is a brief résumé of the main developments.

Roman maps clearly show the main towns of the area that were to be buried by the AD 79 tephra. Nevertheless, the towns rapidly became lost, after some early looting. The existence of a buried town, Herculaneum, in the area south of Portici was known by 1594, and the existence of the remains of a town below La Civita was clear by 1637, on the basis of fragments of buildings excavated while digging irrigation channels. It was thought by most that the latter was the ancient town of Stabiae despite the discovery of a tablet inscribed with the name Pompeii.

The exploration of Herculaneum was triggered by a peasant who, while digging for a well, found marble blocks clearly belonging to a building. The land was bought by a Prince Elbouf, who was constructing a country house nearby. He employed workmen to be lowered into the well and dig horizontal exploratory tunnels, a dangerous exercise because of trapped CO_2 gas underground. There followed incredible finds of statues and other artefacts in splendid buildings; most objects of art were to make their way into Elbouf's new house, or be shipped to dignitaries elsewhere in Europe. That phase of exploration ceased in 1716, but was renewed with vigour in 1738. Then, until 1765, shafts were cut, without discrimination, in all directions, punching through walls, destroying frescos and other objects of art. Although the excavations were crude and inflicted archaeological damage on the site, they did produce amazing finds. Visitors to Naples were led round this underground city by the light of smoking torches.

Excavations at La Civita began in the mid-eighteenth century and the site was confirmed to be the fabled city of Pompeii in 1763. This was a much easier area to work than Herculaneum, and whole buildings could be uncovered rather than be explored by tunnels (Fig. 2.10).

Fig. 2.10. Excavations at Pompeii showing the discovery of the Temple of Isis. As depicted by Pietro Fabris in a painting commissioned by Sir William Hamilton (Hamilton 1776).

The early work was cloaked in secrecy, and when the German archaeologist, Johann Winckelmann, arrived at Naples in 1758 he was rebuffed and not allowed to examine the site. He returned 4 years later and was convinced that from an archaeological point of view the excavations were being bungled; greed, he considered was the prime motive behind the work. He wrote a widely distributed 'open letter', followed by a supplement, expressing rather forcibly his views. They were in German, and as a consequence, were not read in Naples until a French translation became available, a copy being in the hands of Sir William Hamilton, who took a great interest in the excavations and even collected some of the artefacts. The discoveries at Pompeii became well known over Europe and many famous people arrived to admire them. What they saw had a strong influence on art and decoration of the time.

At Herculaneum, work to expose buildings by removing the overlying materials began in 1828, although initially it was not very successful. The first systematic excavation and recording at both sites began in the mid-nineteenth century under the direction of Giuseppi Fiorelli, who invented the technique of making plaster casts of the cavities left by the bodies of those buried in Pompeii. Objects and paintings were left *in situ* as far as possible. By the end of the century, villas in the surrounding countryside had also been discovered.

Major advances in uncovering both Herculaneum and Pompeii were made in the early twentieth century, but this ceased during the Second World War. Post-war excavation began in 1951 with emphasis on conservation. In the 1980s important new discoveries were made at Herculaneum, when the seafront to the town was excavated.

Oplontis figures as a major city on Roman maps, but it was only discovered in 1964 at Torre Annunziata. Only one large villa has been discovered, but exploration is difficult because the site is completely built over.

Prehistoric stratigraphy

Knowledge of the rocks below Vesuvius comes from a borehole drilled on the southern slopes of Vesuvius and reaching a depth of more than 2000 m within the Mesozoic carbonate basement. Pre-Vesuvius volcanic rocks range in age from 400 ka and involve tephritic lavas and some trachyandesitic tephra fall, possibly from Campi Flegrei.

The most ancient dated rocks of Vesuvius are around 300 ka old, based on K/Ar and Ar/Ar age determinations. The initial construct of Vesuvius, the Somma volcano, is made of both lavas and pyroclastic rocks, which built a mountain at least as high as the present Vesuvius. Part of this sequence is exposed in the walls of the Somma caldera (Plate 3) where it is cut by numerous dykes. It is also seen in the floors of valleys and in deep quarries at the volcano's foot.

How much explosive activity occurred during the Somma part of the history of Vesuvius is not known, but at least two major explosive events are recorded in the sequence. The first, known as the Codola eruption, took place about 25 ka BP (Fig. 2.11) and deposits from this event are poorly exposed. The first products are a white pumice fall deposit that grades up to a green and green and white banded pumice. Above this is a massive

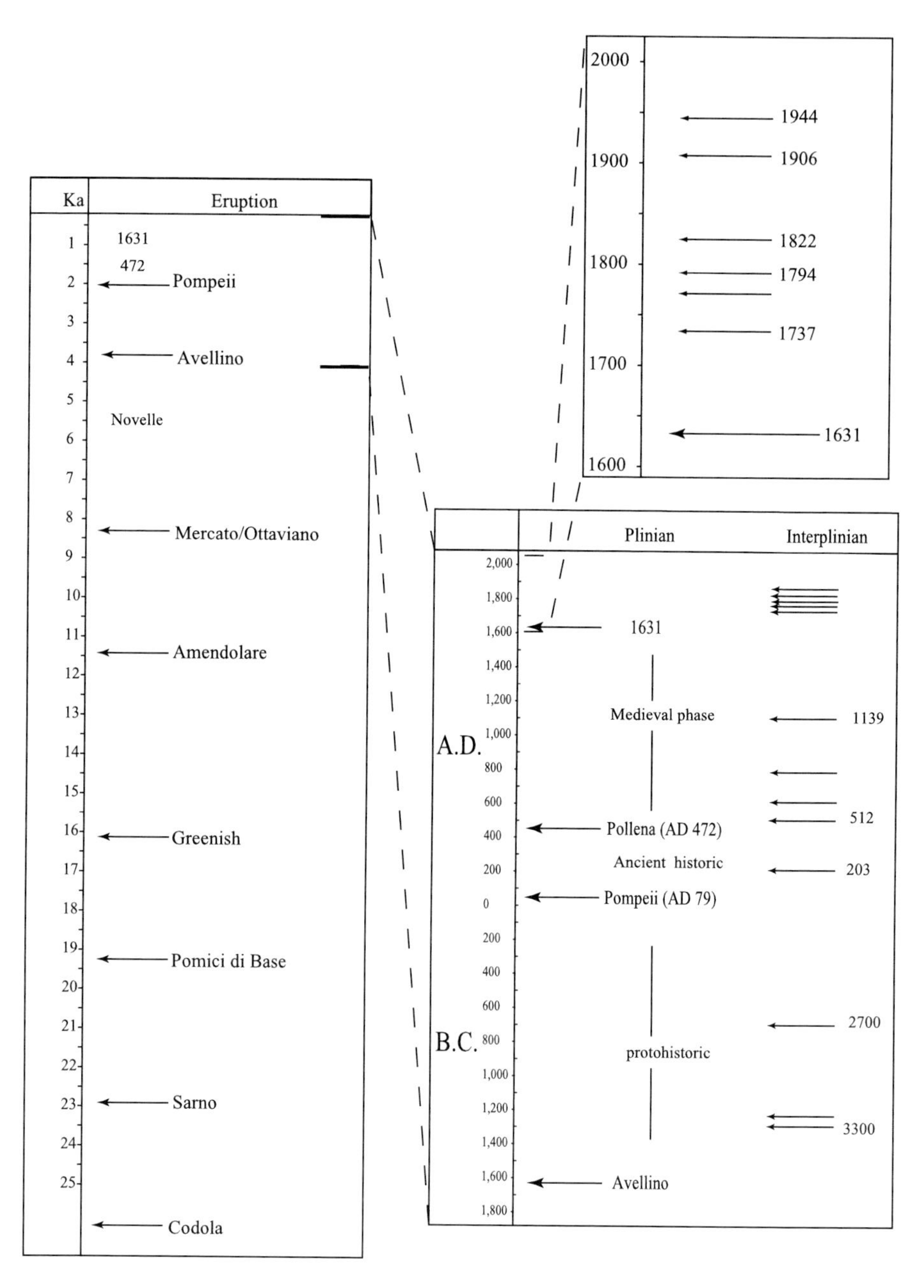

Fig. 2.11. Chronological chart of eruptions from Vesuvius.

ash deposit probably of phreatomagmatic origin. At 20 km from the volcano the deposit from this eruption is half a metre thick, indicating a substantial eruption.

A second major explosive eruption occurred about 22 ka BP and is referred to as the Sarno eruption. Again, there are few outcrops of the deposits and all are in the plains east of the volcano up to 12 km from the vent. The deposits show mainly fall materials consisting of white pumices at the base grading up to grey ones at the top.

This pattern of a major plinian eruption occurring every few thousand years continued, breaking the volcano's activity into cycles each started by such activity. Probably the largest eruption in the history of Vesuvius took place about 18.5 ka ago and not only started a new cycle, but marked a change in the style of activity from dominantly effusive eruptions to both explosive and effusive activity. Outcrops of the deposit from this eruption, known as the Pomici di Base (Basal Pumice), are limited, but show that the eruption was a strong one of plinian character. It is likely this was the eruption that truncated the Somma Volcano, although other collapses may have occurred since. The youngest lavas on the northern flank of the Somma caldera rim are 20 ka old, indicating that initial truncation of the cone occurred after this time; the Pomici di Base eruption was the next one.

After the Pomici di Base eruption little is known about the activity of the volcano until the next major eruption, apart from evidence of lateral effusive eruptions. One and a half thousand years later the so-called Greenish plinian eruption took place, forming a sequence of deposits familiar on Vesuvius and consisting of early pumice fall material followed by surge and pyroclastic flow sequences. The next large eruption took place *c.* 11 ka ago. The deposits of this eruption, known as the Lagno Amendolare Pumice, have been found in only a few outcrops. It does not have the same pattern as other plinian deposits on the volcano and as such is a useful marker in the stratigraphy. The lowest strata in the deposit are white pumices with a tendency to darken upwards. Above this the pumice is mixed with black scoria, or has sharply defined scoria beds. Whether this deposit represents a plinian or sub-plinian event is not known.

The Mercato (or Ottaviano) eruption was clearly plinian in character. It occurred around 8000 a BP, and the deposits are typical of Vesuvian plinian activity. Outcrops show early pumice fall with later valley-filling pyroclastic flows and surge deposits on the interfluves. Caldera collapse probably occurred during this eruption. Following this eruption, there was a fairly long period of repose of around 4500 years punctuated by at least one sub-plinian event known as the Novelle eruption, which is of unknown age.

The penultimate plinian activity at 3400 a BP is known as the Avellino eruption. This eruption produced a sequence of deposits that are much the same in appearance as the deposits of AD 79; they are so similar that for some time they were considered to be the products of the same eruption. The deposits consist of lapilli-fall material that is of a comparable thickness to that of AD 79, and there is also a similar colour and compositional change from white to grey upwards through the deposit. The dispersal of the Avellino deposit is, however, to the east. Overlying the lapilli is a sequence of sandwave-bedded pyroclastic surge deposits that have been interpreted as being of a phreatomagmatic origin, again similar to the AD 79 sequence. Caldera formation probably accompanied this eruption.

In a striking similarity to the AD 79 eruption, a Bronze Age village has recently been found preserved in the Avellino deposits at Nola near Pompeii. Huts, vases and other utensils have been unearthed, together with an oven containing pots. Skeletons of goats, some in cages, have also been found.

Between the Avellino eruption and that of AD 79 there are records of three smaller eruptions, in the seventh century BC, in 216 BC and an undated one.

In summary, the plinian eruptions of Vesuvius show a number of trends upon which several models for Vesuvian plinian activity have been based. These trends include: all the plinian events begin with a large, sustained convecting eruption column; fallout from the column was dispersed to the eastern side of the volcano, with only one exception, owing to the prevailing wind of the region; many of the lapilli deposits contain carbonate lithic fragments indicating fragmentation of the country rock; there is evidence for phreatomagmatic activity associated with formation of the pyroclastic flows and surges (increased fragmentation, increased lithic content); and Vesuvius appears to have a fairly regular periodicity with major plinian eruptions occurring on average every few thousand years.

The post-AD 79 activity

For the 400 years following AD 79 little is recorded about activity at Vesuvius, apart from a possible sub-plinian event at AD 203; but we do know there was a major plinian eruption (known as the Pollena eruption) in AD 472. This late fifth-century eruption was, based on the deposits, the largest since that of AD 79. That of AD 968 is the first in historical time when it is known that a lava flow accompanied explosive activity. The eruptions of 1037 and 1139 both had lavas that extended to the coast.

The 1631 sub-plinian eruption (Fig. 2.11), which killed over 4000 people and caused some 40 000 people to be evacuated, was again to change the pattern of activity at Vesuvius. Historical records indicate that precursory activity took place around 2 weeks before the eruption with changes inside the crater, and that increased fumarolic activity together with possible red glows from the summit may have occurred several months before. During the week before the start of the eruption there were felt quakes and ground uplift.

The course of this devastating sub-plinian eruption is known from both the deposits and historical accounts. Recent volcanological studies agree on the broad sequence of explosive events that took place over a 3 day period. Explosions started in the morning of 16 December when a sustained column developed, reaching a height of some 20–22 km by mid-afternoon. This activity was accompanied by tremor. The column became lower during the night, but there were more than 100 felt earthquakes. During the following morning pyroclastic flows spread down the mountain towards the sea. Several earthquakes of high intensity were felt during this phase and continued into the next day, when more pyroclastic flows were formed. Pyroclastic flows from this eruption rushed down most of the valleys that drained the volcano. Areas struck included Torre del Greco and Torre Annunziata to the south, Boscotrecase to the SE and S. Anastasia and San Sebastiano to the north. Several of these pyroclastic flows overtopped the Somma caldera rim. Penecontemporaneous reworking of pyroclastic material caused lahars in some areas.

During the eruption, vertical ground deformation caused the sea to retreat, and later return in the form of tsunamis.

There is some controversy over whether there were lava flows during the final phases; from a hazard point of view this is somewhat academic, as pyroclastic flows would have caused far more widespread destruction than any lavas. The eruption ended during the early afternoon of 18 December.

The period of activity between 1631 and 1944 is well documented. During this time Vesuvius was in a state of almost continuous activity mainly at the summit crater. This activity, known as persistent activity, consisted mainly of strombolian explosions, punctuated by mild eruptions that involved lava overflowing from the summit crater (Fig. 2.12), sometimes quietly, at other times accompanied by explosions up to the scale of lava fountains. In some cases lava escaped the central conduit along fractures and erupted on the upper flanks: most of these events were small, but some lavas reached the sea. In other cases effusion near the foot of the summit cone produced slowly forming cupolas of lava. Brief repose periods of a few years break up the periods of persistent activity; and cycles can be recognized each ending in a vigorous eruption known as a 'final eruption'. Cycles range in duration from at least 32 years to about 2 years, with repose periods of just under 2 years to about 6 years. Between 1638 and 1944 there were 18 cycles of activity.

The so-called 'final' eruptions that terminate a cycle typically begin with effusive outpourings of lava on the flanks of the volcano during which time there are explosive detonations at the summit crater. Effusion continues for a few days, threatening towns

Fig. 2.12. Sketch of the summit of Vesuvius during the 1831 eruption. The vent is to the top right with the lava spreading towards the observers. The cliffs of the Atrio de Cavallo are to the upper left. The person facing away from the eruption showing no interest in it is probably a guide who brought a group up to observe the lava. (From the Johnston-Lavis collection, University College London.)

and property on the volcano flanks. Towns such as Torre del Grecco on the western flanks of the volcano have been inundated by lava several times since 1631 (Fig. 2.1). As the effusion diminishes, explosive activity at the summit increases in strength. Many of the final eruptions then begin their most explosive phases, with eruption columns and sometimes fire fountains up to several kilometres in height. During these paroxysmal phases destruction of part of the main cone or 'beheading', as it is sometimes called, often takes place. Such activity fills the population of Naples with both dread and awe in equal measures. There are many beautiful paintings of the volcano at night during these paroxysmal periods of activity.

As noted before, many fine paintings were commissioned by Sir William Hamilton. He kept a detailed log of eruptive activity during the last half of the 18th century. In this he was aided by Padre Antonio Piaggio, whom he paid to make daily observations, between 1779 and 1794, from his home in Resina near the Herculaneum excavations. The Padre produced his Diary of Vesuvius in eight volumes, now in the British Museum in London. Between 1764 and the end of the century, Hamilton was to witness three complete cycles of activity separated by two repose periods of 27 and 44 months, respectively. His detailed records are, therefore, representative of this style of Vesuvian activity.

The classic eruption of 1906 is probably the best documented of any of the 'final' events occurring in the period 1631–1944. The scholars and early volcanologists who were in Naples at the time made several long accounts of the 1906 eruption. The account of the American Frank Perret, who was stationed for much of the time at the Vesuvius Observatory located only 2 km west of the crater, is a classic, and contains many detailed and interesting descriptions of the volcanic phenomena that occurred.

From 1872, Vesuvius had been in a relatively continuous period of mild effusion of lavas. The 1906 eruption (Fig. 2.13), which ended this persistent activity, began on 4 April and lasted for 16 days; some reports indicate that signs of increased activity, marked by the notable ash content of the plume together with elevated seismicity, were first observed on the morning of 2 April 1906. Lava flows during the initial phases of activity on 4, 5 and 6 April from several vents opened at progressively lower altitudes on the SE flank of the cone. The formation of the lavas was associated with moderate explosive activity at the summit that waxed and waned every few hours. The longest of the lava flows reached around 5 km from the cone.

As the eruption progressed, the intensity of explosive activity increased, particularly as the lava flows waned. Many strong detonations on 7 April were associated with what Perret described as 'flashing arcs'. He described at the instant of each explosion, but before it could be sensed by the eye or ear, 'a thin luminous arc would flash upward and outward from the crater and disappear into space'. This phenomenon was interpreted by Perret as a 'condensation-rarcfraction spherical shell caused by the explosion'. What he observed was a type of shock wave.

Overarching of the eruption column to the NE caused particularly heavy fallout in that area. It is also interesting to note that many windows in Ottaviano were broken on the side of buildings facing away from the volcano. This is considered to be due to inrushing winds towards the eruption column. During the day on 8 April there was a continuous eruption column estimated by Perret to be 13 km in height. On 9 April

Fig. 2.13. Photograph by Frank Perret of an explosion during the 1906 eruption of Vesuvius. Note the small pyroclastic flow cloud at the foot of the column. (From the Johnston-Lavis collection, University College London.)

accretionary lapilli were observed to fall, some 'as large as an egg'. During this period and until the end of the eruption activity was characterized by the formation of intermittent moderate ash clouds that declined in intensity. It was at this point in the eruption that the first of the 'hot avalanches' were observed. Hot fine ash accumulated to a depth of 15 m in the region of the summit cone and Perret recognized this ash as being 'dilated', and noted that it was easily dislodged by earthquakes and moved down the mountain in a manner similar to 'silent snow avalanches'. Perret described several of these 'hot avalanches', many of which were triggered by earthquakes and occurred for the next several days. One, on 13 April, travelled directly toward the Observatory but was deflected by the lava cupola upon which it is built.

Based on his observations of this eruption, Perret developed a model for these 'final' eruptions. He argued that in the initial stages of eruption there was a column of magma with a gas phase that was essentially in equilibrium with the ambient pressure. Then, when effusive activity took place on the flank, lava drained from the central conduit above the altitude of the effusive vent, exposing a deeper level in the magma column. This new top of the column was suddenly exposed to ambient conditions and was out of equilibrium with its environment, and there was a release of gas to give an explosive phase. Some modern workers would argue that entrance of ground water into the system was a more important factor in the explosive phase of these eruptions.

The most recent eruption of Vesuvius, in 1944 (Figs 2.6 and 2.14), occurred at a bad time for the city of Naples and the surrounding environs. Naples had just been liberated by the Allies, and food and other essential supplies were in great shortage. It may be for this reason that the 1944 eruption is not very well known, and there are probably more descriptions of the 1906 eruption. The 1944 event was a typical 'final eruption'.

The eruption lasted 11 days. It began on 18 March with effusive activity from the summit cone on its northern and southern side. The southern lava flow lasted only 3 days and travelled less than 3 km. Meanwhile, the northern flow spread through the Atrio del Cavallo and down a steep valley towards the small towns of San Sebastiano and Massa. These towns had already been destroyed by lava three times previously. San Sebastiano and Massa were evacuated with the help of Allied troops, and early on 21 March lava entered the towns. Within hours much of Massa and outskirts of San Sebastiano had been overrun. Lava entering water tanks (cisterne) caused explosions, and two boys were killed by ejected blocks.

Lava effusion continued for the first 3 days of the eruption, and some explosive activity occurred at the summit crater. Because of a northerly wind this explosive activity resulted in ash up to 15 cm thick accumulating to the south. As the initial lava flows began to wane on 21 March, explosive activity became predominant and the eruption entered its paroxysmal phase. This took the form of large lava fountains, which typically ascended to a height of 1 km above the crater rim. Eight or nine distinct fountains occurred, each of which had a duration of 20 minutes to 1 hour. The last fountain was the longest and was sustained for several hours. Seismic activity was at its strongest during this time.

Photographic evidence (Fig. 2.14) also shows short pyroclastic flows occurring on the flanks of the cone during the paroxysm. These flows are similar to those described by Perret during the 1906 eruption and are probably not true pyroclastic flows, but were due to tephra becoming unstable on the steep flanks of the cone and subsequently avalanching (Fig. 2.14). Indeed, avalanche deposits formed during this phase of the eruption are conspicuous on the flanks of the cone (Plate 3). Two types of avalanche were formed, those formed by blocks and ash and those solely formed of ash. These are

Fig. 2.14. The eruption plume of Vesuvius in March 1944 looking north. Note small pyroclastic flows descending the cone. Such flows may have been formed by the overloading of tephra on the most proximal regions immediately adjacent to the vent and then dislodged by associated seismic activity. Similar 'pyroclastic flows' were described during the 1906 eruption.

interpreted to have been triggered by the strong seismic activity that was literally shaking the summit cone apart.

On the following day (22 March), explosive activity became more ash-rich with distinct detonations and helical ash columns rising to at least 6 km in height. This activity caused serious tephra fall, with ash falling often in clumps 15 cm in diameter in the region of Terzigno and Pompeii where there was a military airfield. Allied aircraft were seriously damaged. Tephra fall was such that the main trunk road between Pompeii and Salerno was open only to four-wheel-drive vehicles. There was ashfall for 4 hours in Bari and fallout occurred as far as Albania, more than 500 km distant. During the week following until 29 March, intermittent detonations and seismic crises with increasing repose intervals took place.

In total, 47 people were killed, mostly from collapsing roofs overburdened by accumulations of tephra. Emission of CO_2 through the soil continued after the eruption ended; the gas collected in pockets including basements of buildings and caused danger to life. Two people and numerous animals died as a result of asphyxiation by this odourless gas.

At the time of writing, Vesuvius has not erupted again.

Petrology

The K-rich products of Vesuvius can be assigned to three magmatic phases (Fig. 2.15). The first, Group 1, ended at about 11.5 ka BP with the Amendolare eruption, and consists of slightly undersaturated trachybasalts to trachytes. The second magmatic phase, from 7900 BC to AD 79, consists of tephrites and phonolites, whereas the third, from AD 79 to the present, is characterized by leucititic tephrites to phonolites. All the

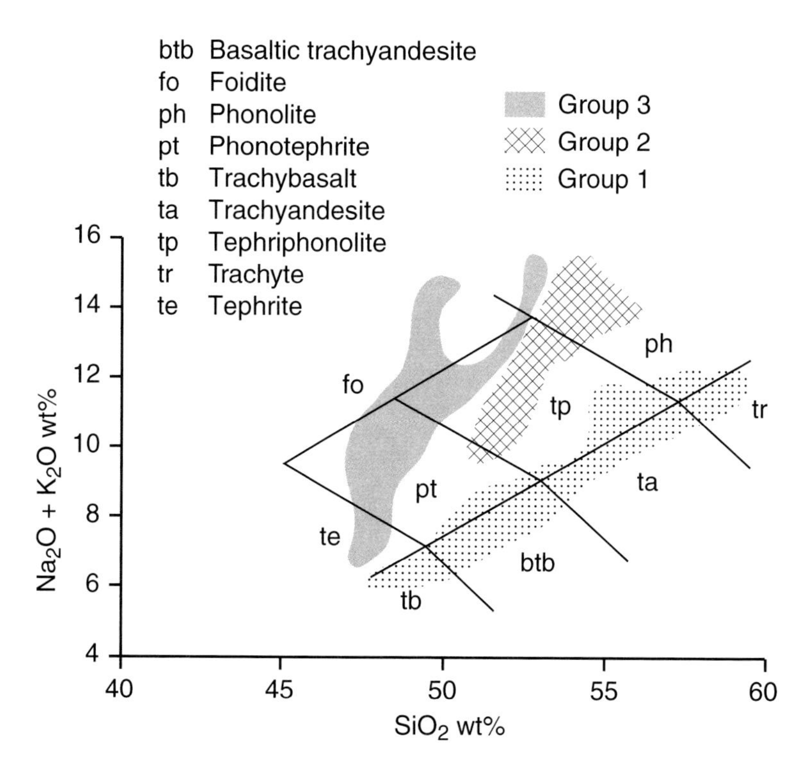

Fig. 2.15. Total alkalis–silica (TAS) plot of chemical analyses of rocks from Vesuvius (adapted from Ayuso *et al.* 1998).

products range from 47 wt% to around 59 wt% SiO_2, but Mg-number values are less than 50 and no compositions approach the values of probable mantle-derived primary liquids. This may be because mafic magmas become trapped by lower-density crustal magma reservoirs and undergo some fractionation before eruption.

The rocks of Group 1 consist mainly of trachybasalts to trachyandesites, and tephrites to tephriphonolites. Clinopyroxene, biotite, plagioclase and sanidine are the main phenocryst phases, with subordinate olivine and plagioclase. Group 2 rocks are mostly tephriphonolites with clinopyroxene, biotite and sanidine phenocrysts, with subordinate amphibole, nepheline and melanitic garnet. The products of the most recent magmatic phase, Group 3, are tephrites, phonotephrites and foidites with phenocrysts of leucite, diopside and plagioclase, with subordinate amphibole, biotite, sanidine, nepheline and melanitic garnet. There is a clear evolutionary trend towards the eruption of more undersaturated, potassic magmas throughout the history of the volcano. Leucite is present in pumices of the 1631, AD 79 and Pollena eruptions, but is absent in the deposits of older plinian events.

A wide variety of xenolith types occur in the erupted products of Vesuvius: old lava, carbonates, metamorphosed carbonates and ultramafic nodules. The metamorphosed carbonate nodules include dolomite, brucite and periclase, and are interpreted as derived from skarn-type development resulting from a high degree of metasomatism at the contact between a magma reservoir and carbonate country rocks. Fluid inclusion data indicate that these skarns equilibrated at 1.5–2.0 kbar and 850–100 °C. This would indicate that magma is stored in a reservoir system at around 5–7 km depth within crustal carbonate rocks, and this is in accord with the geophysical data, which place the carbonate sequence at between 2 and 11 km beneath the volcano.

There appears to be a correlation, as with many volcanoes, between the length of the repose time following an eruption and the degree of magma evolution and size of the subsequent eruption. The evolved magmas of trachytic–phonolitic composition give rise to explosive, typically plinian, eruptions. The pumice in the deposits of the sub-plinian and plinian eruptions show a range in their chemistry reflecting eruption from a compositionally zoned magma reservoir. This is particularly marked in the Avellino, Pollena and AD 79 eruptions. In the AD 79 eruption this is seen with the more evolved phonolitic white pumice forming the early lapilli fall beds, giving way to more basic grey hybrid tephritic–phonolitic pumice at higher levels in the sequence.

Cumulate nodules of biotite pyroxenite, wehrlite and dunite occur in the fall deposits of the Avellino, Pollena and AD 79 plinian eruptions. These nodules are distinctive in that they contain abundant CO_2 or H_2O inclusions, suggesting elevated H_2O in the magma reservoir before plinian eruptions. Fractional crystallization may lead to saturation in volatile species, which can be an important trigger of explosive activity from a shallow, evolved magma reservoir. Overpressure of H_2O, in particular, can be generated by fractional crystallization. The CO_2 and $CO_2 + H_2O$ inclusions in the cumulate nodules indicate that there was a supercritical immiscible fluid in the melt at the times these minerals crystallized.

Since 1631, eruptions have been characterized by a restricted range in magma composition from K-tephritic to K-tephriphonolitic, and it is considered that the volcanic system operated as an open conduit during this phase. Oscillatory zoning and melt inclusions in clinopyroxene phenocrysts provide a record of events in the magma reservoir before eruption. Determination of the homogenization temperature of the melt inclusions provides an indication of melt temperature.

Melt inclusions within clinopyroxene phenocrysts in tephra from the 1906 eruption reveal a fluctuation in homogenization temperature from 1100 to 1200 °C and in composition from Fs (ferrosilite)$_s$ to Fs_{14} within a single oscillatory zoned crystal. It is proposed that during open-conduit conditions the magma reservoir is of limited volume and sensitive to temperature perturbations caused by the influx of batches of hotter, more mafic magma. The variation in homogenization temperature of melt inclusions and pyroxene composition within the alternating zones of phenocrysts records the thermal and compositional fluctuation of the magma reservoir in response to injection of batches of hot, mafic magma.

The larger plinian eruptions follow extended periods when the magma reservoir was blocked and the volcano was in repose. Before the AD 79 eruption a compositionally zoned reservoir with dominantly two-fold layering developed. The layers are of contrasted composition and temperature, with an upper layer of phonolitic magma (850–900 °C) overlying phonotephritic magma (1000–1100 °C). The dynamics of eruptive extraction result in mixing of the phonotephritic magma with the more evolved upper layer and no unmixed phonotephrite is erupted.

The first real attempt at the interpretation of the petrogenesis of the magmas of Vesuvius was undertaken by Alfred Rittmann and is presented in his text on volcanoes, *Volcanoes and their Activity*. Rittmann adapted R. A. Daly's model of limestone assimilation causing desilicification resulting in undersaturated alkalic magmas. He proposed that assimilation of dolomite by trachytic magma would lead to the formation of a strongly undersaturated potassic magma:

$$\underset{\text{Orthoclase}}{2KAlSi_3O_8} + \underset{\text{Dolomite}}{CaMg(CO_3)_2} = \underset{\text{Leucite}}{2KAlSi_2O_6} + \underset{\text{Diopside}}{CaMgSi_2O_6} + 2CO_2.$$

He considered that the trend with time from trachytes to feldspathoidal phonolites was a function of progressive assimilation of carbonate rocks in the magma reservoir. The model was based on the presence of the metamorphosed carbonate nodules and the association of these strongly undersaturated potassic magmas with carbonate country rocks.

On the basis of strontium and oxygen isotope geochemistry, large-scale assimilation of carbonate metasedimentary rocks has now been largely discounted. Trace element and isotopic data suggest that the magmas of Vesuvius are derived from different source regions within a heterogeneous mantle that has been enriched in incompatible elements. The source of the fluids giving rise to the enrichment could be upward migration of fluids from depth in the mantle, or they may be derived from a subducted slab. There is, however, no evidence for current subduction beneath Vesuvius, but, as discussed in Chapter 1, this region has had a complex tectonic history, and a subduction signature in the mantle source region may reflect an older episode. Experimental work supports the idea that the primary magmas are generated by small degrees of partial melting of phlogopite-bearing peridotite under CO_2-saturated conditions.

The products associated with each of the three magmatic phases in the evolution of Vesuvius are characterized by distinct isotope ratios but there appears to be a genetic linkage between the magmas within a group. Hf/Th variation within each group is arranged along a distinctive array, indicating a systematic relationship with the erupted magmas for that group being derived from a compositionally zoned magma reservoir that remained in operation for the duration of the phase.

Each of the major plinian eruptions followed a similar pattern. That of AD 79 is the best documented and serves as an example of this activity. The initial white phonolitic pumices consist of colourless glass. The denser grey phonolitic–tephritic pumices that followed consist of brownish glass with abundant crystals, and show evidence of having been mixed with more salic phonolitic magma. It is clear that the eruption was fed from a compositionally zoned magma reservoir located within carbonate basement rocks at a depth of 3–6 km. The chemical zonation of the reservoir is interpreted as a two-fold stepwise gradation rather than a continuous compositional variation.

Petrological characteristics indicate that some of the crystals in the AD 79 grey pumice are cumulates that crystallized from different basic magmas before the eruption. Indeed, some of the diopside crystals with K-basaltic glass inclusions may have been derived from residual magma of the Avellino eruption (3400 a BP). It is proposed that the parental magma feeding the AD 79 magma reservoir ranged between K-basanitic and K-tephritic in composition. This is similar in composition to the magma feeding the open-conduit conditions that have been in operation between 1631 and 1944, and supports a steady-state model with supply of mafic magma from depth operating over the last 3400 years. If the mean magma supply rate for the 1872–1944 period of $(3.5–4) \times 10^6\ m^3\ a^{-1}$ estimated by Roberto Scandone and colleagues is taken for the last 3400 years then 2.5–3 km^3 of mafic magma will have entered the Vesuvius magma reservoir during the 700 year interval that preceded the AD 79 eruption. This would require that *c.* 2 km^3 of magma erupted in AD 79 was residual magma remaining in the system after the Avellino eruption.

Forecasting, hazard and risk

Naples and all the towns and villages surrounding Vesuvius, as well as those in the neighbouring Campi Flegrei, are at serious risk from both volcanic and seismic activity. Devastating eruptions have occurred in the past. History will repeat itself, but with much greater devastation because never before has the area under threat been so densely occupied (Fig. 2.2). For most of the region's history the inhabitants have remained remarkably fatalistic about the volcano despite the not infrequent reminders of how dangerous a place it can be. This was recognized as long ago as 1632, when Viceroy Emmanuele Fonseca erected a marble plaque in the small town of Portici saying in Latin: 'be attentive. Twenty times since the creation of the sun has Vesuvius blazed, never without a horrid destruction of those who hesitated to fly. . . . Sooner or later it kindles . . . and will give birth to a vent . . . If you are wise, hear this speaking stone. Neglect your domestic concerns, neglect your goods, and chattels, there is no delaying. Fly.'

It is today clearly recognized in Naples that a programme of public understanding of risk is required. Efforts are being made to do this through the schools, where young, receptive minds are able to understand the problems and assimilate the responses required of the population in a future eruptive event.

With regard to an evacuation plan, there is inevitably a deep controversy about the best approach. To enter into this political topic is not our purpose here. Two vital factors are required: recognition of an impending eruption, and rapid evacuation, preferably not in a downwind direction. In addition, plans need to be in place to provide food, water and shelter for at least 600 000 people, together with medical support for the infirm, injured, young and old. No mean task for any governmental body!

How do we assess the problem? The danger comes from several phenomena: earthquakes before and during the eruption; heavy fall of tephra downwind of the volcano; pyroclastic flows and surges potentially all round the volcano; lava flows; and lahars as a result of aqueous reworking of the tephra both during and after the eruption.

We can only realistically forecast future eruptions based on those that have occurred in the past. The official civil protection plan is based on the supposition of the most likely maximum-sized eruption being of the magnitude of that of 1631 described earlier. Unofficially, others have looked at the possibility that the real 'worst case' is that of AD 79. Nevertheless, based on estimates of the actual amount of eruptable magma in the present reservoir, it is considered that the next eruption will have a magnitude equal to, or less than, the eruption of 1631. Given this, hazard maps have been produced (Fig. 2.16) and evacuation plans devised for those areas at most risk. These plans assume that there will be 15–20 days advanced notice, to allow an evacuation to be set up in an orderly manner.

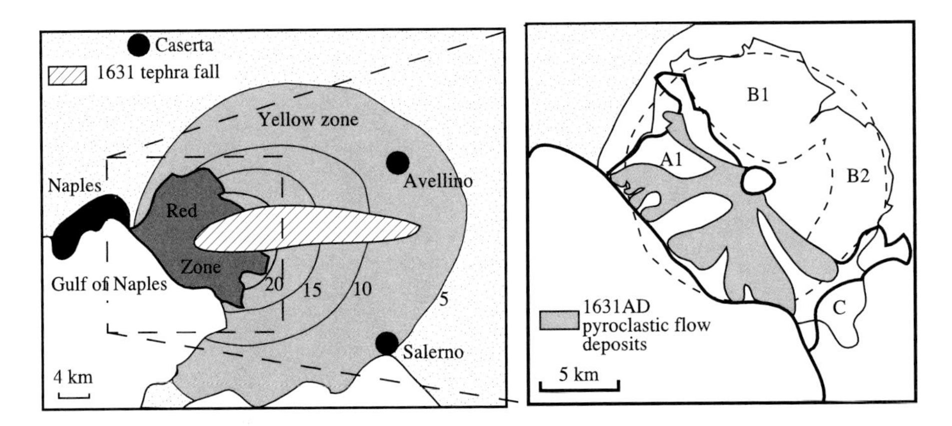

Fig. 2.16. Hazard map for Vesuvius (from Santacroce 1996). This is based on the possibility of a sub-plinian eruption of the magnitude of that of 1631. The inner 'red zone', shown in dark grey is considered to have the highest hazard level. The outer 'yellow zone', shown in light grey, is considered to have a high hazard level. The enlarged map to right shows the distribution of 1631 pyroclastic flows in grey and the zones A, B1, B2 and C correspond to the time sequence of recommended evacuation.

Places to visit

Any visit to Vesuvius by car will probably involve negotiating the autostrada. If the summit is the goal then one should take the 'Ercolano' exit. Approach by the Circum-Vesuviana railway from Naples from Piazza Garibaldi below the main platform. For Herculaneum the station is 'Ercolano' and for Pompeii the station is 'Pompeii Scavi' (care should be taken to ensure the correct train is boarded).

The Royal Volcano Observatory is no longer used as such, but in 2000 was renovated as a museum that is well worth a visit. It has a splendid exhibition of old seismic instruments, as well as historical photographs and maps.

The summit crater is a standard tourist attraction and is approached by two well-kept tracks (payment required). The track from the west and the paved road that leads to it from Ercolano provide fine views of the Somma Caldera wall, the dykes cutting Somma strata, and a cross-section through a cone showing the feeding dyke. The lava of 1944 is also accessible from the paved road, as are the deposits of 1944 debris flow deposits across which the road is cut. The crater itself is just a steaming crater.

Of the archaeological sites Herculaneum is more compact than Pompeii. It is the best choice for a short visit; but surrounded as it is by the modern town, it is much less attractive. There are, however, good sections available through the deposits. For Pompeii, much larger and set in a rural environment, a long half-day visit at least is best. There are a few outcrops of the deposits available. Several villas including Oplontis, which is located in the town of Torre Annunziata (well signposted), and the Villa Regina at Boscoreale are well worth visiting. At Oplontis a nearly complete section through the AD 79 deposits is exposed. On the ramp down into the villa one passes through lithic-rich pyroclastic flow deposits into pumice-rich pyroclastic flow deposits, surge deposits and the pumice fall. The Villa Regina has particularly good plaster casts of trees that were initially buried by the Plinian pumice and then bent over by the following pyroclastic surges and flows.

Quarries through pre AD 79 deposits are particularly good at Pollena. The Terzigno quarry also exposes both pre and post AD 79 deposits.

Notes

General

For wonderful pictures and an interesting text, *Pompeii; the Day a City Died* by Etienne (1992), is to be recommended. As usual, the *Blue Guide to Southern Italy* (Blanchard 2000) also provides useful information, including detailed descriptions of Pompeii, Herculaneum and other AD 79 sites. For rather personal, and non-technical books on Vesuvius, there is that by Trevelyan (1976), *The Shadow of Vesuvius*, which includes an account of the history of discovery of Pompeii and Herculaneum, and *Volcano* by Hoffer (1982), who emphasizes the 1944 eruption and effects on the people. For an account of life in Naples in 1944 from the perspective of a British Intelligence Officer, *Naples '44* by Lewis (1978) is a fascinating read. The Touring Club Italiano (Anon. 1980) map is useful for getting around.

The most recent geological map of Vesuvius is accompanied by a memoir (Santacroce 1987), which has been the source of much of the stratigraphy discussed in this chapter. There have been two thematic issues of *Journal of Volcanology and Geothermal Research* (in volumes 58 and 82) dedicated to Vesuvius, containing a total of 35 papers covering many aspects including physical volcanology of individual eruptions, geophysics, monitoring, and hazard and risk. There is also a special issue of *Mineralogy and Petrology* (De Vivo & Rolandi 2001), which has 12 papers on Vesuvius and volcanism of the Campanian Plain.

The AD 79 eruption

An English translation of *The Letters of the Younger Pliny* is available (Radice 1963), but there are also a number of publications that reproduce Pliny's account of this eruption with comments. Sigurdsson (1999) has given an authoritative account, as, in a more popular way, has Scarth (1999). More details of the eruption and its products have been given by Sigurdsson *et al.* (1985). Barberi *et al.* (1989) and Lirer *et al.* (1993, 1995, 1997) are also valuable sources for information on this eruption and its products.

Height of eruption column

To calculate eruption column heights from lapilli fall deposits good isopleth (equal clast size) maps are needed for both pumice and lithic clasts. Densities of the pumice and lithic clasts must also be determined. Lithic clast isopleths provide the most reliable method as these clasts were more resistant to breakage on impact. The area enclosed by each of the isopleth lines is then calculated and can then be plotted on graphs given by Carey & Sparks (1986) or Wilson & Walker (1987) and column heights read off. Values of height in the later paper are slightly lower than those in the former.

Pre AD 79 activity

Information on the sub-Vesuvius geology obtained by the Treccia borehole on the southern flank of Vesuvius was reported by Brocchini *et al.* (2001)

One of the first major plinian eruptions to occur at Vesuvius, the Pomici di Base, was described by Bertagnini *et al.* (1998). The 8000 a BP Mercato or Ottaviano eruption was described by Rolandi *et al.* (1993*b*). The 3500 BC Avellino eruption has been documented by Rolandi *et al.* (1993*b*). Lira *et al.* (1973) were the first to compare deposits from the AD 79 eruption with those of the Avellino eruption. The smaller eruptions that took place between the larger plinian events have been described by Rolandi *et al.* (1998); this account includes eruptions both before AD 79 and those after. Evolution of the caldera is given by Cioni *et al.* (1999).

Post AD 79 activity

Rosi & Santocroce (1983) described the sub-plinian AD 472 Pollena eruption. A number of the recent eruptions have been the subject of more than one study, often with conflicting ideas. The 1631 eruption was described by Rolandi (1993*a*) and Rosi *et al.* (1993). Hamilton (1776) reported his observations of eruptive activity in the last half of the 18th century. Post-1631 explosive activity was discussed by Arrighi *et al.* (2001).

The great eruption of 1906 was the subject of classic monographs by Johnston-Lavis (1909) and Perret (1924). More recently, Bertagnini *et al.* (1991) and Mastrolorenzo *et al.* (1993) have described and interpreted the 1906 deposits. Our account of the 1944 eruption is based largely the reports of Giuseppe Imbo, Director of the Observatory and advisor to the Military (Imbo 1951) at a most difficult time. He remained at the Observatory during the most violent phases of the eruption, determined to make the best observations possible. We also use the notes of J. V. Stephens, who during peace time worked for the British Geological Survey, but at the time of the eruption was serving in the British Military based in Naples.

Petrology

Overall discussion of the petrology of the volcanic products of Vesuvius and assignment of these to three magmatic groups has been provided by Ayuso *et al.* (1998). Of interest in interpretation of the petrogenesis are the early ideas on limestone assimilation by Rittmann (1962), but more recent ideas have been presented by Joron *et al.* (1987) and Belkin *et al.* (1993). Belkin & De Vivo (1993) have given an account on the petrology of the ejected nodules.

Tectonics, sub-volcanic structure and plumbing

Bianca *et al.* (1998), Bruno *et al.* (1998) and Bruno & Rapolla (1999) have provided information on the regional structure of the Campanian Plain. Interpretation of gravity data (Berrino *et al.* 1998) has added to the understanding of the structural relationships. Seismic tomography (Zollo *et al.* 1998) has shed light on the sub-volcanic crustal structure beneath Vesuvius. Petrological information and interpretation on the nature of a compositionally zoned magma reservoir has been provided by Cioni *et al.* (1995); and based on evidence from phenocrysts and melt inclusions, Cioni *et al.* (1998) have proposed a model for the thermal and compositional evolution of the shallow magma reservoirs of Vesuvius. According to their model the shallow magma reservoir of Vesuvius would currently be in its narrow, low-volume, high aspect ratio stage, possibly explaining why it has not been identified by seismic tomography. De Natale *et al.* (1998) discussed seismicity at Vesuvius and its implications for 3D tomography. See also Mirabile (1988).

Hazard

Much has been said in recent years about hazard and civil defence in the Vesuvius region. We have tried here to avoid the controversy. A short summary of the ‘official’ stand has been given by Santacroce (1996). There is an emergency plan (Anon. 1995) to cater for a future eruption including evacuation. Needless to say, not all Italian volcanologists or politicians agree with the plan, and some are vigorously against it.

Risk assessments of the Vesuvian area have been made by Scandone *et al.* (1991) and Lirer *et al.* (1997). An article by Roberto Santacroce appeared in *IAVCEI News*, outlining the hazard assessment and risk assessment for Vesuvius based on a 1631-type eruption (Santacroce 1996).

Chapter 3. **Campi Flegrei**

Geography

Campi Flegrei consists of a 12 km diameter depression surrounded by cliffs to the east and north, but is less well defined to the west (Fig. 3.1). It is a major caldera complex, the centre of which lies in the Gulf of Pozzuoli to the south. Seen on satellite images it looks like a war zone, peppered with craters; there are at least five nested caldera depressions within it, as well as more than a dozen cones and a crater lake (Figs 3.2 and 3.3). Like Naples, which sprawls into its eastern half, Campi Flegrei is densely populated, containing about a million people, about 62 000 of whom live in Pozzuoli.

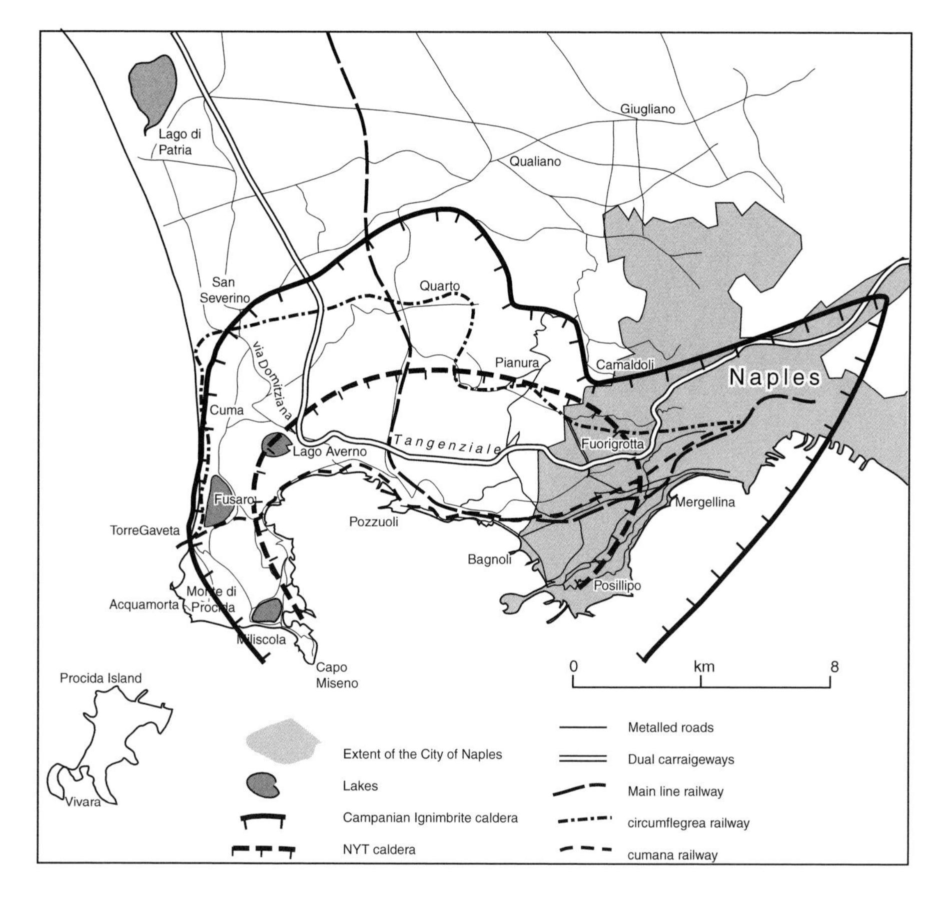

Fig. 3.1. Map of the caldera rims that make up the Campi Flegrei complex. Main roads and railways within Campi Flegrei are also shown.

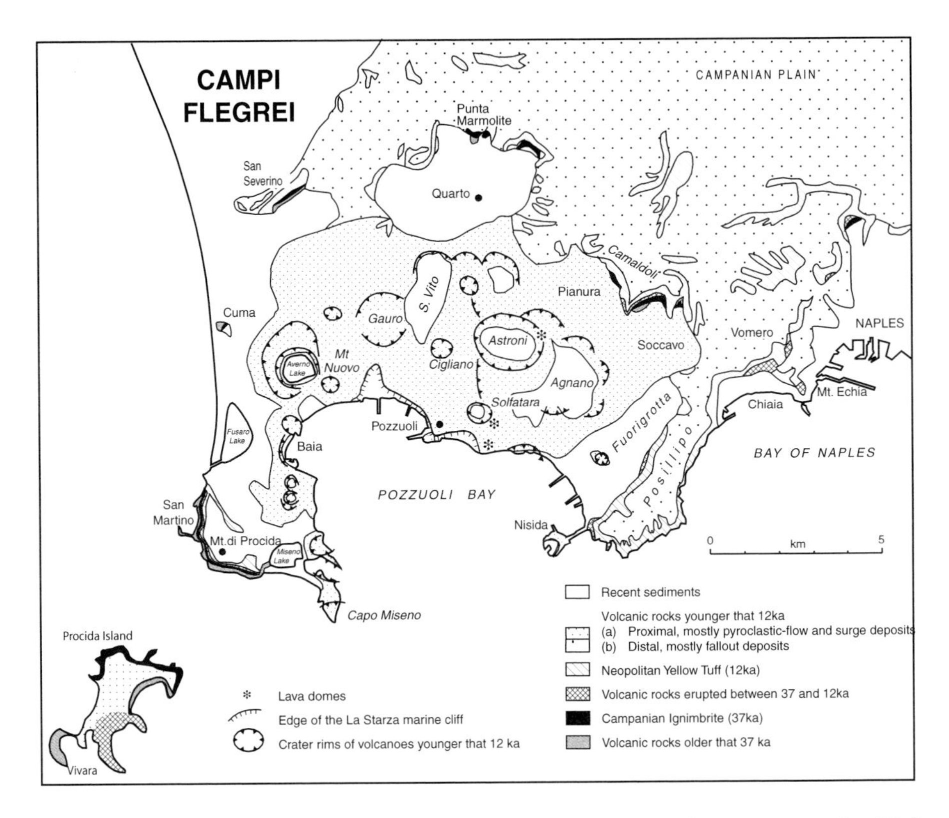

Fig. 3.2. Geological map of Campi Flegrei. The main caldera walls are shown in Fig. 3.1 (modified from Di Vito *et al.* 1985).

The main towns, small spas and fishing villages lie along the coast as an almost continuous urban strip. Inland there are ribbons of development in the gaps between the many volcanic cones. This is an area with a long and fascinating history. It is also of strategic importance as it hosts the NATO Southern European Headquarters as well as the Mediterranean base of the US Navy.

Campi Flegrei is clearly an active caldera, and although the last eruption was in 1538, ground movements during the last part of the 20th century suggest that another eruption could well occur before the first few decades of the third millennium are over. The nearby island of Procida is part of this volcano, but the larger, adjacent island of Ischia is a separate active volcano in its own right (see Chapter 9).

History

To Greek colonists, who were political exiles from Samos, the mild climate and beauty of this area were great attractions. The first to arrive settled on the island of Ischia; but the most important Greek colony was that of Cuma (Cumæ) established in the eighth century BC on the western side of Campi Flegrei. These early settlers named the whole area, including the Bay of Naples and Vesuvius, the Phlegrean Fields (i.e. Burning Fields), apparently because of its resemblance to an area in Greece with a similar name.

Fig. 3.3. Lago Averno within the crater of a Campi Flegrei tuff ring. The remains of the Temple of Apollo are seen in the foreground.

It does imply that the volcanic nature of the area was known, and, although there is no evidence that any volcanic activity occurred during this time, there may have been verbal records of earlier activity. Nevertheless, the presence of unusual underground heat was exhibited by the numerous hot springs and fumaroles, and the early colonists witnessed eruptive activity on the nearby island of Ischia (see Chapter 9).

Apart from the thermal waters, the area also lent itself to housing development because of extensive outcrops of mildly indurated tuffs, which were easily cut to form underground dwellings. One of the most remarkable of these is the Cave of the Sybil at Cuma. This is a 45 m long tunnel (Fig. 3.4) hewn out of pyroclastic rock (the Neapolitan Yellow Tuff). It has a trapezoidal cross-section and is oriented north–south. It is here that, according to Virgil (Book VI of the *Aeneid*), Aeneas came to consult the Sybil and plan his descent to the underworld through the crater lake of Averno (Fig. 3.3), which was considered to be the entrance to Hell. It was said that birds flying over the lake died, presumably an early observation of the fatal effects of CO_2.

The Greeks rapidly spread their power over the whole area as new settlements were established. Pozzuoli, the coastal town in the centre of the Campi Flegrei complex, was founded in 530 BC. Naples also came under Cumaean control. The whole area fell in 421 BC to the Samnites, a warlike people from the southern Apennines; and then to the Romans in 338 BC during the Punic wars.

The Roman period in Campi Flegrei (also known then as Campania Rex) was extremely fruitful. Pozzuoli, then called Puteoli, became one of the most important, and cosmopolitan, ports in the Mediterranean; its industries included glass,

Fig. 3.4. The Cave of the Sybil at Cuma cut into the Neapolitan Yellow Tuff.

terracotta, perfumes and textiles, based on Hellenistic, Phoenician and Egyptian traditions. The amphitheatre in Pozzuoli is the third largest in Italy. Saint Paul, in AD 60, stayed in Pozzuoli for a few days, meeting with the small Christian community there on his way to Rome where he was executed. Pozzuoli lost some of its commercial importance when the port of Ostia was built at the mouth of the River Tiber, close to Rome.

Campi Flegrei was to become the largest spa in the whole of the Roman Empire. Holiday-making in a sunny climate and soaking in hot mineral waters was definitely to the Roman taste, as the baths at Baia demonstrate. A visit to the ruins shows the remains of a superb spa town where visitors could relax with the vast luxury and excesses of the Imperial Court. There is even a pool surrounded by a semicircle of rooms built almost 2000 years before the concept of the US-style motel.

The Romans also had a strong military presence in the area. Lago Averno was turned into a naval dockyard by Agrippa in 37 BC when it was linked to the sea. Also used by the Roman Navy was the bay at Miseno, where Pliny the Elder set forth in AD 79 to view the eruption of Vesuvius. Using the easily worked, but durable, tuffs nearby, the Romans excavated the basilica-like, 15 000 m^3 *Piscina Mirabile*, an underground water storage reservoir designed to supply the fleet with fresh water.

The commercial importance of the area declined rapidly in the Middle Ages. Pozzuoli became a small fishing port, although the area as a whole continued to be a popular spa. There were, and still are, many sites of interest to the tourist because of their curiosity value or historical interest. Solfatara, close to Pozzuoli, is a crater with bubbling mud pools, fumaroles and a very hot sauna. Not far away, near the hot springs of Agnano, is a cavern, the *Grotta del Cane*, into which CO_2 leaks to form pools of the gas up to half a metre deep. Nineteenth-century visitors were 'entertained' by the spectacle of dogs walking into the lethal gas, collapsing and dying without any apparent cause. This is just one example of the evidence of the volcanically active nature of the region, which is exhaling gases over much of its area. Hot water in boreholes and springs testifies to the presence of a heat source at depth.

The Romans, and those who followed, were well aware of the instability of the area. The whole region steadily sank. Much of the Roman town of Baia is now under water and the rectilinear pattern of its streets can still be seen from the air. The so-called Temple of Serapis, actually a market place built in the second century BC, sank until only the tops of pillars remained above water. Nevertheless, it is now well above sea level, first because of the dramatic uprise before the 1538 eruption, and second, because of changes that occurred in two periods of uplift since 1970.

Communications and industry

The Via Domiziana, the main Roman highway from Rome to Naples, runs through Campi Flegrei and is still a major communications route (Fig. 3.1). However, the new autostrada (the Tangenziale) now takes most of the traffic through Campi Flegrei. It passes via spectacular tunnels through the caldera walls west of Naples; it is here that one sees the way in which densely populated Naples is 'flowing' over into Campi Flegrei. The rest of the area is served by a network of narrow roads that are generally overcrowded.

Three railway lines run through the area. The main line from Rome to the south passes through Pozzuoli and Bagnoli; and one of the local lines, the Cumana, runs from Naples close to the coast of Campi Flegrei with a number of stops ending at Torre Gaveta, a small seaside resort. A third, the Circumflegrei, goes through northern Campi Flegrei to the western coast. For visitors without transport, the railways provide a useful way of getting around.

The area is a seething mass of people. Industries include fishing, light manufacturing, textiles, dock-related activities, and until recently, a major steel works. Tourism is also significant, with the many sites of historical interest to visit as well as such attractions as the Solfatara, seaside resorts and the country club at the foot of Monte Nuovo. A major source of income for the area comes from military personnel and their families associated with the NATO base at Bagnoli, and the nearby US naval base.

The volcanic history of Campi Flegrei

Introduction

Whereas the eye is drawn to the striking edifice of Vesuvius, Campi Flegrei is a more subtle collection of craters, cones and calderas, more complex than its visually attractive neighbour (Fig. 3.5). Campi Flegrei has captured the interest of European geologists for well over 200 years. The first descriptions and observations were probably made by Sir William Hamilton; subsequently there were classic discussions in Lyell's *Principles of Geology* of Pozzuoli and the so-called Temple of Serapis. In the late nineteenth century, H. T. Johnston-Lavis was probably the first to make detailed descriptions of the volcanic rocks of Campi Flegrei. He identified the 'Piperno' and 'Breccia Museo' because of the

Fig. 3.5. View looking east across Campi Flegrei from the southeastern rim of Monte Barbaro, one of the many tuff cones. In the foreground is the tuff cone of Cigliano (C) and the Astroni tuff ring (A). Vesuvius is in the background beyond the city of Naples.

variety of rock types within it. The work of DeLorenzo in 1904 was a milestone in the understanding of this region. He identified eruptive centres and divided the activity into three periods, the first two being submarine and the third subaerial. Extensive work by Alfred Rittmann proposed the existence of an old buried edifice which he called 'Archiflegrei'.

During the last two decades of the twentieth century, considerable advances, and debates, about the geology and the possibility of future activity have been achieved. These, in part have been stimulated by two periods of unrest in the area. We will first discuss the general geological history of the volcano and then turn to historical activity.

Pre-Neapolitan Yellow Tuff activity

The Neapolitan Yellow Tuff is a striking deposit that, because of its thickness and relatively continuous outcrop, forms a useful marker horizon around Campi Flegrei (Figs 3.2 and 3.6). It has been radiometrically dated at about 12 ka BP. Thus we may discuss the geology of this area in two parts: pre and post Neapolitan Yellow Tuff.

Before the eruption of Neapolitan Yellow Tuff, about 12 ka ago, the products of more than 18 eruptions from Campi Flegrei have been identified. It should be stressed that with increasing age, resolution of previous eruptive events inevitably becomes more difficult. This situation is aggravated by caldera collapses, which have destroyed structures existing within them. In addition, several pumice fall deposits have been identified, which have been suggested to originate from activity on the island of Ischia, demonstrating that the geology of one volcano may be in part composed of the products of another.

The oldest dated rocks of Campi Flegrei are from about 47 ka BP. Following this, the products of a number of small localized centres have been dated at around 40 ka BP. These include a number of formations in western Campi Flegrei and on Procida island as well as the Torre Franco tuffs below Camaldoli in NE Campi Flegrei. The products include small tuff cones such as Vivara and some lava domes on Procida island, Milliscola and the San Martino dome around Monte di Procida region in southwestern Campi Flegrei.

In the city of Naples similar products have also been identified, including trachytic lava domes and several tuff cones. Although no exact dates of these products in Naples are known it is possible that they relate to the same period as the similar products in western Campi Flegrei. Early activity was not entirely localized, as some pumice lapilli beds resulting from large, possibly plinian, explosive eruptions are exposed in western Campi Flegrei.

The Campanian Ignimbrite

Without doubt, the largest eruption to have taken place in the Campi Flegrei region was that which formed the Campanian Ignimbrite. We described ignimbrites in the last chapter, but these produced small-volume deposits (less than a few km^3) compared with that of the Campanian Ignimbrite, estimated to be some 150 km^3. The exact transport and emplacement mechanisms of pyroclastic flows are, as previously commented, highly controversial and the Campanian Ignimbrite has played a part in this debate.

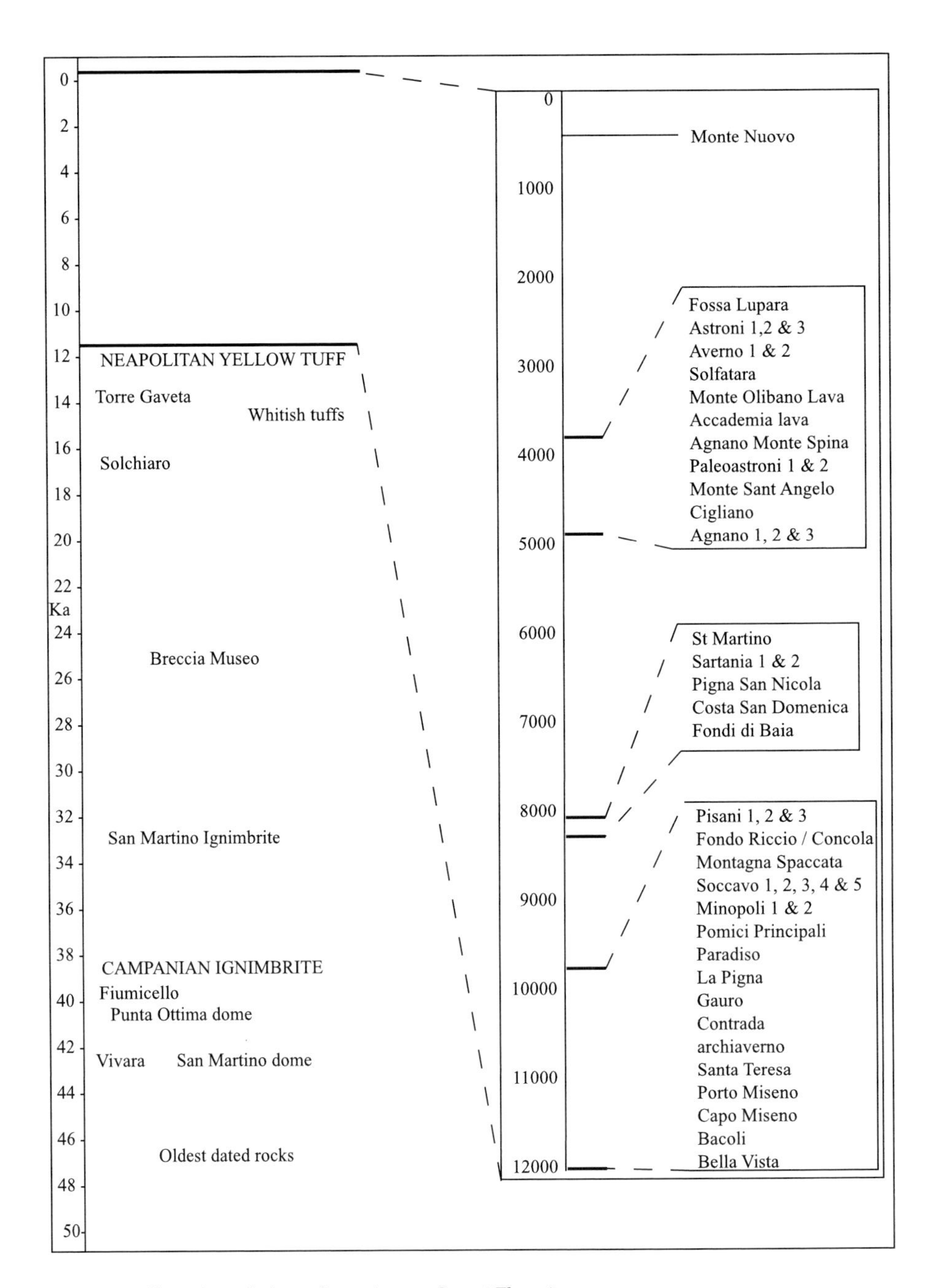

Fig. 3.6. Chronological chart of eruptions at Campi Flegrei.

The Campanian Ignimbrite was formed by a pyroclastic flow that was so powerful that it overtopped mountains more than 1000 m high and travelled over 100 km from the probable source vent. Outcrops of the ignimbrite occur within the Roccamonfina caldera some 60 km to the north at about 600 m a.s.l. and also high in the Apennines. The

Campanian Ignimbrite has an associated Plinian lapilli-fall deposit that crops out below the ignimbrite in the Apennine mountains, demonstrating that a large convecting ultra-plinian eruption column existed before formation of the pyroclastic flow from which the ignimbrite is derived.

The ignimbrite is a poorly sorted deposit of larger scoria or pumice clasts set in a finer-grained matrix. Within the vicinity of Campi Flegrei it has a welded facies and it was even hot enough to form well-developed columnar jointing on the lower northern flank of Roccamonfina volcano some 70 km from its source (Fig. 4.9). Within the Campanian Plain two facies can be identified; a grey one with dark scoria clasts and a yellow facies with grey–white pumices. Another important field characteristic is the presence of extensive lithic breccias north of Campi Flegrei associated with it.

The source vent of the Campanian Ignimbrite is, however, a matter of debate. Some workers suggest that the Campanian Ignimbrite was erupted from Campi Flegrei and was responsible for collapse of a single caldera that encompasses all of Campi Flegrei. Others, on the other hand, suggest, based on the distribution of thick and extensive co-ignimbrite breccias, that it was erupted from a fissure just north of Campi Flegrei. Much of the controversy arises from the poor exposure in the region.

The age of the Campanian Ignimbrite is not well constrained because dating of carbonized wood from within the ignimbrite has yielded a range of ages from 28 ka to 42 ka BP with a mean age of *c.* 35 ka BP (from nine dates). Moreover, the palaeosol below the ignimbrite yields dates that give an average age 3000 years younger than the ignimbrite. There is clearly a problem with using radiocarbon dating for older rocks in this CO_2-rich, volcanic environment. Ar/Ar dating shows that age of the Campanian Ignimbrite may be around 39 ka BP.

The Breccia Museo–Piperno Formation

Since Johnston-Lavis first described the 'Breccia Museo' it has become famous. Similar breccia deposits have been recognized at several localities on the topographic border of Campi Flegrei: in the Camaldoli area, Pianura, Punta Marmolite, Cuma, Monte di Procida and Procida island where a sequence exists composed, more or less, of a welded grey eutaxitic tuff, the 'Piperno', overlain by a coarse lithic breccia (Fig. 3.7).

The welded tuff or 'Piperno' outcrops intermittently, and is variable in grain size, with individual fiamme ranging from a few centimetres up to 1 m on the eastern side of Procida island. The breccia is a particularly coarse-grained, fines-poor deposit typically containing blocks >1 m in size of a wide range in lithologies including several types of lava, hydrothermal altered and metamorphosed rocks. Geologists from Pisa have related all the breccia deposits to the same eruption, whereas some groups of Neapolitans consider that only those on Procida island and in the Monte di Procida region were formed in the same eruption.

The 'Breccia Museo–Piperno' deposits have been correlated with the medial–distal Campanian Ignimbrite, which occurs on the Campanian Plain and in the Apennines. Following this theory it is suggested that the breccias were the proximal facies (lag breccias) of the Campanian Ignimbrite. However, the two facies have never been

Fig. 3.7. The Breccia Museo formation exposed on the beach below the cemetery at Procida island, SW of Campi Flegrei. The main components of this formation are present (from base to top): Piperno, indicated by (p), consists of 2 m of welded spatter blocks; above are two units (4 m total) of lithic breccia (the Breccia Museo proper), and 5 m of ignimbrite, which caps the sequence.

observed at the same locality and, furthermore, recent work by the Neapolitan group on radiocarbon dating of palaeosols indicates that the Breccia Museo ranges between 17.2 and 18.5 ka in age. On the basis of this radiocarbon dating the Breccia Museo is too young to be correlated with the Campanian Ignimbrite.

Below the Breccia Museo on the island of San Martino and at Acquamorta in southwestern Campi Flegrei, there is a grey partly welded ignimbrite, which some workers tentatively correlate with the Campanian Ignimbrite. The palaeosol beneath it, however, has been dated at 26.7 ka BP and if this date is correct, then correlation with the Campanian Ignimbrite is unlikely.

Yellow tuff and the Neapolitan Yellow Tuff

Yellow tuff is a ubiquitous rock type in and around Campi Flegrei and the Neapolitan area. Its physical properties make it a useful building stone and it has been used for this purpose for thousands of years. The origin of the yellow tuffs has been the subject of much scientific interest. Early workers considered all yellow tuffs to be part of the same formation, whereas later workers interpreted yellow tuffs to be formed by numerous, separate localized eruptions. It is currently thought that neither of these interpretations is correct. Following extensive field studies it has been proposed that there was one large explosive eruption (about 12 ka BP) that produced the thick and extensive deposits of yellow tuff that occur on the periphery of Campi Flegrei, and this is called the Neapolitan Yellow Tuff (NYT). In addition, there are deposits of tuff that are yellow but were formed by localized explosive activity that built cones and rings of different ages (e.g. Gauro, Nisida, Miseno). The fact that a tuff is yellow is due to a combination of factors, which include magma composition, magma–water interaction, and the mineralization–zeolitization process occurring during diagenesis: it is not a diagnostic criterion for correlation.

The Neapolitan Yellow Tuff crops out extensively around the edge of Campi Flegrei, in the city of Naples and across the Campanian Plain. It occurs as both a lithified yellow and an unlithified grey facies, termed pozzolana (Fig. 3.8). The sharp transition between the lithified and unlithified NYT occurs around the border of Campi Flegrei, with the lithified facies occurring in proximal areas and the unlithified part in the more distal outcrops.

The eruption sequence has been divided into two members; A and B. Member A is composed of a distinctive basal laminated phreatoplinian ash fall unit that has been identified at all localities and is overlain by sandwave-bedded surge deposits and pumice lapilli fall layers. This member has been traced up to 42 km from the proposed vent in NE Campi Flegrei. The upper part, Member B, is made up of the deposits of numerous pyroclastic flows, which ranged widely in their transport and emplacement mechanisms. Deposits are present that represent a spectrum of flow types from dilute, low-particle concentration pyroclastic surges to dense high-concentration flows. The relatively fine grain-size of all the NYT and the widespread presence of accretionary lapilli and vesicular tuffs strongly suggest that water–magma interaction played an important role in both phases of the eruption. The calculated volume of the eruptive products for the NYT is about 50 km^3.

(a)

(b)

Fig. 3.8. Sections through the Neapolitan Yellow Tuff at Zaccaria NW of Campi Flegrei. (**a**) Parallel to flow direction, which was from the right; (**b**) perpendicular to flow direction. Note the complex multilayered nature of the deposit formed by many individual pyroclastic flows. The deposit approaches 30 m thickness at this locality. R, reworked deposits. Note person for scale.

Post-Neapolitan Yellow Tuff activity

The numerous craters and cones that dominate the present-day landscape of Campi Flegrei are the result of over 56 separate eruptive events since the NYT eruption some 12 ka ago. It is this hydromagmatic activity that is apparently responsible for the construction of the many tuff cones and rings that are seen today, with tuff cones such as Gauro, Nisida and Cigliano and tuff rings including Astroni, Averno and Baia. Field studies of deposits formed in the last 12 ka have revealed that magmatic and hydromagmatic activity have both played important roles in eruptive activity. Many deposits are formed of numerous pumice or scoria lapilli beds produced by magmatic activity interbedded with ash-rich layers containing abundant accretionary lapilli and vesicular textures related to hydromagmatic phases. Sandwave bedforms and cross-stratification are also typical of the ash-rich beds and formed by low particle concentration pyroclastic currents: pyroclastic surges. Some of the lapilli beds represent fallout from eruption columns that were plinian in magnitude. A fine example of this style of activity is the Averno tuff ring formed *c.* 3.7 ka BP. Several thin pumice lapilli layers interbedded with the ash-rich deposits indicate that short periods of magmatic activity were interspersed with the phreatomagmatic activity.

It is worth noting that radiometric dating suggests that eruptions over the last 12 ka have not been evenly spaced in time (Fig. 3.6). Thirty-four eruptions occurred between 12 and 9.5 ka BP, which means that on average during this period there was an eruption every 70 years. Six eruptions occurred in the 400 years between 8.6 and 8.2 ka BP, indicating an average of an eruption every 65 years. The third cluster occurs between 4.8 and 3.8 ka BP, which yields an average of an eruption every 62 years. The hazard implications of such periodicity are considerable because if a new phase of activity were entered then it could suggest a series of many eruptions occurring on a relatively frequent basis for tens of years.

The volcanoes of Naples

Excavations through the Vomero and Posillipo hills in Naples at the end of the nineteenth century and in the early twentieth century for the funicular and railway tunnels yielded a wealth of information regarding the volcanic activity in the region of the city, older than the Neapolitan Yellow Tuff (12 ka BP). The earliest activity was effusive with domes and possibly some lava flows. Exposures near the Chiaia region and below Posillipo hill (Trentaremi) show sections through tuff cones and rings relating to minor explosive activity.

At Monte Echia near the Castel Dell'Ovo exposures of pyroclastic surge deposits and lapilli fall deposits sit on a promontory or topographic high surrounded by NYT. The relations between these two formations is unclear; however, the possibility exists that the Monte Echia deposits were associated with explosive activity from a vent in this region of the city in the last 12 ka, after the NYT eruption. Other researchers indicate that the Monte Echia deposits are older than the NYT.

Calderas

Today Campi Flegrei is dominated by volcanic craters, rings and cones. The whole region lies within a general topographic depression bound, in places, by steep scarps. It is this depression that defines the border of the volcanic complex. It has been proposed that this depression is a single caldera collapse structure related to either the Campanian

Ignimbrite eruption or the Neapolitan Yellow Tuff. However, a careful look at the geomorphology reveals that Campi Flegrei is more complicated than simply a single caldera structure and is a complex structure of coalescing calderas developed over time (Fig. 3.1). Other than the recent craters and cones, several distinct plains can be recognized. They are, from the north in a clockwise direction; Quarto, Pianura, Soccavo and Fuorigrotta, each of which impinges on, or forms, the border of Campi Flegrei. Some of these plains, such as Soccavo, Pianura and Fuorigrotta, coalesce, whereas others, including Quarto, are distinct and individual structures. Each of the plains has a different floor height. For these reasons it seems probable that there are the result of separate, smaller, collapse structures related to different eruptions, or different phases of the same eruption.

If the Campanian Ignimbrite was erupted from Campi Flegrei, any caldera that formed as a result has since been superimposed by later smaller collapses that formed the plains of Quarto, Pianura, Soccavo and Fuorigrotta. The exact location of the boundaries of the main caldera are poorly defined. Recent studies have suggested that the eastern border may run through Naples, based on the depth of probable Campanian Ignimbrite recorded in boreholes.

Geological evidence rules out the possibility of the NYT being related to many of the collapse structures in the northern and western part of Campi Flegrei as it drapes several of the caldera scarps, and in some places it is underlain by deposits that also drape the caldera margins. The NYT must, therefore, postdate the formation of these structures. It is considered that the NYT caldera is related to the Fourigrotta plain collapse. This 10 km diameter caldera is largely buried, but its eastern margin is marked by a well-defined scarp (Fig. 3.1). Boreholes within the centre of Campi Flegrei show a dramatic increase in the thickness of the NYT as expected in the centre of a caldera, and the western margin is marked by a line of vents older than 8 ka BP. Which deposits relate to eruptions responsible for each of the other collapses remains to be determined.

Unrest at calderas

Uplift and continued seismic activity can be precursors of volcanic activity. Indeed, it was the activities of Campi Flegrei in the early 1980s, together with those at Rabaul in Papua New Guinea and at Long Valley in California, that emphasized to the volcanological research community the serious problem of future eruptions in calderas that contain a large population. As a result of this two US volcanologists, Chris Newhall and Dan Dzurisin, compiled an exhaustive review, published in 1988, of calderas that have shown unrest in historical time. This is an invaluable starting point for anyone involved in this subject.

Unrest does not necessarily result in an eruption in the short term. Sometimes there are several periods of unrest before an eruption takes place. Of the three calderas mentioned above that have shown recent unrest, only one has given rise, at the time of writing, to an eruption following unrest. This occurred at Rabaul and started on 19 September 1994 from two vents on either side of the caldera floor. There was very little warning. During the last few days of August there was a sudden increase in seismic activity for a few days. Then, the day before the eruption there was a magnitude 5.1 earthquake below the caldera, followed by swarm of shallow earthquakes. At dawn on 19 September, it was seen that areas of ground had been uplifted by as much as 6 m, and soon after the eruption started, causing virtual destruction of the town in just a few days. Good civil defence policies and the natural common sense of the inhabitants led to an orderly evacuation of 30 000 people, and loss of life was limited to five.

Unrest can take several forms, but the most important are seismic and thermal activity, and ground deformation. On average, about 18 calderas of all types show unrest in any one year. Most calderas, particularly those associated with basaltic volcanoes, do not pose life-threatening possibilities if an eruption occurs; but a small number of more silicic calderas, such as Campi Flegrei, do, even from the smallest of eruptions. Campi Flegrei has the longest documented record of unrest of any large caldera. In Italy such unrest is known as a *bradyseism*. We will return to this later, but first we discuss unrest in general because a knowledge of this phenomenon is vital to understanding calderas in general, and in predicting dangerous eruptions.

Seismic events are dramatic and may take several forms. They are usually of relatively low magnitude, less than five on the Richter scale, which is a measure of the energy released by the earthquake. The intensity (i.e. a measure of violence of the earthquakes based on damage caused) may be high, nevertheless, if the quakes are shallow; such quakes will be felt only locally, but may cause considerable damage. They may be isolated events, but it is common in episodes of caldera unrest for there to be periods of some hours when swarms of quakes occur in high numbers, even almost continuously. This can be very frightening and at times dangerous for those in the area.

Ground deformation, involving upward or downward movement, is a common sign of unrest. It may or may not be accompanied by seismic activity. Uplift may indicate inflation of the magma reservoir by an addition of magma from below, but it may also be the result of volume changes in the magma reservoir by vesiculation resulting from crystallization, or of volume changes in the hydrothermal system. Downward movement may result again from changes in the volume of the hydrothermal system, or from drainage of magma away from the reservoir, for example along rift zones outside the caldera.

Unrest may also involve changes in the composition of fumarolic gases. Proportions of SO_2, H_2S, HCl, HF and CO_2 may change, and in some cases there may be an increase in H_2 and Rn. In addition, discharge rates of gas may increase, and temperatures may rise, sometimes by several hundreds of degrees. Hot springs also may show changes in temperature and rate of discharge, but these are usually small.

It is evident that the floor of the Campi Flegrei caldera has been far from stable during historical times. Indeed, it was observations in this region that provided the first such graphic evidence of instability of the Earth, even on short time scales. As mentioned earlier, the most striking evidence comes from the famous pillars of the Roman marketplace in Pozzuoli (Fig. 3.9). The marble columns have been bored by marine molluscs between 6 and 8 m above the base. The interpretation is that the Romans built the market at or just above sea level. A second, higher floor was built at a later date, suggesting that even then the land was sinking relative to the sea. Continued downward

(a)

(b)

Fig. 3.9. 'Temple' of Serapis, Campi Flegrei, (**a**) in May 1982, and (**b**) in September 1984. The change in water level reflects the ground uplift during the bradyseismic crises of 1984. These are the remains not of a temple, but of a Roman marketplace.

movement caused the columns to sink below sea level, and while the lower parts of the columns were buried in sediment the upper portion within the water was bored by the molluscs. The general trend for the region was sinking of the land, without changes in sea level. However, at Pozzuoli in the early sixteenth century movements went against this trend, lifting the pillars out of the water again.

Over several thousands of years the floor of the Campi Flegrei caldera has undergone tens of metres of vertical movement. This history of movements is recorded in the sequence of interlayered marine and volcaniclastic deposits exposed in the Starza terrace, a well-defined ancient sea-cliff that runs above the shore front at Pozzuoli. It is considered that the uppermost marine layer may have been more than 70 m above present sea level.

The 1198 eruption

It is unlikely that this eruption was magmatic, and it probably consisted of a steam explosion within the Solfatara crater. This crater is at present the most visually 'active' phenomenon in Campi Flegrei. It lies just outside and to the NE of Pozzuoli, and is about 600 m in diameter and is understandably a major tourist attraction. The crater even contains a camp site usually full of caravans and tents. The attractions are the bubbling mud pools and fumaroles. Visitors have steamed themselves in the incredibly hot 'sweating' rooms for centuries, and still do! It is quite normal, but infrequent, for fumarolic areas such as this to explode. Gas pressures become too high, the delicate equilibrium is suddenly disrupted, and a small explosion occurs. Such explosions are not easy to predict, but when they do occur can cause injury and loss of life to those nearby. Sudden ejections of boiling water accompanied by fragments of surface rocks cause damage over some tens of metres from the centre of the explosion.

This is almost certainly what happened in 1198; such explosions may have taken place since then, and could occur in the future. The effects may normally be expected to be contained within the crater, but could cause damage to homes on the outer rim of Solfatara.

The 1538 eruption

The most recent eruption within the Campi Flegrei caldera complex occurred over 400 years ago. Compared with some eruptions in the area, it was small; but, despite this, such an eruption today would have devastating effects on people, property and the local economy. Although a much larger eruption cannot be ruled out as the next in this area, a similar one to that of 1538 is probably the more likely. The site is marked today by a well-defined cone known as Monte Nuovo just to the east of Lago Averno (Fig. 3.10).

We are fortunate that there are several contemporary accounts of the eruption, notably by Marco Antonio delli Falconi and Pietro Giacomo da Toledo. These two documents were discovered by Sir William Hamilton, whose translations of them into English were published in 1776. He also donated the original Italian versions to the British Museum

Fig. 3.10. Monte Nuovo, built during the eruption of 1538, seen from the bay of Pozzuoli. Note the asymmetric form of the cone that is probably the result of the prevailing westerly wind causing preferential accumulation of falling tephra to the east.

in London. The following account of the eruption is based on these together with an account by Francesco Marchesino, who was in Naples when the eruption started, but later travelled by boat to Pozzuoli to observe the phenomenon.

How did it all begin? Probably the first precursor of the eruption was in 1502 when there was a sudden uplift of the coast around Pozzuoli. The new land was given by King Ferdinand and Queen Isabella to the people of Pozzuoli and, apparently, the local university. Further new land became available in 1511, indicating that continued uplift had taken place.

In 1537 earthquakes started to be felt again in the area, most strongly in Pozzuoli, but also in Naples and the surrounding area. Two days before the eruption began, this activity reached a climax when continuous earthquakes were felt accompanied by rapid uplift of the land around Pozzuoli manifesting itself in the emergence from the sea of a wide new tract of land near where the eruption was about to start. Cracks appeared in the ground from which, it is reported, water bubbled out. This is not surprising as the area was a spa with hot baths, or sweating rooms. Indeed it still is, and the nearby Country Club at the foot of Monte Nuovo has hot pools filled with water pumped from a well in the grounds.

In the early evening of Sunday 29 September, a fissure was seen to open near the baths, and extend towards the village of Tripergole. Eyewitnesses saw 'flames of fire' burst from the fissure accompanied by loud thunder-like bangs. Great quantities of pumice and wet ash were thrown out from what was described as a 'horrid hole'.

The following morning the inhabitants of Pozzuoli, struck with fear, were to see the whole drama unfold in front of them. The volcano continued to spew out pumice and ash, which had rained down on the town all night, covering everything with a muddy wet layer of ash. They fled to Naples, carrying infants and sacks of belongings, their faces black with the falling ash. Many were reported as collecting and carrying away dead animals and fish. Large numbers of fish had been stranded on the land raised at the start of the eruption, and many animals appear to have died in the eruption area. The death of animals may have been from a number of causes, but it is most likely that they suffocated in the fine ash. However, some may also have died from CO_2 emissions.

During the night, the people of Naples had no idea what was going on. Ash was falling on the city like snow and they could hear the thunderous roars from the other side of the Posillipo ridge. The arriving refugees informed them of the stupendous activity. Sightseers from Naples, including the Viceroy of the region, appeared on the scene later in the day and observed the conflagration. They noted that the sea had retreated a considerable way, and was completely obscured by floating pumice. Clouds of black ash and white fume swirled above the vent, and blocks 'as big as oxen' were seen to be thrown out for the distance of a crossbow shot. Hamilton later confirmed that blocks this size do indeed occur in the materials of Monte Nuovo. It was also noted with perception by delli Falconi that different sizes of material fell according to distance from the vent, finer material falling further away.

By Tuesday, the eruption had died down, the air was clear and good views were obtained of the new cone, which was some 140 m high and had a basal diameter of 1.5 km. In an effort to stop the eruption, a procession carrying relics of San Gennaro made its way to the Chapel near Pozzuoli where San Gennaro had previously had his head cut off.

On Wednesday, calm continued, but on Thursday the eruption started again with thunderous force. From his viewpoint on a boat in the Gulf of Pozzuoli, delli Falconi observed 'many columns of smoke shoot up, with the most terrible noise I ever heard, and bending over the sea, came near our boat, which was four miles or more away'. On the same day trees up to 5 km from the vent were ripped out of the ground and thrown over. We interpret these observations as evidence that pyroclastic surges were being formed, probably by hydromagmatic activity.

Thursday to Saturday were again calm and Neapolitans were able to visit Pozzuoli. Francesco Marchesino arrived there by boat, but with difficulty because of rafts of floating pumice through which they had to push their way. The town was abandoned and devastated. The sight was of fallen or partly fallen houses, some smashed to pieces. Half the Cathedral had fallen, and the other half was in a precarious state. Most of this devastation was probably the result of earthquakes, but some must have been from the weight of wet ash that covered the roofs, and also from surges that had torn through the town, uprooting trees and destroying gardens. Francesco and others were intrepid enough to climb Monte Nuovo. Hot cracks were observed and there was a coating of sulphur over everything. Those visitors were fortunate, because on Sunday 6 October, 24 curious observers climbing the cone were killed by the final explosion. A cloud of ash spread over Naples, and that was the end of an eruption.

The area was one of complete devastation. Ash covered almost the whole of Calabria. Naples was painted a dirty grey with a thick layer of ash, and everywhere in the Campi

Flegrei area was rendered almost uninhabitable. Despite this, life rapidly resumed in the area, and today something like a million people live within the caldera complex.

Based on the historical record, and field observations of the rocks, we can now interpret the events of that frightening week. The main cone was produced in the first 2 days of the eruption. Observations of red hot material at the very beginning of the eruption may suggest that it was at this stage magmatic rather than hydromagmatic. However, the prodigious amount of wet ash reported indicates that hydromagmatic activity soon became important, although the last phase may have become magmatic again. The pauses in the eruption are a sober reminder that a break in activity at any volcano does not mean the end of the eruption, and those who venture too close at such a time could be in serious trouble, as indeed were those who climbed the cone on the last day of the eruption and lost their lives.

After the dramatic events of 1538, the land started slowly to subside, and seismic activity occurred on a frequent basis until the end of the century.

Recent bradyseismic events

With knowledge of the events leading to the 1538 eruption, it is not surprising that there was considerable concern in late 1969 when uplift, centred on Pozzuoli, started once again. Over a period of 2 years the ground rose 1.7 m (Fig. 3.11) and much of the old town of Pozzuoli was rendered uninhabitable, standing as a dilapidated pile of buildings cut off from the rest of the town by large gates.

In early 1982 ground movements began again and the land began to rise. The crisis lasted until 1984. The area was wracked by seismic events as well, sometimes continuously for hours on end. Buildings crumbled and people fled the town. The quakes were of low magnitude, less than five on the Richter scale, but shallow, and therefore of a high intensity.

A new town of high-rise buildings was constructed on the western side of the caldera complex so that inhabitants in the worst hit part of town could be evacuated. In all there was uplift of *c.* 2 m. A new quay had to be built at a lower level to accommodate ships in the busy port (Fig. 3.12). The upper storey of some buildings had to be taken down to prevent them falling on people and property. Other houses were in a state of constant repair, and buildings, and whole streets were supported by scaffolding (Fig. 3.13). The ceilings of some shops and archways were supported by pit props. It was a very serious situation indeed.

Regular sampling and analysis of water and gases was carried out at Solfatara and other hot springs and wells. The temperature of the water appeared to be steady during the crisis, and there is no evidence for large changes in temperature over many centuries. Small changes in composition were observed for a short time at the start of uplift. All the evidence points to an increase in pressure in the magma reservoir, although there is no evidence from gravity measurements to suggest a fresh influx of magma. Some argue that the whole Campi Flegrei system was shaken up by the 1980 Avellino earthquake in the Apennines. Certainly there was also a correlation of lunar tides and the timing of seismic swarms, illustrating the delicate equilibrium of such systems.

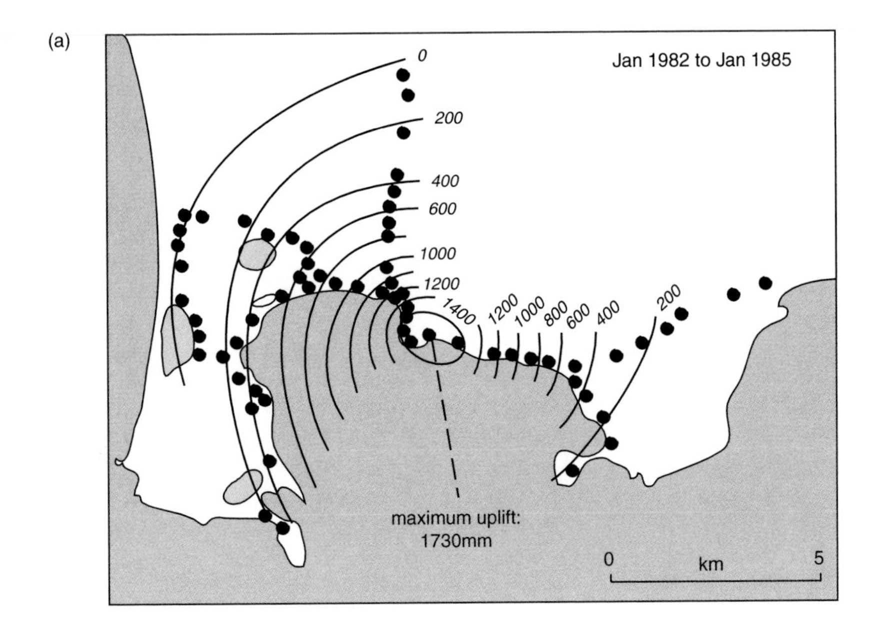

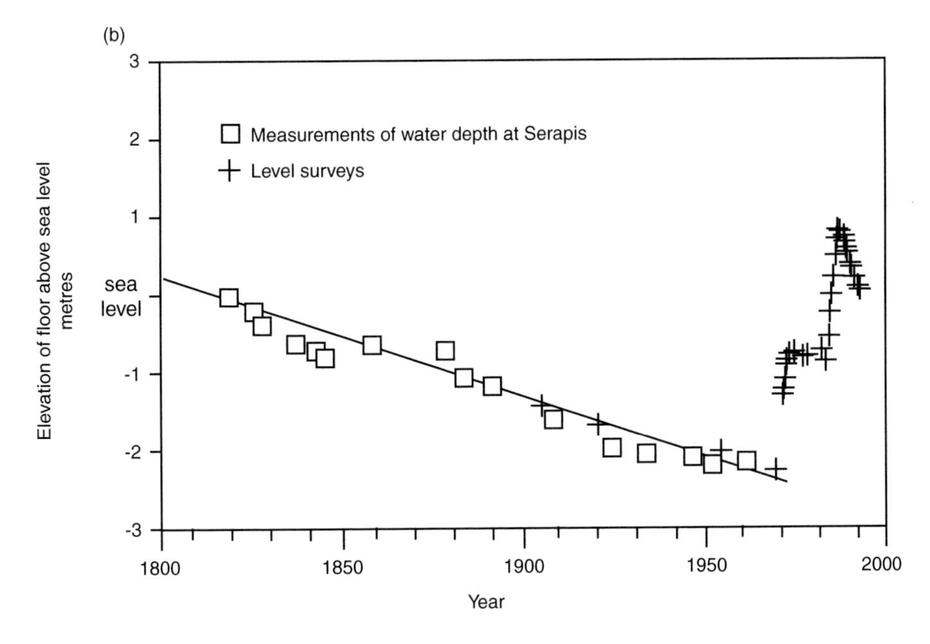

Fig. 3.11. Ground deformation at Campi Flegrei. (**a**) Map showing uplift in millimetres between January 1982 and Jan 1985 (black spots are measured stations); (**b**) elevation of the floor of Serapis with respect to sea level Note the rapid uplifts in the early 1970s and 1980s.

Fig. 3.12. The new jetty at Pozzuoli harbour, built at a lower level than the one behind to accommodate for the uplift in 1984. The height of the new jetty approximately represents the amount of uplift that occurred in 1984.

Few of the inhabitants were aware that Pozzuoli is at the heart of an active caldera, and the main concern was the earthquakes. The possibility of an eruption was very real, but few other than the scientists knew this during most of the crisis. The first public statement of the real concern of a future eruption came surprisingly in a documentary programme on television in the United Kingdom. This outlined the possibility of a potential eruption, and devastating effects if one should occur in this densely populated area, as well as in Naples and elsewhere. The programme promoted additional concern to that already felt by everyone in the area, including those based at the NATO Southern Europe Headquarters in the requisitioned World War II Gestapo buildings in Baia just east of Pozzuoli. One of us (J.E.G.) was asked by the Ministry of Defence in London to go to Campi Flegrei to explain the situation to the UK personnel. Earlier, a US Geological Survey team had been to advise the US Navy in the Mediterranean. The situation was clear; the possibility of an eruption similar to that of 1538 did exist. The US team assessed the possibility of an eruption as 50%.

As well as describing the possible effects of different sizes of eruption and how to deal with them, the report to the UK NATO group included the following recommendation: 'It is clearly prudent to have an evacuation plan well worked out before an eruption takes place and it would be advisable to base this on the possibility of phreato-plinian eruption.'

Inevitably in Naples, this report found its way to the newspapers. Because this was the first public suggestion of volcanic activity, in addition to earthquakes, it became headlines. One of the first of these was: 'Goodbye Napoli!' From then on chaos reigned.

Fig. 3.13. Buildings in Pozzuoli encased in scaffolding for repair following their being rendered unsafe by seismic activity during the 1984 bradyseism. Mt Nuovo is in the background behind the church tower.

The Press were highly critical of the authorities for not keeping the public better informed. The authorities accused the UK group of suggesting that Britons should be evacuated from the area, when in fact it had been argued that what was needed was a well-organized plan of evacuation.

Shortly after, the comprehensive, official report by Italian volcanologists became available, showing that they too considered there were real dangers, and, indeed, that a plan of evacuation existed, but not till then made public. The dangers to those who live in Campi Flegrei are still there, and, as with all active or potentially active volcanoes, a constantly upgraded emergency plan is of fundamental importance.

At the time Pozzuoli was suffering these phenomena, Rabaul Caldera, similar in size to Campi Flegrei with a diameter of 12 km, in Papua New Guinea, was also having a period of uplift and seismicity. But Rabaul, as described earlier, did erupt 12 years later in

September 1994. It is worthy of note that the eruption of Rabaul took place with only 48 hours warning.

The magma chamber

Being predominantly pyroclastic rocks, many of the products of Campi Flegrei have suffered significant alteration, hampering geochemical studies. The products range from trachybasalts to peralkaline phonolitic trachytes, with trachytes being volumetrically most abundant. There is a clear compositional gap between the trachybasalts and the more evolved products (Fig. 3.14). The trachybasalts are rare, mainly pre-caldera in age with a few younger representatives such as the products of Minopoli (8–9 ka BP). Some of the products of individual eruptions show variable chemistry, suggesting evacuation of a compositionally zoned magma reservoir; the temporal sequence is always from more evolved to less evolved where this can be determined. The compositional variation of the erupted products of Campi Flegrei can largely be explained by fractional crystallization involving the phenocryst phases.

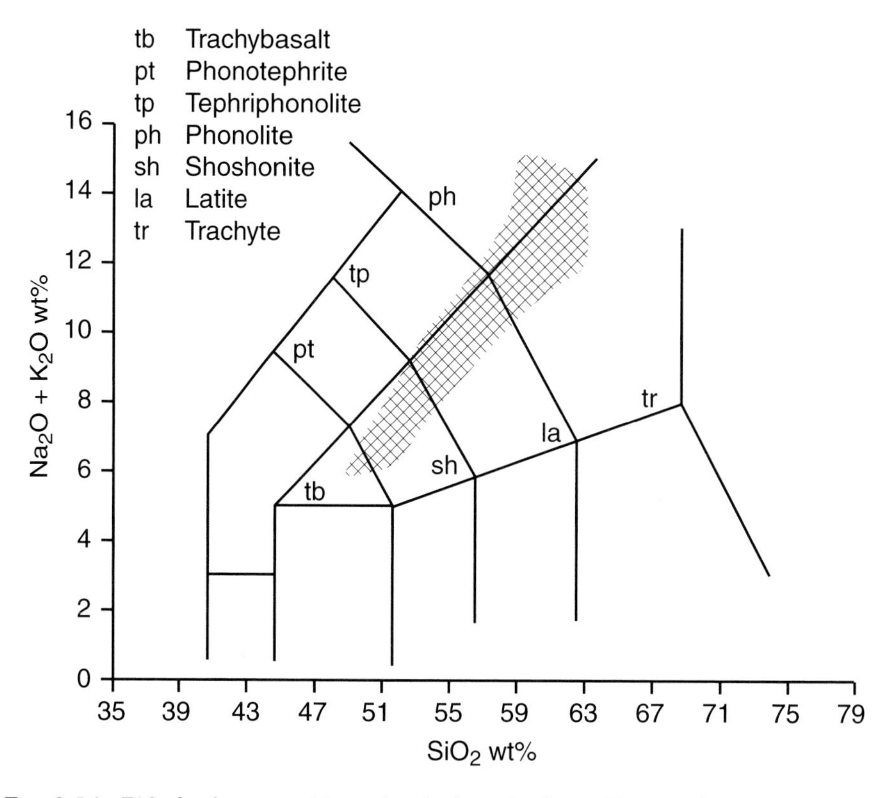

Fig. 3.14. TAS plot for compositions of rocks from the Campi Flegrei volcano (adapted from D'Antonio *et al.* 1999).

A possible progressive decrease in the volume of the erupted products from the Campanian Ignimbrite to that of the 1538 eruption is said by some to imply a decline in the volume of magma available within the magma reservoir. This idea may also be supported by the migration with time of vents towards the centre of the caldera. Trachytic lavas tend to be erupted progressively towards the centre of the caldera complex, whereas more basaltic lavas are erupted at the periphery. This has been interpreted as a consequence of the progressive solidification and contraction of a compositionally zoned magma reservoir, which has acted as largely a closed system over the last 10 ka.

The levelling surveys carried out since 1970 of the ground deformation of Campi Flegrei provide a wealth of data for interpreting the cause of these uplift episodes. Attempts to mathematically simulate the observed ground movements using various modelling approaches have been undertaken by a number of research teams using various assumptions.

There is debate as to whether the uplift was due to increased pressure exerted by the magma reservoir, or due to heat transfer to a confined shallow aquifer. This discrepancy in interpretation is due in part to dispute about the depth of top of the magma reservoir. There is, however, general consensus that a shallow magma reservoir is located at 3–5 km below the surface and that it is overlain by an active hydrothermal system.

The pattern of seismicity during the 1982–1984 uplift episode and the gravimetric Bouguer anomalies support the presence of an inner collapsed zone within Campi Flegrei. This collapse zone, with a funnel-shape' structure, may have formed as a result of the eruption of the Neapolitan Yellow Tuff, and some consider that this structure has controlled the recent deformation and thus explains why the same pattern of movements recur.

An important question concerning the recent episodes of uplift is whether they resulted from the injection of fresh magma into the high-level reservoir. Input of fresh magma into the system might be expected to lead to a distinctive signature in the composition of fumarolic gases. There has been detailed monitoring of the chemical variation of fumaroles before, during and after the 1982–1984 crisis. H_2O, H_2S and CH_4 in fumaroles all increased as early as 1 year before the beginning of uplift and began to decline for about 9 months before the end of the uplift stage. It is clear that the system responds chemically more quickly than it does mechanically. Isotopic data for fluids showed no increase in magma-derived species during the 1982–1984 episode. This lack of an increased magmatic signature in the fumaroles and thermal fluids was taken to suggest that there was no fresh magmatic input into the reservoir. However, it is also possible to argue that the gas and fluid geochemistry indicate only that no magmatic component is being released at the surface, and not that no fresh magma is being injected into the reservoir.

Theoretical models conclude that the tensional stress exceeds the lithostatic load immediately above the pressure source and also near the surface, but between 1 and 2 km depth the magnitude of the tensional stress goes through a minimum falling below that of the lithostatic load. Gas and fluids might be expected to flow freely near the surface and around the intrusion, but not to migrate through the zone of minimum tensional stress where fractures will be closed. If this is the case, injection of fresh magma would not necessarily be reflected in the composition of the discharged gases. Thus the injection of fresh magma, probably hot, more mafic melt, into the silicic magma reservoir is a strong possibility as the cause for the uplift events at Campi Flegrei. The longer-term subsidence, on the other hand, may be due to movements of fluids within the hydrothermal system.

The most recent erupted products, those of the 1538 eruption, are peralkaline phonolitic trachytes and among the most evolved on the volcano. If fresh magma was emplaced into the shallow reservoir to initiate the 1538 eruption, there was no mixing with the erupted silicic material. It is well known that the ascent of a new batch of mafic magma can be halted on encountering a body of more silicic melt, either through experiencing a change in density or because of rheological properties of the magmas. It is thus possible that this eruption may have been triggered by injections of small amounts of mafic magma into the high-level silicic reservoir causing pre-existing magma to be erupted.

It is important to assess what factors might trigger the next eruption of Campi Flegrei. With successive uplift in the 1970s and 1980s, pressure has built up in the rocks overlying the magma reservoir. It can be calculated that little extra pressure is required to open pathways from the magma reservoir to the surface, leading to a possible eruption. For this to occur another uplift event of 1.5 m would be expected within the next few decades.

Hazard

This is clearly an area at great risk. With a million people virtually entrapped in the caldera with poor road communications, an eruption of the magnitude of that of 1538 would have a devastating effect. We might expect only a few days warning; there would be earthquakes and ground uplift. Once the eruption started, explosive activity spreading ash and lapilli over the whole area would make motorized transport virtually impossible. Pyroclastic surges and possibly pyroclastic flows could affect the whole of Campi Flegrei. Central Naples would be protected from all but the worst of the surges, but could suffer from heavy ash fall. We could expect that downwind for hundreds of kilometres there would be a covering of ash enough to destroy agricultural land at least in the short term. Such a small eruption would be devastating.

Much larger eruptions have occurred. Intermediate eruptions similar to, but larger than that of 1538, would affect a wider area in terms of tephra, but much the same in terms of surges and pyroclastic flows. An eruption like that which produced the Neapolitan Yellow Tuff would be expected to erupt pyroclastic flows that travelled for at least 15 km.

We have, however, to consider that a really large ignimbrite eruption could occur. The last in this area, the Campanian Ignimbrite eruption, was about 39 ka ago, and another will almost certainly happen in the future. The last such eruption to occur in Europe was the one that occurred in *c.* 1500 BC on the Greek island of Santorini only some 700 km away to the SE. There has been much speculation about the part played by the Santorini eruption in the destruction of the Minoan civilization; whatever the answer, there is no doubt about the dramatic effect of such an eruption today on such a densely inhabited area. The next from Campi Flegrei could devastate the Italian peninsula from at least Rome south; the ash fall could cover much of Europe, the Middle East, or less likely North Africa depending on the wind direction.

Places to visit

The late Maurice Krafft, in his guidebook to European volcanoes, suggested that the best place for an overall view of Campi Flegrei was the Monastery at Camaldoli. He was quite right, but the smog levels over the caldera are normally so high as to prevent decent views. Only after heavy rain or on cold winter days may a good panorama be experienced. A climb to the top of Monte Nuovo through the cultivated flanks can provide a good overview; even better is the view from Monte Barbaro (Gauro), but it is a stiffer climb especially when it is hot. Other good overviews are from Monte di Procida, and from Capo Miseno at the end of a single-track road through a tunnel cut in the cone from which Pliny observed the AD 79 eruption of Vesuvius

A visit to the classical geological site of the so-called Temple of Serapis is a must, and a walk round Pozzuoli and the port area is instructive both from a neotectonics point of view and as an indication of the damage that can be caused by a bradyseism. Most of the damaged buildings have been patched up, but the new, lower-level, landing area built to take account of the uplift is clear to see.

One of the best places to observe the many pyroclastic deposits of the region is the island of Procida. This is only a short distance by boat and has excellent exposures. In particular, some of the best exposures of the Breccia Museo are found here, showing associated facies including welded tuffs, piperno and normal ignimbrite.

Torre Gaveta has excellent cliff exposures. The NYT is seen banked up against a steep unconformity, below which is the Breccia Museo and older rocks of this volcanic complex. Rocks of the NYT are exposed in many places within the city of Naples, especially the Mergellina and Posillipo hill area. These are all lithified deposits, but unlithified examples can be seen in many quarries, such as those on the NW margins of the area at San Severino. One of the easiest places to see the NYT is at the archaeological site of Cuma.

Outcrops of the 1538 deposits occur on the seaward side of the cone. For outcrops of some of the younger cones within the caldera complex, those on the coast road north of Baia are particularly instructive.

Notes

Geography, history, communications and industry

There are many guide books to the region, but we find the Blue Guide (Blanchard 2000) to be packed with information and generally reliable. The Touring Club Italiano produces a useful map of the area including Naples and Vesuvius at a scale of 1:50 000 (Anon. 1980).

Volcanic geology

The first really detailed descriptions of the volcanic geology were probably made by Johnston-Lavis in a series of papers (1888, 1889*b*). De Lorenzo (1904) was the first to consider the whole stratigraphy of the area. Major contributions to the stratigraphy were also were made by Rittmann (1950*a*,*b*).

The two main schools currently working on Campi Flegrei described the stratigraphic framework in a modern volcanological context in a number of papers during the 1980s. From Pisa was the work of Rosi *et al.* (1983), and a geological map with accompanying memoir by Rosi & Sbrana (1987); and from Naples the work in considerable detail by Di Girolamo *et al.* (1984), followed by their geological map (Di Vito *et al.* 1985). There are two special issues of *Journal of Volcanology and Geothermal Research* devoted to Campi Flegrei (in Vol. 48 (1991) and Vol. 91 (1999)).

The pre-NYT activity stratigraphy was dated by Scandone *et al.* (1991), incorporating earlier work such as that of Capaldi & Gillot (1985). In the Naples area it was described initially by Johnston-Lavis (1889*a*) and more recently by Cole *et al.* (1994).

General description of the Campanian Ignimbrite at medial and distal locations was given by Barberi *et al.* (1978). Fisher *et al.* (1993) described features of the ignimbrite that argue for emplacement as an expanded turbulent flow. Lithic breccias that crop out to the north of Campi Flegrei have been described by Di Girolamo *et al.* (1984) and Scandone *et al.* (1991). The ultraplinian phase of the Campanian Ignimbrite eruption has been described by Rosi *et al.* (1999). The location of the source vent for the Campanian Ignimbrite is highly controversial. There are three theories: (a) that it was erupted from Campi Flegrei (Rosi *et al.* 1983; Rosi & Sbrana 1987; Barberi *et al.* 1991); (b) that it was erupted from a fracture north of Campi Flegrei located in the Campanian Plain (Di Girolamo *et al.* 1984); (c) that it was erupted from the Acerra depression north of Naples (Scandone *et al.* 1991). Extensive radiocarbon dating of the Campanian Ignimbrite was made by Alessio *et al.* (1971, 1973, 1974); many of these results were also presented by Scandone *et al.* (1991). Ar/Ar dates for the Campanian Ignimbrite have been provided by De Vivo *et al.* (2001).

The origin of the Breccia Museo and its correlation with other deposits is highly controversial. Workers arguing that all outcrops of breccia were formed by a single eruption include Rosi *et al.* (1983), Rosi & Sbrana (1987) and Barberi *et al.* (1991). These workers also consider the Breccia Museo to be the proximal facies of the Campanian Ignimbrite. Proponents of a multiple eruption origin include Lirer *et al.* (1991), Scandone *et al.* (1991), Perrotta (1992) and Perrotta & Scarpati (1994). On the basis of radiocarbon dating these workers have proposed that the Breccia Museo of SW Campi Flegrei is too young to be correlated with the Campanian Ignimbrite.

Correlation of the breccia with the medial distal Campanian Ignimbrite has been made by Rosi *et al.* (1983), Di Girolamo *et al.* (1984) and Rosi & Sbrana (1987). Dating of Breccia Museo has been carried out by Lirer *et al.* (1991), Scandone *et al.* (1991) and Perrotta (1992). Scandone *et al.* (1991) suggested that older San Martino Welded Ignimbrite might correlate with the Campanian Ignimbrite.

All the Yellow Tuff in the Campi Flegrei was initially considered a single deposit by De Lorenzo (1904). Other workers proposed that the yellow tuffs were the result of many small eruptions (Rittmann 1950*b*; Capaldi *et al.* 1987). Recent detailed studies support the view that although the Yellow Tuff is a single mappable unit it is the product of many eruptions (Scarpati 1990; Orsi *et al.* 1992*a*; Scarpati *et al.* 1993). Detailed descriptions and interpretation of the upper part of the Yellow Tuff (the NYT) are given by Cole & Scarpati (1993).

Field studies indicating that magmatic activity formed an important component of post-NYT explosive activity at Campi Flegrei were made by Rosi *et al.* (1983), Di Vito *et al.* (1987), Rosi & Sbrana (1987) and Mastrolorenzo (1994). The Agnano–Monte Spina eruption is discussed by Di Vita *et al.* (1999). The geological evolution of the Averno tuff ring was described by Lirer *et al.* (1990) and Mastrolorenzo (1994).

Excavations into rocks of the volcanoes of Naples were described by Johnston-Lavis (1889*a*,*b*). More recent descriptions are by Cole *et al.* (1994) and Di Vito *et al.* (1999).

Calderas

The idea that Campi Flegrei was formed by a single caldera collapse event related to the eruption of the Campanian Ignimbrite is supported by Rosi *et al.* (1983), Rosi & Sbrana (1987) and Barberi *et al.* (1991). That the NYT eruption formed the caldera is argued by Lirer *et al.* (1987). It was Scarpati *et al.* (1993) who pointed out that NYT drapes over some of the caldera scarps within the Campi Flegrei complex. More recently, Orsi *et al.* (1996*a*) have extended the margin of the Campi Flegrei caldera to the east, so that it now includes most of the city of Naples. Such an interpretation is based on the depth of the Campanian Ignimbrite in boreholes in the city and takes into account the tectonic lineaments. De Natale & Pingue (1993) discuss ground deformation in caldera structures. See also De Natale *et al.* (1991).

Unrest at calderas and recent unrest

The two-volume compendium of unrest at calderas on a global basis (Newhall & Dzurisin 1988) was stimulated by the simultaneous unrest at Campi Flegrei, Long Valley in California and Rabaul; it provides a valuable source of information. A special issue of *Bulletin Volcanologique* (Barberi *et al.* 1984; a curious date of publication as many of the papers were not accepted for publication until the following year) is a collection of papers on the 1982–1984 bradyseism. The seminal work on archaeological evidence for sea-level changes in the western Mediterranean is that of Flemming (1969). The work of Flemming has been expanded by Dvorak & Mastrolorenzo (1991). A valuable summary of the interpretations of the early 1980s unrest has been given by Dvorak & Berrino (1991).

Gas geochemistry

Paper on this subject include Allard *et al.* (1991) and Tedesco *et al.* (1990).

Chapter 4. **Roccamonfina and Vulture**

Introduction

Both Roccamonfina and Vulture are generally considered to be extinct volcanoes. There are reports in the classical literature of unusual events that could be indicative of historical activity, but these events were probably the result of more mundane activities. Nevertheless, although there is no direct evidence to suggest they are still active, the possibility cannot be disregarded.

At both volcanoes the stratigraphy is not easy to determine, first because outcrops are limited, and second because correlation between outcrops is sometimes difficult. Extensive ignimbrites, however, form good stratigraphic horizons and specific patterns of local sequences can help in establishing the position of an outcrop in the overall stratigraphy. Outcrops, mainly road cuttings and quarries, tend to be temporary; but new outcrops are continually being made, so improving the potential for understanding the stratigraphy.

Roccamonfina

Roccamonfina volcano does not have a distinctive landform when viewed from the east, for example from the Rome–Naples autostrada. Only when seen from the SW does it have a recognizable volcanic form (Fig. 4.1). Nevertheless, it has a well-formed caldera (Fig. 4.2) at its summit, within which a prominent dome complex has formed. The huge lava domes of Monte Croce and Lattani, some of the largest domes in Europe, rise from the centre of the caldera structure and loom impressively above the town of Roccamonfina at their base.

Fig. 4.1. Roccamonfina volcano from the SW showing caldera rim and lava domes (D) contained within the main caldera. (Photograph by courtesy of Guido Goirdano.)

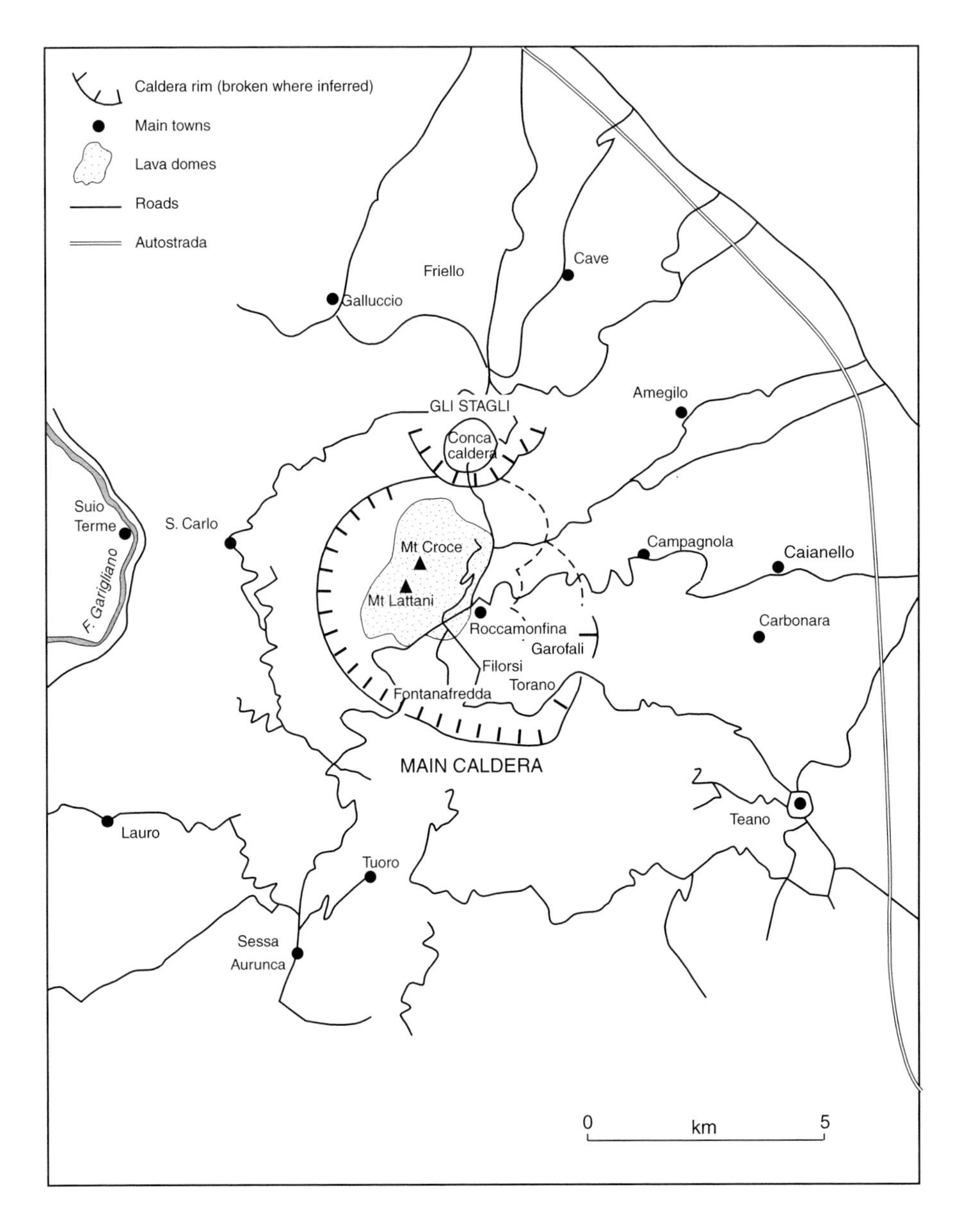

Fig. 4.2. Location map and roads for the Roccamonfina volcano.

From a petrological point of view, Roccamonfina is well known from the work, in the early 1970s, of James Appleton, then at Edinburgh University, who provided the basis for the current classification of the K-rich volcanic rocks of the Roman and Campanian Provinces based on studies at Roccamonfina. He recognized that the lavas belonged to two distinct magma series, which he designated the High-K Series (HKS) and the Low-K Series (LKS). These two series have been subsequently identified as being fundamental throughout the volcanoes of the Roman and Campanian Provinces. The

HKS is strongly undersaturated, incorporating leucitites and leucite tephrites to leucite phonolites, whereas the LKS ranges from basalts to trachytes.

Geography

Roccamonfina volcano lies some 60 km NW of Naples, and sits in a topographic depression surrounded by imposing fault-bounded mountains of mainly carbonate Mesozoic–Cenozoic basement rocks. It is situated at the intersection between the main NW-trending normal fault system that runs along the western side of the Apennines, and the NE-trending Garigliano graben (Fig. 4.3). This regional tectonic pattern has played an important part in influencing the growth of the volcano. Many of the vents on the flanks of the volcano are aligned along NE lineaments parallel to the Garigliano graben. Regional tectonics also played a part in the development of the summit caldera. Although a NE lineament clearly cuts the rim of the caldera with a distinctive notch there is little evidence of displacement. The western and northern part of the summit caldera has a clear arcuate outline, but the overall shape is rather rectangular, suggesting that tectonic trends, in particular the NW trend, have influenced the form of the caldera.

On the eastern side of the volcano, intense fluvial dissection has occurred through the soft pyroclastic materials, forming deep valleys. These are heavily vegetated and difficult to penetrate, but expose the volcanic products. The interfluves are wooded and form the main lines of communications radial to the caldera.

Traditionally, Roccamonfina has sustained a rural community. It is fertile and relatively highly populated on the lower slopes. There are many agricultural hamlets, especially on the eastern side. Crops include vines and olives, together with cereals, vegetables and sweet chestnuts, for which Roccamonfina is famous. In recent years the area has increasingly become important for second homes, and the peasant life style is rapidly disappearing.

The Autostrada del Sole (Fig. 4.2) from Rome to the south swings round the foot of Roccamonfina on the east side and some of the products of the volcano can be seen in road cuttings. Junctions at Caianello and Capua link the autostrada to secondary roads that climb the volcano to the town of Roccamonfina in the main caldera. Most communications in the north, east and south are radial to the caldera, running along the interfluves in this deeply incised terrain. To the west, where there has been less dissection, circumferential communications are more practical. Apart from Roccamonfina, the two main towns of the volcano are Teano, which has a railway station on a line between Rome and Naples, and Sessa Aurunca.

An interesting geological aside is that just before the Second World War there was interest in obtaining alumina. Leucite was seen as a potential source, and together with the possibility of also obtaining potash, such extraction might have been economic. The leucite-rich lavas in the Sessa Aurunca area were seriously considered for exploitation.

At the western foot of the volcano, in the Garigliano Valley, is the spa resort of Suio Terme (Fig. 4.2). The mineral-rich waters here are claimed to have wide curative

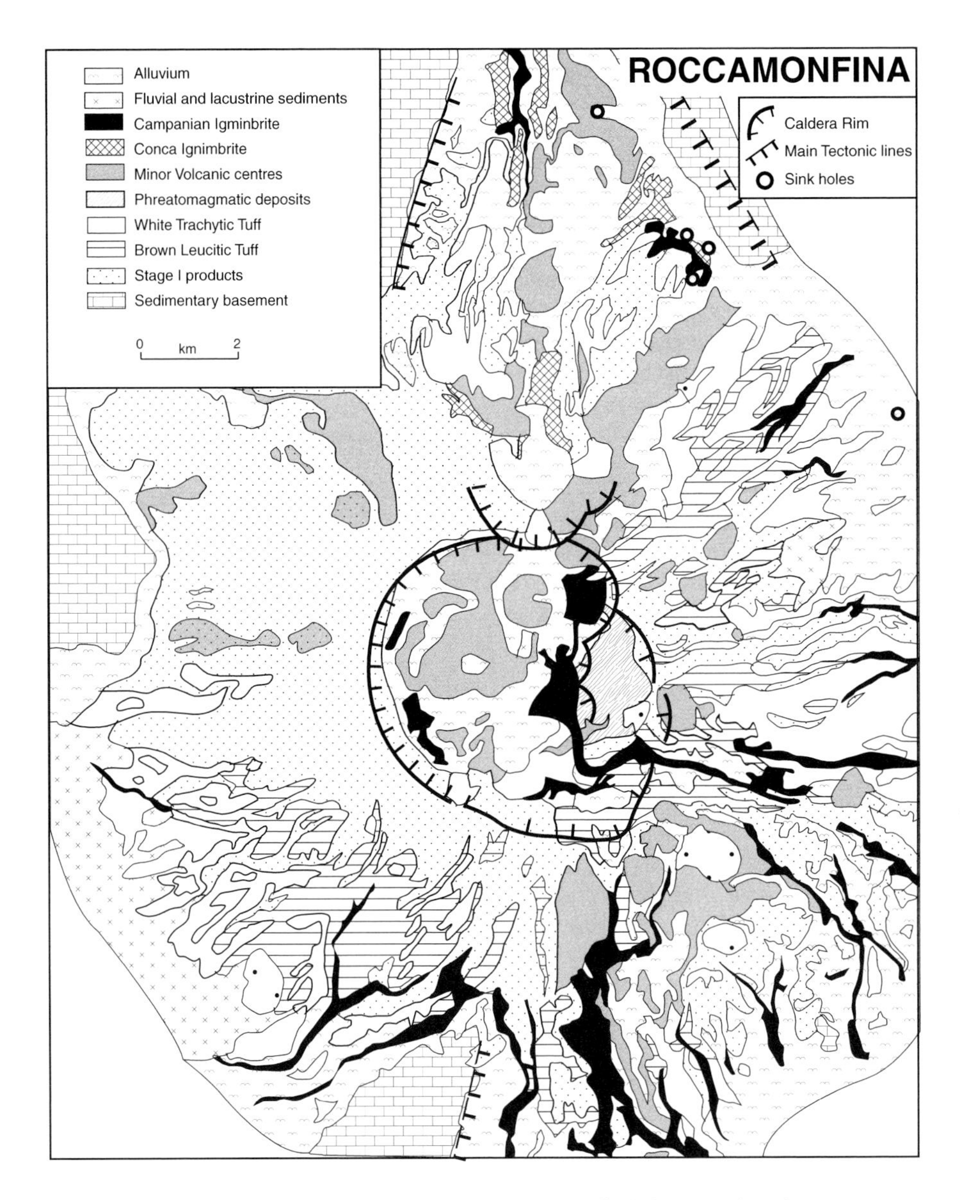

Fig. 4.3. Geological map of Roccamonfina based in part on Luhr & Giannetti (1987).

powers; as far back as Roman times the resort was visited by the aristocratic classes and it was used, for example, by the Emperor Nero. Spas are considered a part of the health care regime in Italy and there is extensive hotel accommodation at this resort. Bubbling mud pools occur on the valley sides and the carpet of dead insects on the ground attests to CO_2 emissions. High levels of radon gas are also emitted.

History

As far as we know there have been no eruptions on Roccamonfina during historical times. The inhabitants have had a more peaceful time than their counterparts on the nearby Campi Flegrei and Vesuvius. Nevertheless, damage has been caused by earthquakes.

The site of the present town of Sessa Aurunca, on the south flank, was once the capital of the Aurunci tribe, and remains of baths and a theatre attest to the presence of the Romans there. Sessa continued as an important centre and became an impressive walled town with imposing gates at either end of the main street.

Teano, another town with ancient roots, became famous as the place where, in 1861, Garibaldi and King Victor Emmanuel met. Garibaldi arrived from the south with his troops, having taken Naples from the Bourbons, and Victor Emmanuel came from the north, having defeated the Papal troops. Thus Italy was united under the House of Savoy with Victor Emmanuel as king.

The volcanic history of Roccamonfina

Roccamonfina has had a long and complex history of activity stretching back over at least 600 ka, with the latest major eruptions probably taking place around 50–100 ka BP (Fig. 4.4). Much of the early pioneering study of the volcano was done by the Italian geologist Bernadino Giannetti, and his work has provided much of the basis for the understanding of this volcano. Giannetti, and his US collaborator, petrologist Jim Luhr, established the stratigraphic framework of the volcano.

The geological history of the volcano can be divided into two stages. Stage I built up the main cone with the eruption mainly of lavas, followed by ignimbrite-forming explosive eruptions. The products of Stage I are strongly undersaturated, leucite-bearing rocks that belong to the HKS. By the end of Stage I the summit cone had been truncated by a summit caldera. Stage II was initiated about 300 ka ago by a major explosive ignimbrite-forming eruption, and continued until about 50 ka ago. Much of the activity forming Stage II products was explosive, but lavas were produced, including the huge summit domes. The products of this stage in the volcano's history belong predominantly to the LKS, although some of the lavas are more potassic (Fig. 4.5).

The main stratocone building phase (Stage I)

The main stratocone cone built up to a maximum height of over 1200 m. The base of the cone, which to the SW rests on the coastal plain, is about 18 km in diameter; and the preserved profile on the western flank has slopes of about 6° and then gradually steepens up to 20°. Activity was mainly effusive, but interbedded pyroclastic deposits, such as lapilli fall beds, were formed, and a few cinder cones resulted from flank eruptions.

In Fig. 4.6 we show our reconstruction of the form of the volcano at the end of the cone-building phase. The western, southern and northern flanks of the volcano, which preserve the general form of the original cone, suggest that the volcano had an

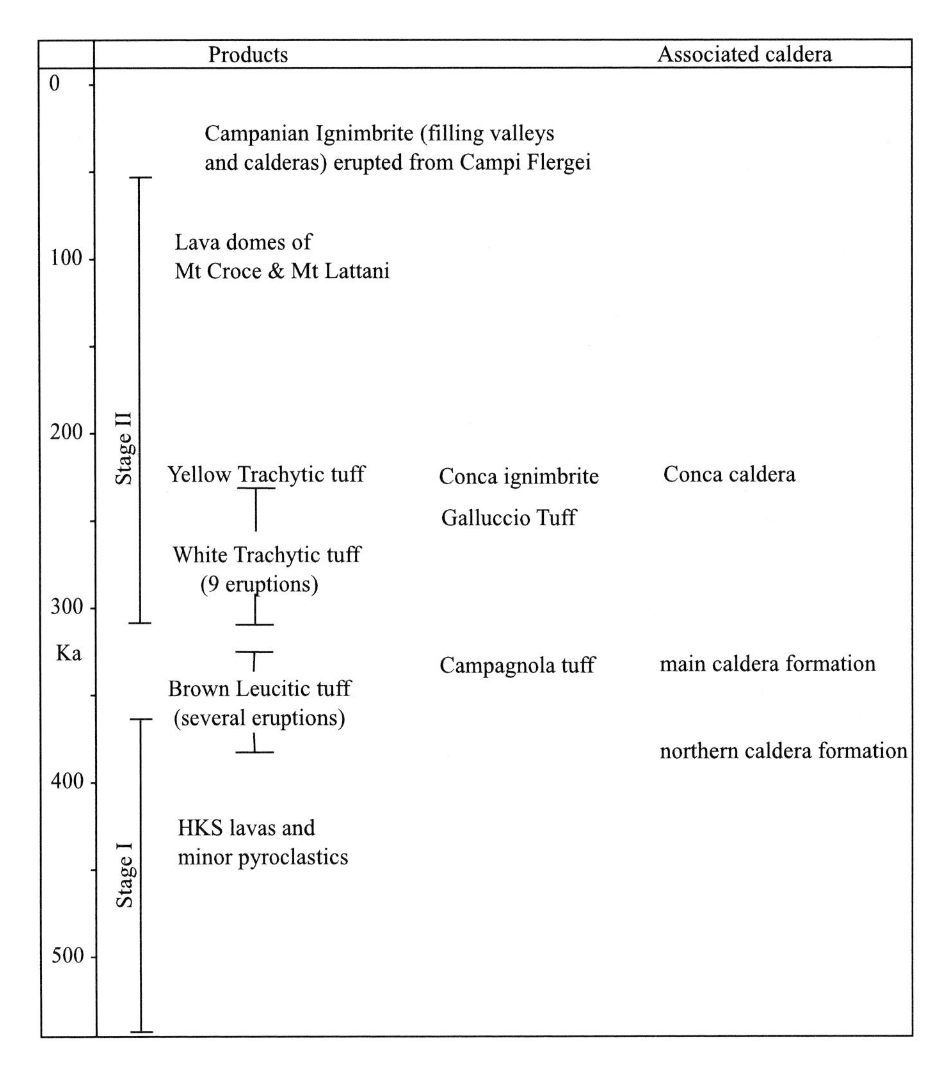

Fig. 4.4. Stratigraphy of Roccamonfina volcano based on Giannetti & Luhr (1983), Cole *et al.* (1992) and Giannetti (2001). The middle column gives units named in Cole *et al.* (1992).

elliptical form in plan view with a NW–SE axis. One explanation of this is that there were two centres, a main one to the NW and a secondary minor one to the SE.

However, to the north, a large horseshoe-shaped scar, Gli Stagli, was formed as a result of sector collapse. The age of this collapse is not known, but it contains within it materials of the later explosive phase of the volcano. It is thus most likely to have formed before caldera collapses started to truncate the summit and end the phase of cone building.

As shown in the post-caldera collapse reconstruction in Fig. 4.6, the main caldera is not centred on the highest part of the volcano but is offset to the east, leaving a high wall to

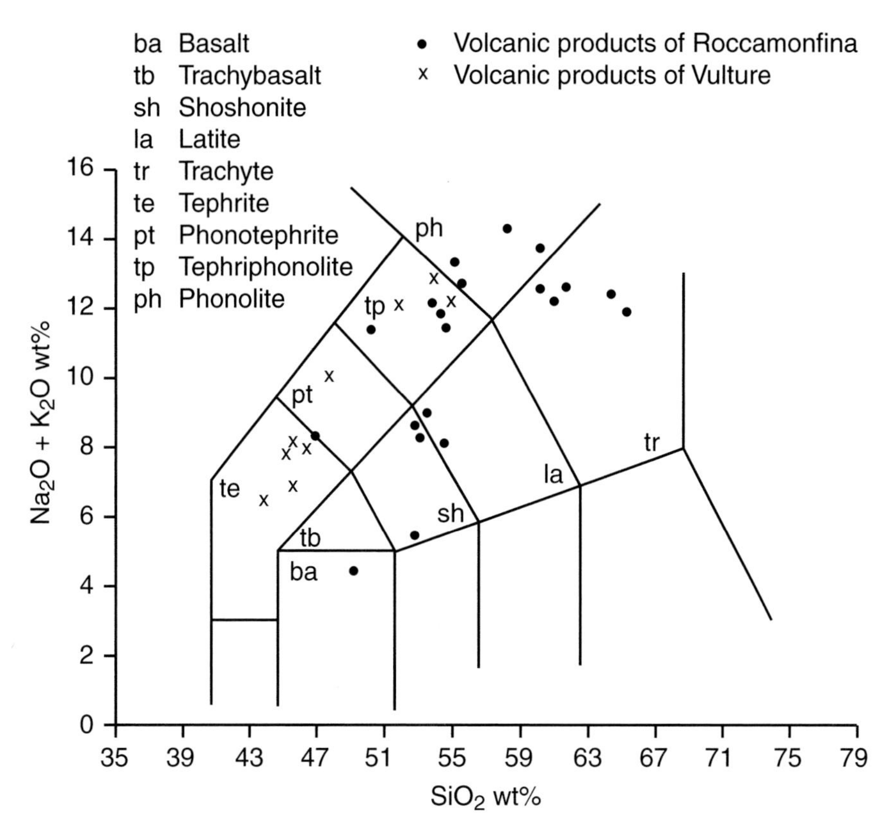

Fig. 4.5. TAS plot of compositions of rocks from Roccamonfina and Vulture volcanoes. Data for Roccamonfina are from Appleton (1972), Giannetti & Luhr (1983) and Luhr & Giannetti (1987); and for Vulture from De Fino *et al.* (1986).

the west and a lower wall to the east. This configuration is important as it may explain the distribution of ignimbrites, which dominate the geology of the volcano's eastern flank and form a complex sequence of cut and fill, the soft pyroclastic rocks being subject to rapid erosion between eruptions and the resulting valleys being filled again by an ignimbrite from a later eruption.

The ignimbrite-forming eruptions

Stage I in the history of Roccamonfina culminated with the eruption of ignimbrite sheets termed the Brown Leucitic Tuff (BLT) by Luhr and Giannetti in the 1980s. Further study has shown that the BLT consists of several distinct ignimbrites of undersaturated potassic trachyte composition separated by soils. Some of the older ones are hard to correlate and are chemically altered. The BLT spans a period of 54 ka starting at 374 ka BP.

The work of Giannetti and Luhr suggests that the BLT involved eruption from a compositionally zoned magma reservoir. The pumice in the lower part of the sequence has <4 wt% CaO with values >4 wt% in the overlying units (CaO is typically used as a

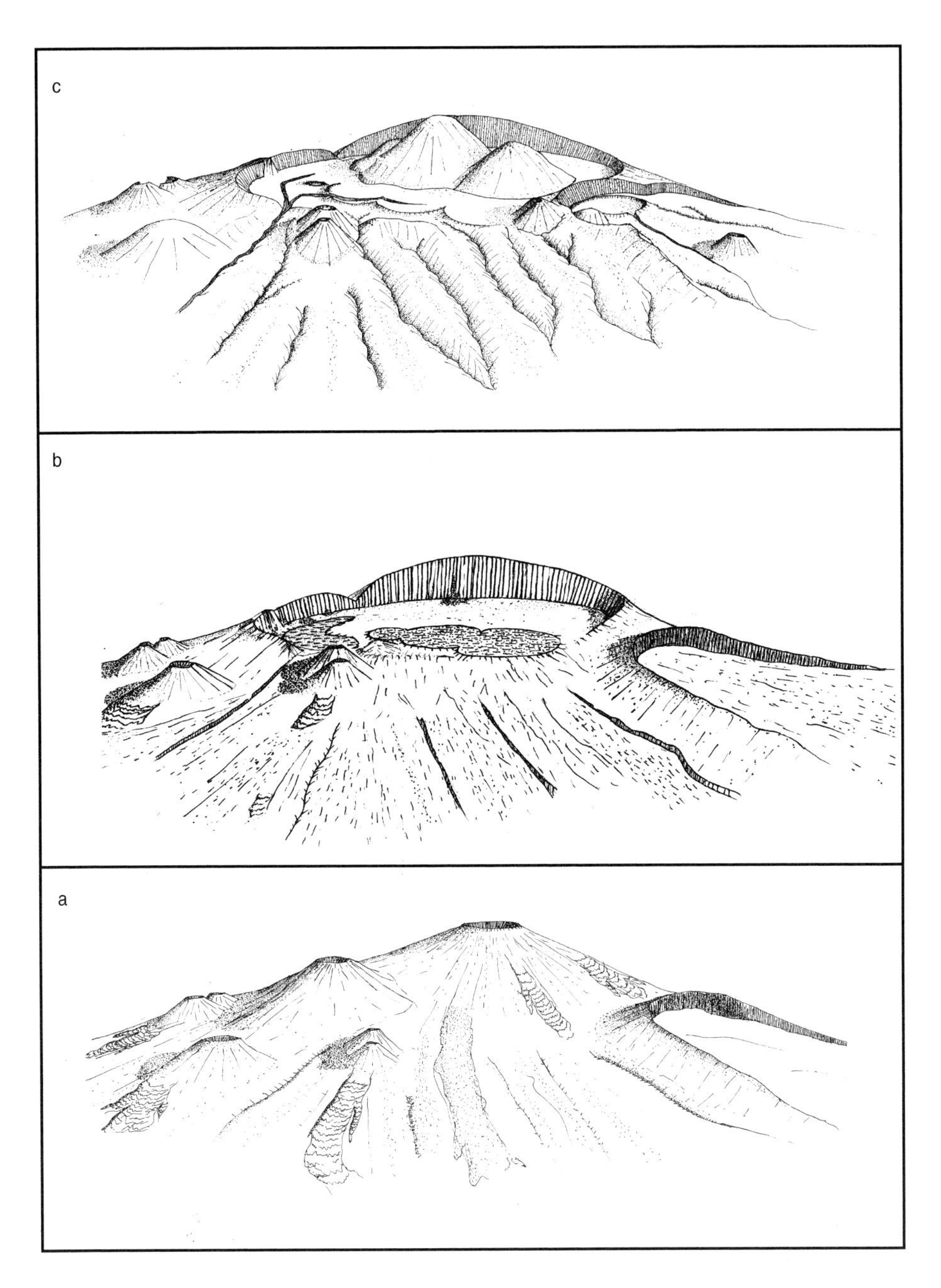

Fig. 4.6. Schematic representation of the evolution of Roccamonfina as seen from the east. (**a**) Pre-main caldera collapse (*c.* 400 ka BP) also showing the northern sector collapse; (**b**) following the main caldera collapse showing ephemeral caldera lakes; (**c**) present-day view with lava domes of Montes Croce and Lattini.

differentiation index in the alkali-rich volcanic rocks of Italy). This suggests that the more evolved reservoir top was tapped first, followed by withdrawal of more mafic melt as deeper levels were erupted. The pumices contain crystals of calcic augite, plagioclase, sanidine, biotite, titanomagnetite, analcime (after leucite) and apatite. The presence also of xenocrysts of olivine and diopside indicates that magma mixing took place, possibly incorporating cumulate crystals. The observed chemical variation can be largely modelled by crystal fractionation of the observed phases and, indeed, nodules of monzonite and syenite are considered to be derived from cumulates generated by this fractionation.

The best preserved of the BLT ignimbrites is the youngest; this we have referred to as the Campagnola Tuff after the town of that name (Fig. 4.2) on the east flank of the volcano. Over most of its extent it is a massive, brown homogeneous ignimbrite with a valley-filling aspect, and a ground surge deposit. However, near the caldera margin, it shows a chaotic facies that includes cross-bedded horizons, lithic breccias and pumice concentrations, which grade horizontally as well as vertically into the normal massive facies.

The second major ignimbrite sequence was identified by Giannetti and Luhr as the White Trachytic Tuff (WTT). This sequence represents the opening phase of Stage II in the volcano's history. Again, further work has shown that these tuffs are the product of several eruptions, probably as many as seven with sufficient time intervals between them to allow the formation of soils. This sequence of ignimbrite-forming eruptions occurred between 317 and 230 ka BP.

One of the WTT deposits is well preserved and we have termed this the Galluccio Tuff because it is exposed in a quarry near that town (Fig. 4.2). The Galluccio Tuff has three eruptive units distinguished by the vesicularity of the pumice, and the crystallinity. Of particular interest are a wide array of co-ignimbrite lithic breccias (Fig. 4.7). Many of these breccias are near breaks in slope that occur between the steeper proximal and more shallow distal flanks of the volcano. Pumice concentration zones are also distinctive, particularly within more distal regions on the flanks.

The Galluccio Tuff includes both white and grey pumice. The white pumice has CaO content as low as 1.2 wt%, up to 66 wt% SiO_2 and is crystal poor, whereas the grey pumice has up to 3 wt% CaO, SiO_2 content as low as 60 wt% and is crystal rich. In any one deposit both varieties of pumice are likely to occur, indicating mixing during eruption. However, the Lower Galluccio Tuff at the base is richer in white pumice and the Upper Galluccio Tuff is richer in grey pumice, suggesting progressive evacuation of a compositionally zoned reservoir. Dark inclusions in the pumice indicate that the compositionally zoned trachytic magma in the reservoir overlay more mafic melt of trachyandesitic composition. Again the chemical variation can be largely explained by crystal fractionation, and the mineralogy of the syenite nodules in the Galluccio Tuff closely matches the calculated fractionation assemblages.

Cumulate nodules are present as lithic fragments in these ignimbrites. As well as the syenitic material described above there are very distinctive nodules of pyroxenite, which represent more mafic cumulates.

A third significant trachytic ignimbrite-forming event occurred on the northern flank of the volcano after the Galluccio Tuff eruption. This eruption, which has been dated

(a)

(b)

Fig. 4.7. Coignimbrite lithic breccias in the Gulluccio Tuff, just NE of Sessa Aurunca. Both photographs are of the same locality and show the heterogeneous nature of the breccias. Flow direction is from right to left. (**a**) The basal contact of the breccia is linear and the breccia pinches out to the right; (**b**) two layers of lithic breccia, the lower one having a sharp, undulation base, whereas the upper breccia has a gradational contact with the ignimbrite below. The lower breccia is 2 m thick in the foreground.

at about 227 ka formed what we refer to as the Conca Ignimbrite (Yellow Trachytic Tuff of Giannetti and Luhr). It erupted from a vent at the head of the northern flank caldera, Gli Stagli. The pyroclastic flows that formed it were apparently confined by the walls of this caldera. The ignimbrite can be traced for over 13 km downslope from the vent. It is as much as 40 m thick where it has ponded in valleys, and consists of a distinctive, massive, mildly indurated tuff. In the past this tuff has been quarried for building stone. In the vent region, the Conca Caldera, it is overlain by poorly sorted fall and phreatomagmatic surge deposits representing the last phase of this eruption.

The calderas and intra-caldera events

As stated above, there are two caldera complexes on Roccamonfina: the main summit caldera complex, and the northern sector collapse with a contained small caldera. As well as the widespread ignimbrite-forming eruptions, which produced pyroclastic flows that swept down valleys on the flanks of the volcano, there were localized eruptions contained mainly within the calderas.

The main summit caldera complex is 6.5 km by 5 km with the long axis trending NW (Figs 4.2 and 4.3). It has a rectangular shape, except to the west, where the high walls (nearly 300 m) have a semicircular planform. Within the main caldera are three nested calderas (Fig. 4.6), the eastern rims of which can be clearly seen from the viewpoint on Monte Lattani.

The age of the main caldera is not easy to establish. The Campagnola Tuff is draped over the subdued eastern caldera wall, implying that the original collapse was related to earlier events. The formation of the caldera appears to coincide with a distinct change in both the chemistry of erupted materials and the style of eruption from stratovolcano-building lavas and associated pyroclastic materials including flank cones, to activity that included ignimbrite-forming events.

An exploratory geothermal borehole has provided a core through the caldera fill and encountered a tuff interpreted to be the BLT as well as breccias. The oldest material exposed on the floor of the caldera is, however, the Galluccio Tuff, consisting of a massive ignimbrite with several flow units and some cross-bedded surge deposits. The presence of lacustrine beds up to 20 m thick within the top part of the Galluccio Tuff and above it demonstrates that lakes formed within the caldera. There follows a thick sequence of hydromagmatic deposits, termed by us the Garofali Formation, containing the products of surges, ashes of fall origin, small ignimbrites and a limited amount of scoria of strombolian origin. Interbedded with these are lacustrine beds of fine ash and diatoms, and pumice beds, some showing reverse grading.

The picture we have is of a caldera with extensive lakes, or a single lake (Fig. 4.6). As a result, much of the eruptive activity involved water–magma interaction with 'wet' surges, as evidenced by fine-grained deposits and abundant accretionary lapilli. In some cases, pumices falling on the water floated, the larger pumices floating longer and thus producing reverse graded beds. The lakes appear to have become less extensive with time as successive deposits filled them. Some purely magmatic activity occurred, and the final deposits have the characters of 'dry surge' material. It is possible that this activity was the precursor to the next and final phase of intra-caldera activity, the formation of the dome complex, one of the youngest events on the volcano.

The massive domes (Fig. 4.8), rising some 400 m above the floor of the caldera, have a volume of nearly 1 km^3. There are two coalesced main domes, the larger, Monte Santa Croce, and the smaller to the NE, Monte Lattani; the former has been dated at 155 ka BP. If we assume that the domes grew at a rate of 4 $m^3 s^{-1}$ (based on the growth of Montserrat dome in the 1990s) we calculate that they may have taken some 10 years to form. There is no evidence to suggest extensive dome collapses, although a young scoriaceous ignimbrite near Fontanafredda has the right composition and position in the stratigraphy to be related to explosive activity from the dome. The lack of collapse deposits may suggest that the domes formed mainly by exogenous growth, and may have built up over a longer time than suggested above.

The Gli Stagli caldera on the northern flank contains deposits erupted from within it, and from the main caldera. The oldest units are a brown and a white ignimbrite. These are overlain by a thick sequence of lahars and water-borne deposits resulting from a sustained wet period reworking heavy ash fall on this flank, or possibly an overflow from a lake in the main caldera complex.

Most of the present surface of Gli Stagli is made of the Galluccio Tuff, which flooded the depression. At the Galluccio quarry, moulds of tree trunks have been found within the ignimbrite in a horizontal position, having been knocked down by the associated pyroclastic flow. Above the Galluccio Tuff is a very distinctive unit of alternating pumice

Fig. 4.8. The lava domes of Monte Croce (left) and Lattani (right), seen from the village of Garofali to the east, in the main caldera of Roccamonfina volcano. These lava domes are among the largest in Europe. The town of Roccamonfina is visible at the base of the dome.

and highly comminuted ash with a thickness of more than 6 m. It is likely that this unit correlates with one of the pumice-forming eruptions in the main caldera.

The most prominent feature in Gli Stagli is the Friello cinder cone, which represents one or more strombolian eruptions. At about the same time as this cone was forming, a deep valley was cut into the Galluccio ignimbrite and partly filled with volcaniclastic material. This valley was also filled to overflowing with the products of the youngest major eruption on Roccamonfina, the Conca Ignimbrite associated with the formation of a 1.5 km caldera at the head of Gli Stagli. This caldera, known as the Conca Caldera, cuts the main caldera rim, indicating its relative youth.

At the foot of the volcano to the north and NE are several distinct pits. These may be maar craters and could have resulted from magma–water interaction punching a hole to the surface by phreatic activity, but without magma reaching the surface: another explanation is that they are simply sink holes in the limestone.

Evidence for historical activity is dubious. The Roman historian Orosius reports that 'a flame shot up and burned for three days near Cales'. If it occurred at all, this event, whatever it was, probably took place in 269 or 276 BC. It appears unlikely to have been volcanic.

The Campanian Ignimbrite

Round the whole of the Roccamonfina edifice in the floor of many of the deep ravines, and within the main caldera, is a distinctive grey, relatively fine-grained ignimbrite.

Fig. 4.9. Outcrop of the Campanian Ignimbrite on Roccamonfina showing columnar jointing.

This ignimbrite, although a prominent deposit on the volcano, is not a product of Roccamonfina, but is identified as the Campanian Ignimbrite erupted from Campi Flegrei (see Chapter 3). In places on Roccamonfina this ignimbrite displays well-developed columnar jointing (Fig. 4.9), indicating it was still hot on emplacement up to 70 km from its source.

Vulture

Introduction

Vulture is the only Quaternary volcano east of the Apennines (Fig. 1.1). It lies at a similar latitude to Naples in northern Basilicata, named after the Emperor Basil II (976–1025). It forms a prominent cone that dominates the surrounding countryside; nestled in a crater near the summit are two crater lakes that provide a wood-lined tourist attraction. Of particular interest at Vulture is the apron of lahar deposits that surrounds much of the volcano, and the associated fluvially redeposited volcaniclastic deposits. Although the volcano has the K-rich products characteristic of the region, it is distinctive in that it has erupted material of carbonatite composition.

Geography

Monte Vulture (Fig. 4.10) sits on a pre-existing structural ridge between two major parallel valleys. To the west is the Ofanto Valley. This is deeply incised with a depth of about 300 m, and has no terraces. In contrast, the Arcidiaconata Valley to the east is half the depth and has a well-defined aggradational terrace of fluvially reworked volcaniclastic materials. To the south is the Atella Valley, a tributary of the Ofanto. The total height of the present volcano is about 1000 m.

The volcano forms an oasis in a barren region (Plate 4). Rural poverty in Basilicata in general has been a constant feature of the region. Eroded mountains cover some three-quarters of the area, and little forest remains. Winter rains, following deforestation, have removed much of the topsoil, and land management has been poor. The summers are dry, whereas convective storms in autumn cause erosion and flooding. But Monte Vulture, apart from the weather, is an exception to this picture of agricultural poverty. It has good soil on the volcanic substrate, and significant aquifers providing better conditions for agriculture. Melfi, at the northern foot of the volcano, is an extensive centre of the olive oil and wine trade (the Aglianico wines are rich and almost black). It is more wooded, and chestnuts are a major crop, as they are on Roccamonfina. As with the rest of Basilicata, the rural economy has been based as well on cereals and pasture.

A 'geological' plus to Vulture is the Monticchio mineral water. This is bottled at Sorgente Guadianello on the west side of the mountain, and sold widely in Italy. It is particularly unusual because it is naturally carbonated. Thus at public taps one can freely drink, or bottle for oneself, this bubbling water, straight from the ground.

Vulture lies some 20 km south of the autostrada (A17) about halfway between Naples and Bari. The volcano is surrounded by roads that connect towns round the foot of the volcano; and there is a road to the Monticchio craters and to the disused cable-car

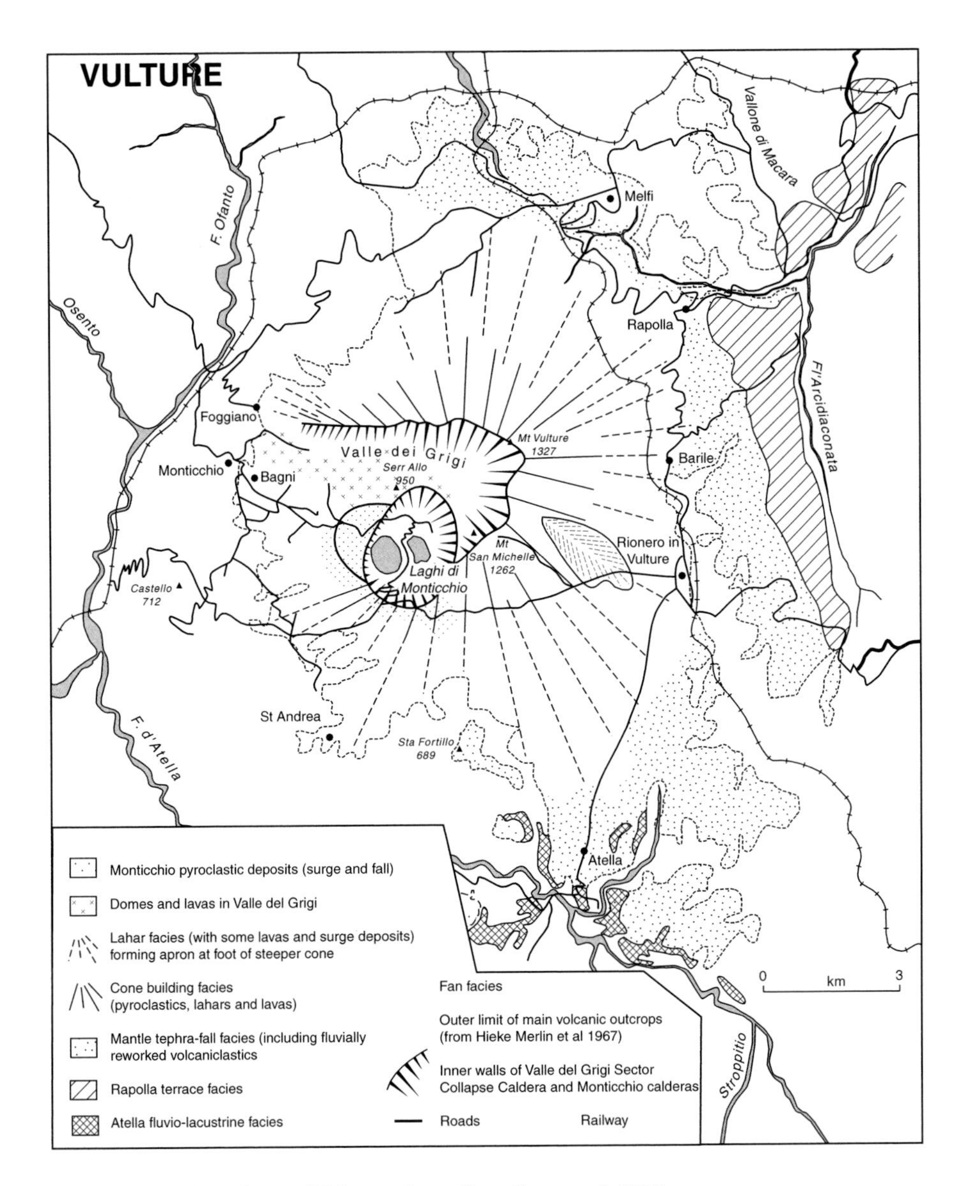

Fig. 4.10. Geological map of Vulture volcano (from Guest *et al.* 1988).

station. The main railway line from Potenza to Foggia runs round the eastern foot of the volcano, with stations at Melfi, Rapolla, Barile and Rionero–Atella–Ripacandida.

History

The Greeks colonized the area in the seventh century BC and turned it into a thriving agricultural region. Many Roman remains testify to their settlement, and Horace mentions Monte Vulture as a place of beauty. In Medieval times, the town of Melfi became the first capital of the Norman conquest of southern Italy. The Norman castle in the centre of Melfi was an important military post. In 1042, William Iron Arm became accepted leader of the Normans, who defeated Byzantine troops on several occasions. A descendant of William, Robert Guiscard, completed the conquest of Puglia and Calabria, and in 1059 Pope Nicholas II invested Robert with the Duchies of Apulia and Calabria. The first crusade was proclaimed from Melfi in 1089; and in 1129 the Constitutions of Melfi were published, unifying the Norman kingdom as a state.

The area round Vulture did not retain its importance after the fall of the Normans, but remained more prosperous than most of the rest of Basilicata. The small town of Barile was established in the 15th century by Albanian refugees, and the inhabitants still retain their language and ethnic traditions. Throughout their history, the towns in the area have suffered repeatedly from earthquakes, most recently in 1851 and 1930.

As in many other regions described in this book, the history during the last two decades has shown great changes. Industrialization has complemented agriculture, for example with a Fiat–Sata car plant at Melfi. Tourism has also increased, especially that with an 'eco' flavour, emphasizing rare flora, as one example. The crater lakes, Laghi di Monticchio (Fig. 4.11), are a focus of attention for tourism, as is the spa resort at Rapolla.

Fig. 4.11. The Monticchio lakes that fill the carbonatitic maar type craters, Vulture.

Volcanic geology of Vulture

The Monte Vulture volcano is close to the western margin of the Bradanic Trough, and to the regional left lateral shear zone that trends at 100° and is known as the 41st parallel. The volcano sits in a graben, which is infilled with Plio-Pleistocene continental conglomerates

The first signs of volcanic activity at the Vulture centre were the eruption of phonolitic–trachytic lavas about 1 Ma ago (Fig. 4.12). These were the precursors to an explosive eruption that produced a sequence of phonolitic–trachytic ignimbrites and surge deposits. The pyroclastic flows swept down the valleys and over the hills round the volcano. At about 3 km to the north of the inferred eruption site, there is more than 20 m of ignimbrite. There are at least four individual sheets up to 7 m thick. The ignimbrites are white and contain abundant pumice, but few lithic fragments. There are

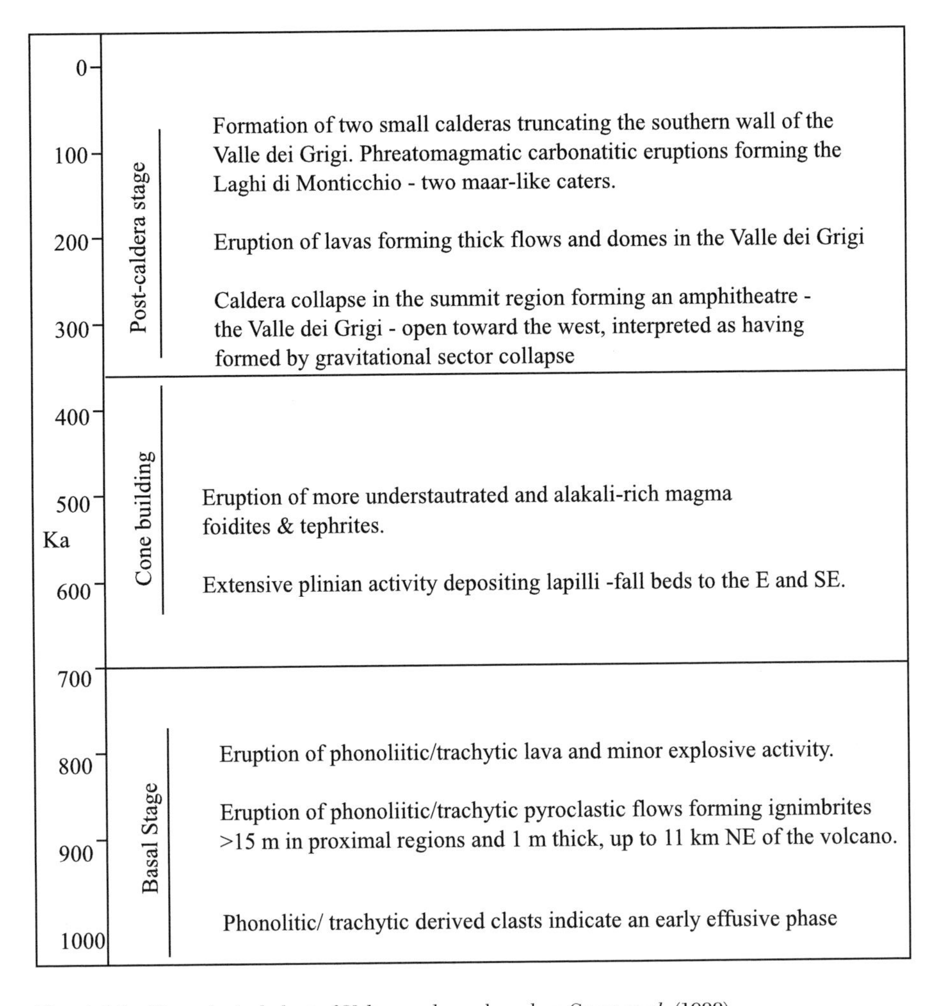

Fig. 4.12. Chronological chart of Vulture volcano based on Guest *et al.* (1988).

concentrations of pumice near the top of two of the flow units. Thin, finely laminated beds and cross-bedded units of surge origin separate the ignimbrites, but only make up about 20% of the material exposed. However, at greater distances from the vent in the Arcidiaconata Valley, the amount of surge material increases until it makes up about 50% of the material. The magnitude of the eruption is difficult to determine as outcrops are limited, but it may well have been of intermediate size comparable with those on Roccamonfina.

Little is known about the volcanic history immediately after the ignimbrite-forming eruption. Phonolitic lava and pyroclastic deposits have been found with an age of 83 ka BP. At some stage after this a central conduit developed and a cone built up. Plinian activity appears to have been the dominant style together with effusion of lavas, some of which accompanied the explosive activity. We have found examples of lavas both underlain and overlain by the same tephra unit, indicating contemporaneous effusive and explosive activity.

Deposits in the main cone, which has a diameter of just under 20 km and maximum slopes of about 19°, consist, where exposed, of bedded scoria, pumice and ashes. There are also surge materials, intimately associated with the fall deposits, filling depressions and valleys. These represent the proximal plinian materials. However, these deposits of unconsolidated tephra were not stable and aqueous reworking in the form of lahars sloughed newly formed materials off the upper parts of the cone to be emplaced lower down where slopes are more gentle and below 11°. The result is a zone consisting mainly of debris flow materials forming an apron round the volcano to the north, east and south (Fig. 4.10).

The lahar deposits of the apron are generally valley filling and typically have a thickness of up to 10 m. The apron is thus mainly a sequence of 'cut and fill'. The matrix (material less than 2 mm diameter) of the lahar deposits is generally brown, and makes up between 20 and 50% of the rock. There are a few clast-supported lahar deposits with little matrix. All are poorly sorted. Clasts range from lapilli to metre-sized blocks, and consist of lava and pumice, as well as fragile rafted blocks of bedded fall deposits (Fig. 4.13). Grading is common, typically with concentrations of dense material near the top of the flow and lava blocks that project above the flow top. In some units, there is normal grading of clasts, either just in the upper portion of the flow or throughout the whole unit.

Most of the lahars have the above characteristics that imply that they came to rest as a coherent flow with strength enough to support the clasts and raft dense material. In addition, many of the debris flow deposits have convex top surfaces and were clearly emplaced *en masse*. Large clasts of friable bedded tephra up to 2 m in diameter can be seen to protrude from the upper surface of some of the debris flow deposits. The transport of such delicate clasts requires gentle flow conditions where they are rafted and precludes a turbulent transport environment. However, some of the flows consist of numerous sub-metre thick lenticular units with load casts implying the beds were emplaced as low-strength material of different densities.

Interbedded with the lahar deposits are strata of other origins. Beds of lapilli or ash of fall origin occur between the lahars, often mantling an eroded surface of the underlying unit. Some lahars are within the same fall bed, indicating reworking of tephra from the

Fig. 4.13. Debris flow deposits on the west flank of Vulture volcano containing large fragile clasts (C) of bedded tephra. At least two units of debris flow deposits are present. Within both units are thin (<0.5 m) reverse-graded subunits. The debris flow deposits are overlain by a lava flow.

cone above during the plinian eruption. In addition there are thin, well-sorted beds of fluvially emplaced tephra. In some cases such beds contain accretionary lapilli and bomb sags, which may imply that reworking occurred during the eruption.

With distance from the volcano, the ratio of lahar deposits to fall material decreases until bedded fall beds make up the majority of material in any outcrop. The deposits consist of beds of pumice lapilli and ash that mantle the underlying topography. Evidence of penecontemporaneous reworking is present, indicating fluvial erosion and and deposition and development of thin slurries of ash.

In summary, it appears that the bulk of Monte Vulture was formed by a succession of plinian eruptions with heavy tephra falls and some pyroclastic flow and surge activity. Eruptions were accompanied and followed by heavy rains that saturated tephra on the cone, causing instability, and, as a result, lahars that swept down the flank left thin deposits on the steeper slopes and thicker ones near the foot of the cone, where they reached their maximum run-out up to 7 km from the central crater. Rain also caused more limited reworking of tephra further from the volcano. Lavas accompanied some plinian eruptions and may also have been erupted with little or no associated explosive activity.

Flank eruptions occurred during the build-up of the main cone and probably after, forming cinder cones, notably Toppo Santa Agata. The hill on which the town of Melfi is built is a separate effusive centre of unknown age, but having a distinctly different composition from the rest of the Vulture rocks.

The main cone probably reached a maximum height of nearly 1000 m at about 0.5 Ma. The cone-building stage was brought to a close by a major collapse, which truncated the cone to form the Valle dei Grigi, a large horseshoe-shaped scar on the west side (Fig. 4.10). The form of this feature, which is open to the west and has a 400 m high back wall to the east, implies that it was the result of a major sector collapse into the Ofanto Valley.

The presence of a carbonated aquifer under the volcano today suggests a hydrothermal system within the edifice during its eruptive period, and thus the possibility of hydrothermal alteration and weakening of rocks at the core of the structure. This, together with the steep slope of the basement into the Ofanto, could explain why a huge chunk of the volcano could slide away leaving a sector collapse. Faulting could also have contributed. The total volume of removed material may have been as much as 3 km^3. This would have been dumped in the valley, damming the river and possibly causing a temporary lake. Active uplift and downcutting in the valley has removed all of the debris avalanche material resulting from the sector collapse.

There followed the eruption of thick lava flows and domes within the Valle dei Grigi, implying that following the collapse the magma reservoir was degassed. Two small caldera collapses took place on the southern wall of the sector collapse feature. The younger of these, with a maximum diameter of 2.5 km, contains two maar-like crater lakes, the Lagi di Monticchio (Fig. 4.11). Surrounding the calderas is a sequence of sandwave surge deposits and associated fall material. Bomb sags are abundant and the fall materials have the characteristics of magma–water interaction (i.e. poor sorting and high levels of fragmentation). This waning phase of the volcano, at about 132 ka BP, suggests that only a limited amount of magma was available, and to erupt it had to pass through a substantial aquifer. It should be noted, however, that Francesco Stoppa and Claudia Principe argue that the deposits were formed by ‘dry’ explosions as evidenced by the lack of accretionary lapilli and ash vesiculation, and suggest that the high level of fragmentation was driven by CO_2 expansion associated with carbonatite melt.

In the 1990s, interdisciplinary teams cored the sediments that fill the larger of the Monticchio lakes. These sediments reach a maximum thickness of 51 m, although cores in the deepest part of the lake encountered slumps derived from the walls of the crater. On the basis of palynological and sedimentological studies, these sediments are interpreted to represent a period of at least 76 ka. Monte Vulture lies 100–150 km downwind of the active Campanian volcanoes of Vesuvius, Campi Flegrei and Ischia, and as such the lake sediments have provided a superb repository for tephra generated by these volcanoes; nearly 160 tephra layers are preserved in these lacustrine sediments.

As we have seen, an important characteristic of this volcano is the fluvial reworking of the pyroclastic deposits that dominate the erupted products. Erosion in this region, where there are torrential rains at specific times of the year, has fed volcaniclastic sediments into the valley systems. The Ofanto had enough energy to keep its valley essentially clear of sediment, but the less energetic Arcidiaconata river to the east deposited its load of volcanic material to form a well-marked terrace some 130 m thick and well exposed at Rapolla (Fig. 4.10). The deposits range from cobble lags to fine silt. Interbedded with the fluvial sediments are fall deposits and possible cross-bedded surge materials with poor sorting (and bomb sags). Most of the cross-bedded material is well sorted and most likely to have been deposited within the fluvial regime. Accumulation of the Rapolla Terrace spanned the whole history of Monte Vulture with the major ignimbrite occurring at its base.

Petrology of Vulture

The erupted products of Vulture range from foidites and tephrites to more evolved phonolites and trachytes (Fig. 4.5). These volcanic rocks belong to a strongly undersaturated suite and are members of the HKS. Although potassic in character the feldspathoid found in these rocks is haüyne. This is related to nepheline with Ca replacing some of the Na ions, the substitution being balanced by incorporation of SO_4 anions. The rather exotic mineralogy of these rocks is also reflected in the presence of melanitic garnet in some of the phonolites. The main phenocryst phases in these rocks, however, are clinopyroxene, haüyne and plagioclase, with sanidine occurring in the more evolved products. It is considered that the observed chemical variation in the volcanic products of Vulture can be largely explained by crystal fractionation from a foiditic parent.

The most recent activity of Vulture, the eruptions that formed the Laghi di Monticchio, involved carbonatitic magma. On petrological criteria it is considered that this is primary carbonatite melt derived directly from the mantle. The tephra that form the ramparts round these craters include two sets of deposits. The first is a lapilli-surge deposit and is considered to be derived from the eruption of the smaller of the maars. A distinctive feature of this deposit is the presence of concentrically shelled lapilli, which show an internal variation from an inner ultramafic melilitite to an outer carbonatitic melilitite. A fragile outer shell of calcite carbonatite is preserved in some cases. Some of the smaller lapilli are made of massive calcium carbonate. The other deposit, associated with the larger maar, is an ash-grade surge deposit with fine lapilli set in carbonate matrix. There are abundant ultramafic nodules of peridotite and wehrlite assumed to be of mantle origin. It is likely, therefore, that these CO_2-rich carbonatite and melilitite magmas rose directly from depth at speed, with minimal interaction with the crust.

Volcanic hazard at Roccamonfina and Vulture

When volcanoes have not erupted within the time of human records, there is a tendency to assume that they are extinct. This, of course, may be far from true. Neither Roccamonfina nor Vulture volcanoes are known to have had any eruptive activity during the last at least 2000 years. Boreholes into the caldera of Roccamonfina show no thermal anomaly, and at Vulture the mineral springs do not have elevated temperatures. There is thus no evidence to suggest an active magma chamber at present at either volcano.

Should new magma rise into either volcano, the risk to life and property is high. Vulture is encircled by towns, but evacuation would not be difficult. The growing industrial activity at Melfi continues to increase the risk there. At Roccamonfina, the vulnerability is higher; the population is spread over much of the volcano including the calderas.

In the extremely unlikely event of activity being resumed at either of these volcanoes, there is the strong possibility that it would be heralded by earthquake swarms, both felt and instrumental.

Places to visit

Roccamonfina

The best place to start on Roccamonfina is the viewing terrace on Monte Lattani above the town of Roccamonfina. From here there is a good panoramic view across the eastern part of the caldera. The caldera walls scarp is clearly seen. The shallow mantled scarps of the younger nested calderas can be seen between the viewing point and Monte Atano, a cone to the east just outside the main caldera scarp. Good views of the main caldera walls and the lavas cut by it are seen from the road that skirts the southern and western foot of the main dome.

It is difficult to recommend outcrops for the pyroclastic sequence, as cuttings and quarries become overgrown and new ones are formed. We therefore suggest some general areas where some of the better outcrops are likely to occur. The road from Campagnola to the caldera rim traverses the Campagnola Ignimbrite. At the rim, its heterogeneous nature can be seen, but this quickly passes into normal, massive ignimbrite. One of the best regions for examining lithic breccias in ignimbrites is on the SW flank of the volcano some 1 km NW of Sessa Aurunca. Some WTT breccia sites are accessible from the Sessa – Roccamonfina road on the NW edge of Sessa Aurunca.

A worthwhile half-day excursion is to walk from the small village of Tuoro SW across the deep valley and onto the next ridge east. Fine-grained Campanian Ignimbrite is exposed filling the base of the valley. Moving up from the base of the valley one passes through older ignimbrites related to the Brown Leucitic Tuff and eventually into WTT. Numerous terraces in this region cut for fruit tree plantation expose breccia both of the WTT and the BLT.

In the Galluccio area quarries have shown remarkable examples of fossil trees within the Gallucio Tuff. These are horizontal and interpreted to have been felled by the pyroclastic flow.

Within the caldera are numerous small outcrops showing intra-caldera deposits. Good examples of pyroclastic surge deposits are seen round the village of Garofoli. Finely laminated lacustrine deposits are exposed below the villages of Filorsi and Torano in the main caldera.

Outcrops of the deposits in the Gli Stagli caldera are well seen on and near the roadsides.

The Suio Terme area is worth a visit. Unless you wish to sample the waters, the best location is the area of bubbling mud pools on the east side of the river. These exhale a stream of CO_2 as evidenced by the mat of dead insects surrounding the vents. Test the depth of CO_2 gas by lowering a match or lighter towards the ground. It is not advisable to take small children close to the pools on foot.

Vulture

The top station of the disused cable-car from Monticchio affords a good panorama, and the road up to it from Rionero provides outcrops of the bedded tephra of the proximal facies deposits. The mass flow deposits of the lahar facies are well exposed in quarries near Barile and Rionero in Vulture to the west and in a road section near the Gaudinella acqua minerale plant in the west. The mantling fall facies deposits are seen in road cuts round the foot of the volcano on the west and SW sides of the volcano. Outcrops of the basal ignimbrite are scattered round the mountain; an easily accessible one is near the acqua minerale plant at the mouth of the Valle dei Grigi. A swig of naturally carbonated spring water from a tap is an unusual experience.

Outcrops of the Rapolla terrace deposits occur east of Rapolla in the valley sides. The lacustrine deposits near Atella are also worth a visit.

The Monticchio lakes are a tourist attraction and thus easy of access. At weekends the area may be crowded.

Notes

Roccamonfina

Structural setting

For more detail on the local tectonic setting of Roccamonfina the reader is referred to the structural analysis by De Rita & Giordano (1996) and the interpretation based on gravity and magnetotelluric data by Capuana *et al.* (1992).

Stratigraphy

As may be expected on a volcano that has scattered and often temporary exposures, there is no detailed agreement about the stratigraphy between different workers. We have essentially adopted the general framework of Giannetti and Luhr's work (Giannetti & Luhr 1983; Luhr & Giannetti 1987) with some additions based on our own work (Cole *et al.* 1992, 1993). Giannetti (1994*a*–*c*) has vigorously objected to any modifications to his own stratigraphy; further interpretations by him have been given in Giannetti (2001).

Broadly, we differ from other workers in that we do not consider it helpful to use colours as rock unit names, especially as the colours are not consistent within the same unit. Within the so-called BLT there are brown, yellow, orange and even white ignimbrites according to Luhr & Giannetti (1987). Giannetti (1979*a*,*b*) originally called the BLT the Yellow Trachytic Tuff, a name he now uses for the much younger ignimbrite in the Gli Stagli caldera.

A second point of difference is that we recognize the products of more than one eruption amongst both the so-called brown and white ignimbrite sequences, based on soil layers. De Rita & Giordano (1996) recognize only one BLT eruption, but do recognize other units under their BLT; they argue that these are from small eruptions only. Neverthless, they do recognize the products of five WTT eruptions including our Gallucio Tuff. Their stratigraphic framework for the whole volcano is based on time units rather that rock units. Giannetti & Casa (2000) have demonstrated that there are seven major WTT eruptions, which they have dated by Ar/Ar at between 317 and 230 ka BP.

The ignimbrites

The physical volcanology of the ignimbrites that occur on the flanks of Roccamonfina Volcano has been the subject of several papers in the late twentieth century. Cole *et al.* (1993) proposed a model for ignimbrite emplacement based of studies of one of the WTT eruptions and part of the BLT (their Campagnola Tuff). The model considered lithic breccia deposition related to hydraulic jumps and pumice-rich facies travelling to distal limits. De Rita *et al.* (1997) also discussed similar processes related to ignimbrite emplacement of four of the White Trachytic Tuffs. Giordano (1998*a*) described different facies characteristics of a number of the WTT eruptions and described how magma–water interaction became more important as the eruptions progressed into caldera collapse phases. Giordano (1998*b*) showed how lithic clasts were coarsest and ignimbrites thickest at the break in slope between the steep proximal and more shallow distal slopes of the volcano

Petrology

The classic paper that provides the basis for recent studies on the petrology of Roccamonfina is by Appleton (1972). This paper concentrated on lavas; the picture was extended by petrological work on the main ignimbrites: the Brown Leucitic Tuff (Luhr & Giannetti 1987) and the White Trachytic Tuff (Giannetti & Luhr 1983). Data and discussion on isotope geochemistry have been given by Hawkesworth & Vollmer (1979), Taylor *et al.* (1979), Vollmer and Hawkesworth (1980) and Ellam *et al.* (1989).

Vulture

Stratigraphy

If anything, the stratigraphy of Vulture is harder than that of Roccamonfina to reconstruct in detail, as there is not the same deep dissection. The broad stratigraphic framework we have used is that of Hieke Merlin (1967). We have chosen to build the rest of our discussion on our own work, where we have looked at process with time and space (Guest *et al.* 1988). La Volpe *et al.* (1984) have added to the 1967 work on the basis of finding distinctive horizons that can be used in stratigraphic correlation, and these have been included in our stratigraphic column. A detailed description of the lacustrine deposits near Atella has been given by La Volpe & Rapisardi (1977).

Lahar deposits

In a study of these deposits (Duncan *et al.* 1996) we demonstrated that there is a range of mass flow deposits on Vulture ranging from those deposited by pyroclastic flows to cold debris flows. The pyroclastic flow deposits, which are limited in abundance, are monolithological, made up predominantly of juvenile clasts, and are matrix supported. The juvenile clasts range in vesicularity through to cauliform-shaped scoriaceous blocks and some are associated with gas escape pipes. Many clasts show breadcrust textures and spindle bombs are present, indicating that these pyroclastic flows were generated by explosive magmatic eruptions. The debris flow deposits are polylithological, made up of angular lava clasts together with with a variable content of juvenile material. The deposits are interbedded with lapilli fall units, indicating that these mass flow deposits were contemporaneous with explosive activity. We suggest that this spectrum of mass flow deposits reflects the operation of a range of processes from primary pyroclastic flows to progressive remobilization of accumulations of tephra and lava by rainfall during phases of explosive eruptions.

Petrology

The classic original work on the volcanic products of Vulture was by Hieke Merlin (1967); more recent work is that on the petrogenesis of the volcano by De Fino *et al.* (1986) and the description of the carbonatite fragments in the deposits of the Monticchio lakes craters by Stoppa & Principe (1998).

Chapter 5. **Vulcano**

Geography and history

This is the southernmost of the Eolian Islands, which form an arcuate-shaped archipelago north of Sicily in the Tyrrhenian Sea (Fig. 5.1). This volcanic island has to be a place of homage for all volcanologists; to be baptised in the hot mud pools is an experience not to be forgotten (and perhaps not even desired again!).

Vulcano is an oval-shaped island (Fig. 5.2), the southern part being a plateau formed by an infilled caldera, the northern part a semicircular amphitheatre formed by a younger caldera open to the NE. In the middle of this depression is the Fossa volcano, the present centre of activity, which forms a cone that rises 391 m above sea level. To the north, joined by an isthmus to the main island, is another cone formed in historical times, known as Vulcanello.

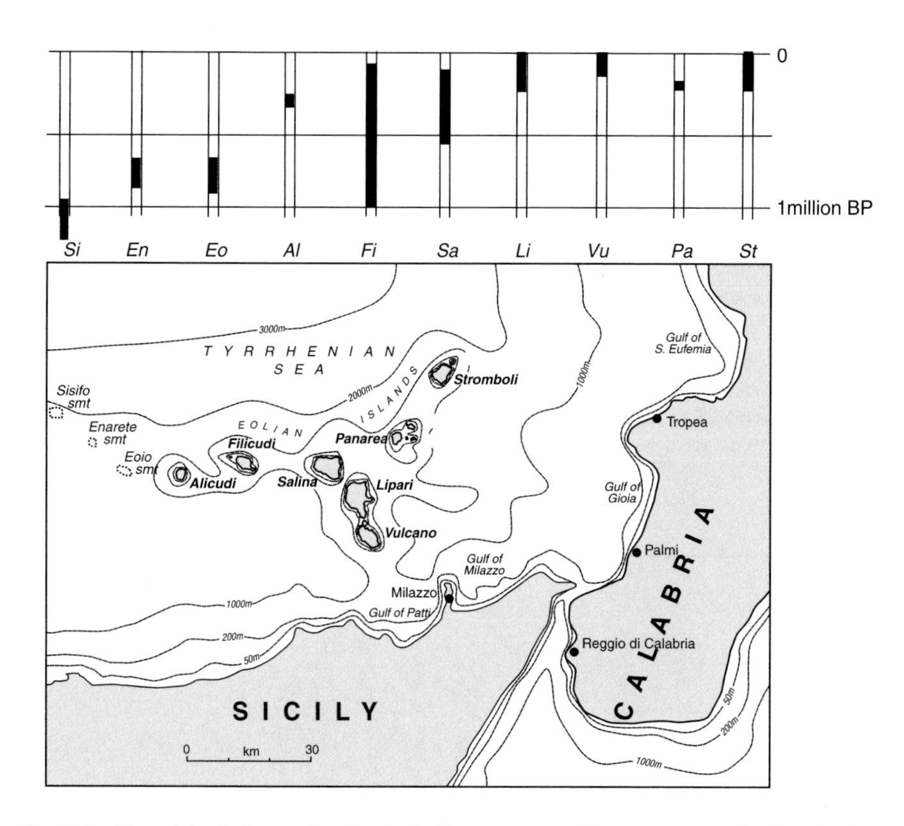

Fig. 5.1. Map of the Eolian archipelago including seamounts. Known age spans for the islands are shown above the map.

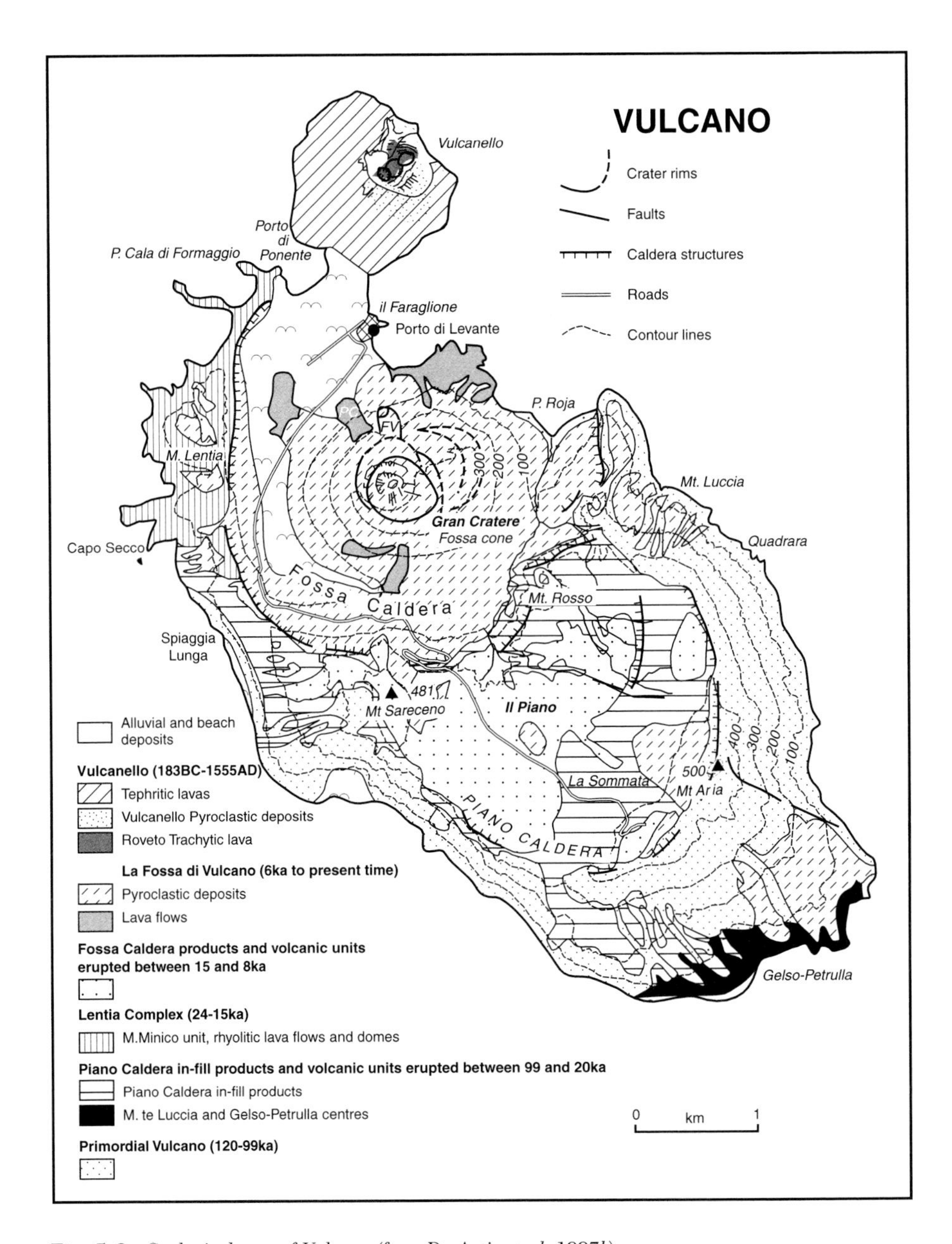

Fig. 5.2. Geological map of Vulcano (from De Astis *et al.* 1997*b*).

The normal way of getting to Vulcano is by sea, from Naples and Milazzo, on the north Sicilian coast, by *aliscafo* (hydrofoil) or ferry; or from one of the other Eolian Islands by small boat. The first impression of the island as one enters Porto di Levante at the northern end of the island is the smell of H_2S that pervades the air; there is the strong feeling that this is an active volcano on the boil! Bubbles rise from under the waters in the port, the rocks around are rotted by steaming fumaroles, and just nearby are hot mud pools much beloved by tourists who believe that bathing in them will cure all manner of diseases (Fig. 5.3). It is common to see visitors standing in the pools smearing the grey mud over one another. An even stranger sight is of people bending over the noxious smelling fumaroles that surround the pool with towels over their heads inhaling the gases, and imagining that it is doing them good.

Vulcano certainly impressed the ancients, who ascribed the obvious venting of hot material to the forge of Vulcan. It is equally impressive today, and has, until recently, deterred people from establishing more than a meagre presence. It is unlikely that there have been many more than 400 inhabitants at any one time throughout the whole history of the island. In 1938 the population was recorded as 401; in 1971 it had risen to 434. The main centre of population, Porto di Levante, is now at the northern end of the island because of the reasonably good natural harbour and tourist attractions. However, this is relatively new, and the settlements on the plateau to the south, and at the southern end of the island have been the main centres of population in the past. They were supported by agriculture inland, and fishing on the coast. For the indigenous population, the island was probably self supporting, although fresh water was limited.

An economic boom occurred with the mining of sulphur and potash in the Porto di Levante area during the early nineteenth century. Mining here probably goes back to classical times, but the main industry was started by the Bourbon General, Nunziante, who built factories and a good complex of roads around the Porto. Eventually the whole island was bought by a Scotsman called Stevenson, who modernized the industry. A mule track was built into the mine, and brick houses were constructed for the workers. His great enterprise was finally brought to an end by the eruption of the Fossa cone only

Fig. 5.3. The mud pool at Vulcano. Vulcanello is visible in the background.

a few hundred metres away in 1888. Viticulture became the alternative industry after the eruption, but it did not attract many new settlers.

Roads on the island are few. There is a single main road from Porto di Levante in the north to Gelso in the south. By-roads serve agriculture around the Piano, and also the growing tourist centre to the north.

Modern, faceless hotel complexes and holiday villas testify to the rapid growth of tourism as an industry on the island. In addition, moored yachts indicate a passing trade of summer sailors. Many second homes have been built. There are thousands of visitors on the island at any time during the summer months, a serious problem if an eruption were to occur during the holiday season.

Tectonic setting and geochemistry of the Eolian Islands

The deep Tyrrhenian Sea in which Vulcano and its sibling islands are set is a marginal basin underlain by thin oceanic-type basaltic crust. This basin opened between 7 and 5 Ma and has a depth of over 3000 m. The Eolian Islands sit close to the edge of the basin between the continental crust of Sicily and the oceanic-type crust of the Tyrrhenian basin. The continental crust beneath the islands is thinned to around 16 km, but thickens to the south.

The archipelago is made up of seven major islands, which are, from west to east, Alicudi, Filicudi, Salina, Lipari, Vulcano, Panarea and Stromboli. All the islands are volcanic and formed within the last 1 Ma; and Lipari, Stromboli and Vulcano have been active in historical times. The name for the archipelago comes from the Greek god of wind Aeolus, who, according to Homeric myth, came to the islands and settled on Lipari where he controlled the winds trapped below. This story may owe its origin to the roaring sound that accompanies explosions on Stromboli. As well as the islands there are also several seamounts or submarine volcanoes that continue the arcuate shape of the archipelago to the west beyond Alicudi (Sisifo, Enarete and Eolo). Seamounts also occur separately from the Eolian arc to the north (Palinuro and Marsili).

The Eolian archipelago is related to at least three main tectonic trends. One to the NW–SE apparently controls the western part of the arc including Filicudi, Alicudi and the western seamounts. A NW-trending lineament relates to Panarea and Stromboli, whereas a north–south-oriented lineament is associated with the most southerly islands Lipari and Vulcano. The north–south lineament continues on to mainland Sicily.

The rocks of the Eolian Islands range from calc-alkaline basalts and andesites to more potassic materials such as shoshonites, similar in composition to the Low-K Series of the Campanian Province. The older products tend to be calc-alkaline, with more recent volcanic rocks showing stronger potassic affinity.

The islands overlie a plane of seismic activity, a Benioff Zone, which dips steeply to the NW, and it is considered that this is a subduction zone with which the magmatism is associated. This concept is supported by the configuration of the islands resembling an island arc, and the calc-alkaline petrology of some of the rocks. The model was originally proposed by Barberi and colleagues in the early 1970s and involves oceanic material from the Ionian Sea being subducted to the NW beneath the Calabrian arc. However, the relationship between the volcanism and regional tectonics is not straightforward. There is no oceanic crust on the fore-arc side, indicating that consumption is now complete.

Early work suggested that the seismicity was chiefly located between depths of about 330 and 250 km. Recent, higher-resolution studies of seismicity in the Eolian arc show a more continuous spread of seismicity with depth, but a gap at shallow depth between 30 and 100 km supports the idea that subduction has ceased.

The petrology of the more recent volcanism has been shoshonitic, which, based on observations of arcs elswhere, is indicative of an arc at a senile stage in evolution. If this is so, with the arc no more than 1 Ma in age this would require very rapid development. There is another problem: the Palinuro and Marsili seamounts, which lie some 50 km to the north of the Eolian Islands (Fig. 1.2), are made of calc-alkaline volcanic rocks and are of comparable age to the volcanic islands of the so-called arc. If we consider these to be seamounts that are part of the system, the arc shape presented by the volcanoes that project above sea level is no longer so convincing. There is also evidence of strike-slip tectonics; Salina, Lipari and Vulcano form a linear chain associated with the Eolian–Tindari–Letojanni dextral transcurrent fault, which extends to NE Sicily. Thus, though there appears to be a clear relationship between the Eolian Island magmatism and subduction, the detailed tectonic picture is far from being fully understood.

Ellam and coworkers undertook an investigation of the trace element and isotope geochemistry of the volcanic rocks of the Eolian Islands. On the basis of this research, they identified two components that they considered to be associated with a subduction origin: first, high Sr/Nd and high Th/Ta, indicative of input from the basaltic oceanic crust slab and, second, very high Th/Ta but relatively low Sr/Nd, derived from subducted sediments. A third component, characterized by highly radiogenic Pb, is similar to the ocean island basalt type source that fed the tholeiitic and alkalic magmatism of Etna.

Such an input to the Eolian Island magmas is interpreted to be derived from the mantle wedge overlying the subducted slab. The heterogeneity of the source region of these magmas reflects the complex and turbulent tectonic history of this area since the Mesozoic associated with the collision of the African and European plates.

Located at the south of the arc, Vulcano sits on about 25 km of continental crust. The island rises 1500 m from the sea floor with the highest point 500 m a.s.l. Much of the subaerial part of this volcanic complex has been destroyed by caldera collapse and strong marine erosion, which may have been aided by faulting on the flanks. The exposed products are thus mainly proximal, or associated with caldera fill.

Volcanic evolution of Vulcano

The early workers on the geology of the island divided the volcano morphologically into four structural units: (1) Southern or Old Vulcano (including the Piano Caldera fill); (2) Lentia mountains; (3) Fossa Vulcano; (4) Vulcanello peninsula. These units form the basis of most studies that have followed (Fig. 5.4).

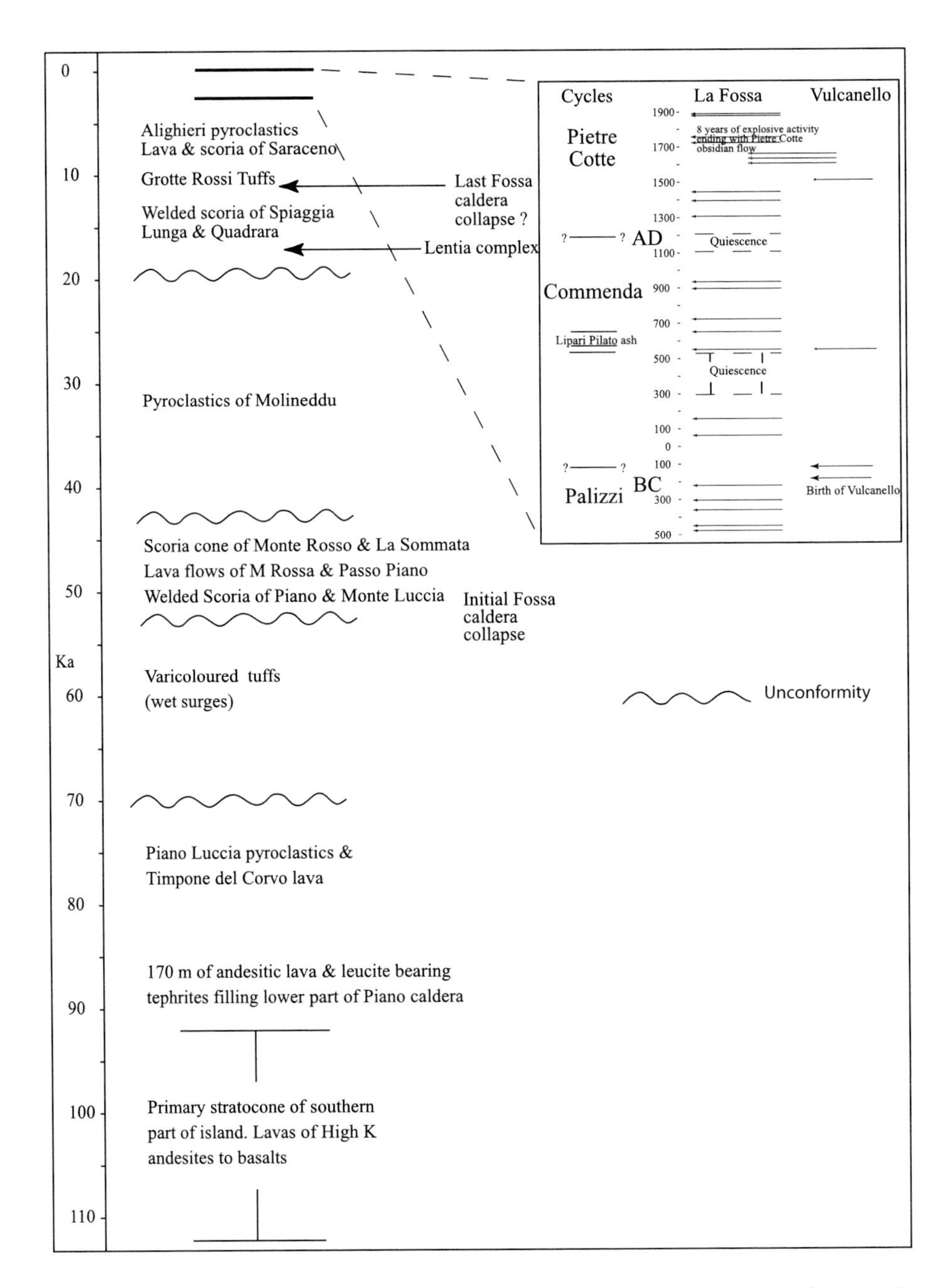

Fig. 5.4. Stratigraphy of Vulcano based mainly on Keller (1980) and Frazzetta (1998). Arrows in insert indicate recorded eruptions.

In modern times the geology of the island was first described in detail by Jörg Keller (this was based on work carried out by him in the late 1960s as a postgraduate), and there have been a number of studies of specific topics by Italian and other geologists. The stratigraphy of the material filling the Piano Caldera has been interpreted more recently by Italian geologists, whose conclusions differ in some respects from those of Keller.

The southern volcano

The southern end of Vulcano (Figs 5.2 and 5.4) forms the oldest part of the island, which, morphologically, is a circular composite volcano with strata dipping towards the sea on all sides at up to 40°. According to Keller, this old volcano is composed of predominantly thin aa lava flows. Numerous dykes, some of which are feeders, have intruded into this construct in a generally radial pattern, and are exposed in the sea cliffs. The rocks of Southern Vulcano yield K/Ar dates of 120–98 ka BP.

The stratocone of Southern Vulcano is clearly truncated by the Piano Caldera, which is roughly circular and has a diameter of 2–2.5 km. Based on a K/Ar date for the oldest exposed lava on the caldera floor, the earliest collapse of this structure is considered to be more than 98 ka old.

Activity within the Piano Caldera then filled it completely, forming the flat Piano plain; this activity spanned a long period from 98 to 8 ka BP with at least eight distinct periods of volcanicity, many of which are separated by unconformities. The presence of several nested scarps cutting the later caldera fill were first noted by Judd in the 19th century. Jörg Keller also recognized this and suggested that collapse had been incremental, successive collapses occurring as the caldera filled. He noted that the collapses migrated northwestwards with time.

The initial filling of the Piano Caldera, probably about 98–77 ka BP, formed a 170 m thick sequence of lavas. Most of the activity following emplacement of these lavas was explosive; wet hydromagmatic activity formed varicoloured tuffs; this varied to dry hydromagmatic activity, and more magmatic explosive activity followed. Two scoria cones can be recognized related to strombolian activity, the La Sommata and 'Monte Rosso', and lavas near these cones have been dated at between 53 and 48 ka BP.

Of particular interest are welded scoria deposits that occur at a number of places around the Piano Caldera. These localities include Spiaggia Lunga, Quadrara, Piano Luccia and Monte Luccia. These scoria deposits are intensely welded and have been referred to as lava-like. The sequence of deposits is similar, with hydromagmatic tuffs underlying the scoria at all localities. There is, however, some disagreement, both as to whether they were formed by a fall or flow mechanism, and also on whether they are all part of the same stratigraphic unit. Keller interpreted the Spiaggia Lunga, Quadrara and Monte Luccia units as being part of the same formation, whereas Gioncada and Sbrana interpreted all four localities as the same unit. Frazzetta, La Volpe, De Rosa, De Astis and their colleagues, on the other hand, consider them to be formed by more than one eruption at different times, based on the differences of K/Ar dates given from similar-looking units in different localities.

The lavas of the subaerial Southern Vulcano are trachybasalts and trachyandesites (Fig. 5.5). They are plagioclase-phyric, and may have phenocrysts of augite, olivine and magnetite. Both lavas and dykes have a fine-grained groundmass with coexisting plagioclase and K-feldspar. The Piano Caldera infill is mainly tephrites and trachybasalts.

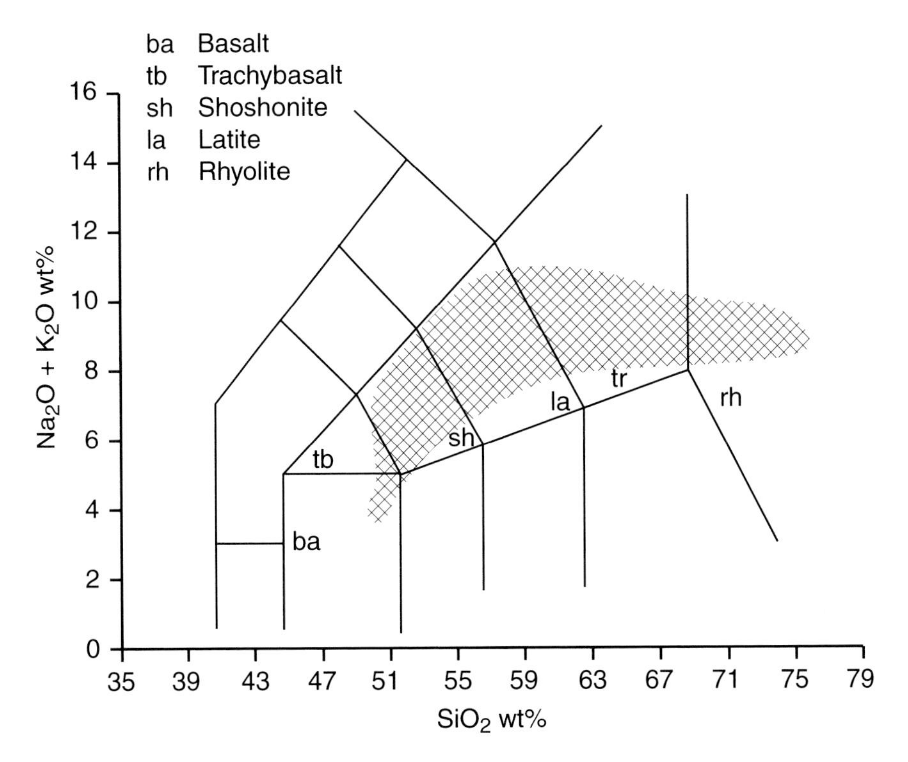

Fig. 5.5. TAS plot of the compositions of rocks from Vulcano (adapted from Gioncada & Sbrana 1991).

Lentia Complex and the Fossa Caldera

The NW part of the island is formed by the Lentia Complex (Figs 5.2 and 5.4) comprising two main parts, the lower Monte Minico unit, which consists of several tephra layers and lavas, and the rhyolites of Capo de Formaggio. The rhyolitic lava flow and dome of Monte Lentia is capped by a trachytic lava flow, which forms the upper part of the complex. Dates for the Lentia Complex range from about 15.5 to 16.1 ka BP. Lavas interpreted to be of the Lentia Complex have been identified at depth in boreholes drilled in the Fossa Caldera. The Lentia Complex is probably related to a much larger volcanic construct largely destroyed by the formation of the Fossa Caldera and by marine erosion. The dominance of rhyolites (with subordinate trachytes) in what is left of this volcano is strikingly different from the older, more basic volcano to the south.

The Lentia phase of activity came to an end with at least one caldera collapse to form the Fossa Caldera, which is open to the sea to the NE and bites into the Piano Caldera fill to the south. The Fossa Caldera clearly post-dates the Lentia complex as illustrated by the large scarps that cut its eastern side, and a date for the Fossa Caldera may be assigned at between 15.5 ka BP, the youngest age of the Lentia Complex, and 14 ka BP, the age of the Punta Roja lava flow, which lies within the lower part of the Fossa Caldera.

Recently a number of Italian workers have considered the significance of the tectonics of the island. The large-scale tectonic setting of the island of Vulcano is dominated by NW–SE-trending right lateral extensional strike-slip faults and by north–south to NE–SW-trending normal faults and fractures. It has been suggested that both the Piano and Fossa Calderas were not formed as the result of engulfment caused by volcanic activity, but were associated with the formation of structural pull-apart basins related to the shifting of volcanic activity northwestwards with time. The lack of plinian deposits or ignimbrites, and the absence of volcanic activity between 50 and 15 ka is cited as being evidence for a structural origin. Although there does appear to be good evidence for the NW shifting of activity with time, the absence of activity for the long period may prove to be false when more tightly constrained dating becomes available. Furthermore, the welded scoria sheets, which have an origin to north of the Piano Caldera, are interpreted by more than one researcher as being of an ignimbritic origin, and plinian fall deposits are associated with this material at several localities. It seems possible that this unit may have been related to collapse of all or part of the Fossa Caldera. It is important to note that all the deposits exposed in the islands cliffs are proximal and most of the distal materials have been eroded away or were deposited at sea.

The existence of a shallow magma reservoir is supported by the data from a geothermal exploratory borehole sunk in 1983–1984 in the southwestern part of the caldera. This penetrated a zoned intrusive monzodiorite at 1365 m. On petrological grounds this monzodiorite was probably the magma reservoir that fed the trachybasaltic activity and that preceded the Lentia Complex.

The Fossa volcano

The view from the point where the main road from the north to the south of the island passes over the Fossa Caldera rim is one of the most spectacular volcanic panoramas in the world, with the steep walls of the caldera encircling the high, fuming and clearly potentially active Fossa cone. This cone (Plate 5, Fig. 5.6), which is starting a new cycle of caldera filling, is thought to have been born about 8600 a BP. Since then it has been built up by repeated explosive eruptions. Some have produced small-volume, short flows of trachyte or rhyolite usually near the end of the eruption when the magma had become too degassed to produce explosive activity. The eruption of such lavas has been taken as a sign that a magmatic cycle has come to an end, and that the next one will start with the introduction of a new column of magma giving violent explosive activity including pyroclastic surges. Although the general composition of the materials making up the cone is trachytic or rhyolitic, some basanites have been erupted as well.

The Fossa cone (Plate 5, Fig. 5.6) is about 2 km across at its base and has a height of 391 m. Its activity has been recorded since Greek and Roman times although, because the island has not been inhabited continuously, some dates are uncertain.

The most detailed studies of the history of this eruptive centre on Vulcano have been carried out by Frazzeta from the International Institute of Volcanology in Catania, La Volpe from Bari University and Sheridan, a pioneer in studies of hydromagmatic

Fig. 5.6. View of Vulcano from the observatory at Lipari. It shows the Fossa volcano, with the Vulcanello centre in front of it and the wall of the Piano Caldera behind.

deposits. The ideas of Sheridan, developed when he was at Arizona State University, have strongly influenced the interpretation of pyroclastic deposits in Italy. He and Wohletz, have made detailed field studies of volcanic deposits interpreted as being of surge origin. They identify two types: wet surge and dry surge deposits. The former are in effect the result of low-temperature surges in which the water content is condensed and the clouds are saturated with water. Such surges produce deposits that are typically hydrothermally altered; there are often abundant accretionary lapilli, bedding deformation and vesiculated horizons. Dry surges, on the other hand, produce deposits that are fresher but show reversed grading, sand wave structures and lenses of massive beds.

Frazzetta and his colleagues divide the exposed stratigraphy on the Fossa into five so-called cycles, each named after the lava flow that terminated the cycle. The first is the Punte Nere cycle, which started with eruptions that produced dry surge deposits, overlain by a thick fall sequence of lapilli that formed the early cone. The trachytic lava flow of Punte Nere dated at about 5500 a BP ends this cycle. The next set of deposits, representing the Palizzi cycle, starts with materials having the characteristics of wet surges, overlain by apparent dry surge materials, capped by a fall deposit dated at about 2200 a BP. The second part of this cycle again begins with wet surge followed by dry surge deposits, capped by the Palizzi trachytic lava.

The third cycle began with the production of a phreatic explosion breccia consisting of highly altered clasts. This unit is reported as grading into pyroclastic flow deposits near the base of the cone. The Pilato ash from Lipari, dated by Keller as *c.* 1400 a BP, lies on top of this deposit. There then followed eruptions that included dry surges before the cycle was ended by the overflow from the summit crater of the Commenda lava.

Wet surge deposits again start the next cycle, followed by dry surge deposits and a pyroclastic fall sequence. The cycle ended with the overflow of lava from the summit crater of the Pietre Cotte lava in 1739. It is likely that the Forgia Vecchia parasitic cone on the northern flank formed during this cycle. Since that time, surges have not been of importance in the preserved deposits and fall deposits have predominated, starting with those of 1771 and followed by explosions in 1780, 1873 and 1876. The 1888–1890 eruption produced deposits that are unique in the geological record of this centre and will be discussed later.

The lavas produced both here and at Vulcanello to the north have ranged in composition from basic leucite tephrites to two-feldspar potassic trachytes, to rhyolitic obsidians. It is considered that complex petrological processes have operated to give rise to the diversity of magma compositions, including fractional crystallization, wall-rock assimilation and mixing. The more undersaturated lavas have been mainly associated with Vulcanello and the oversaturated products with the Fossa cone.

The Vulcanello volcano

Although only about 2.5 km away from the Fossa cone, this volcano is, in many respects, very different (Figs 5.3 and 5.6). The centre is small, with a subaerial diameter of about 300 m, and it is surrounded by an apron of lavas extending for just over half a kilometre from the base of the cone. Based on observations in the Classical period, it is thought to have emerged above sea level in about 183 BC. There are debates about when it finally surfaced as an island. It probably did so several times, but was rapidly eroded away again, only to reappear at the next eruption. It apparently erupted in 126 BC, followed by eruptions in the sixth and 16th centuries AD. This centre became connected to the main island by a sand isthmus in about 1550. Intense fumarolic activity from the craters was present until 1878.

There are three successive cones; the first two are associated with surrounding platforms of lava erupted in a fluid state with a basanitic composition, whereas the third is superimposed on the platform and is composed of trachytic tephra. Between the Fossa and Vulcanello in the Porto di Levante area is an old degraded pyroclastic cone known as the Faraglione. It is intensely altered by fumarolic activity, and was the site of mining of sulphur and alunite. Despite the intense alteration, the materials of this cone are identified as being of similar composition to the early Vulcanello cones.

The 1888–1890 eruption and the present state of the Fossa volcano

This eruption (Fig. 5.7), which lasted 20 months, has given volcanology two names, *vulcanian eruption* and *breadcrust bomb*. The former has had a chequered history, whereas the latter found easy acceptance. *Vulcanian* has been variously redefined; but we stay with the original definition, which is of an eruption in which there are discrete explosions of relatively viscous magma producing mainly polygonal-shaped bombs that typically show a breadcrust surface texture (Fig. 5.8). During the 1888–1890 eruption

Fig. 5.7. Small explosion of the 1888 eruption of the Fossa cone within the crater (from Mercalli & Silvestri 1891).

Fig. 5.8. Large breadcrust block formed during the 1888 eruption (from Mercalli & Silvestri 1891).

the whole island was coated with white ash that appeared like snow. How much of the gas driving the eruption was generated by ground water flashing to steam, rather than magmatic gas, remains in debate.

The eruption was well monitored throughout, especially as it could be observed in relative safety from the southern end of the adjacent island of Lipari, less than 5 km away. A commission was formed to report on the observations. The original president of that group was Professor Orazio Silvestri, an experienced volcanologist from Catania, who had spent much of his life studying eruptions on Mount Etna. Unfortunately, although Silvestri was able to give the benefit of his experience to the members of the commission during the eruption, he died only a few months after it finished, and Professor G. Mercalli from Milan became responsible for much of the preparation of the report that was published in 1891.

The eruption started on 3 August 1888. For the first 3 days only old material, stripped from the conduit walls, was erupted; in other words, the Fossa's throat was being cleared. This type of activity is termed ultravulcanian and is typical of the start of many eruptions on different volcanoes. The ejected material was hot, as it is reported to have set fire to hedges. However, during the next 13 days the amount of fresh magma increased until it became the dominant material ejected. By that time there were large masses of plastic ejecta, rounded in form, elongated or flattened. It was clear to the geologists observing the activity that the introduction of new magma to the system was causing the eruption.

Despite this, there has been argument since about the role of primary magma, and Keller argued that all the material ejected during the eruption was non-juvenile. The situation is confused by the fact that a high percentage of non-juvenile material *was* ejected during this eruption, lithic fragments being coated by a layer of fresh lava; so much so that Johnston-Lavis, on examining samples sent to him, was at pains to argue that the erupted material was 'acidic' despite the presence also of mineral assemblages typical of more basic rocks. All the evidence appears to support the early view that the eruption was driven by fresh magma, but that the crater and vent walls were unstable and much lithic material became incorporated in the juvenile ejecta.

The rate and violence of the explosions were variable during the eruption. They could be as frequent as one every minute or two, throwing up columns of ash as high as 5000 m or more. The more violent explosions were sudden and were normally followed by more feeble explosions or a period of quiet. There were three paroxysmal explosive events. The first occurred on 4 August 1888, the second on 26 December 1889, and the last on 15 March 1890. Johnston-Lavis gives a dramatic account of the final paroxysm. He was in the town of Lipari 7 km away at the time. From there it was not possible to see Vulcano because of the high ground of Monte della Guardia at the south end of Lipari island. A violent explosion accompanied by an enormous bang occurred in the evening. The shock was so strong that windows were broken in Lipari. Pea-sized lapilli with drops of water fell over the town. Even more spectacular, the sky glowed red for some 3 minutes after the explosion. Clearly, this explosion had removed the plug of chilled lava at the top of the magma column in the conduit, exposing fresh red magma, which over the next few minutes was cooled in contact with the atmosphere to develop a new crust. When the cone was visited 10 days later, large numbers of breadcrust bombs were found at its foot. One, termed a 'monster crusty loaf', was 3 m × 2 m × 2 m across and had an obsidian carapace 10 cm thick. Amazingly, there were people in the vicinity of the cone at the time and they survived by taking shelter in caves near the Faraglione. After the paroxysm, explosions continued with diminished violence for a further 2 days, and the eruption came to an end.

The Vulcanian eruption of 1888–1890 is unique in the history of the Fossa. No other eruptions have apparently involved breadcrust bombs. This has led Frazzetta and his colleagues to suggest one explanation may be that this eruption represents the end of a cycle and the breadcrust bombs correspond to the short lava overflows at the end of previous cycles.

The products of the 1888–1890 eruption show a range of compositions and are considered to indicate the presence of a zoned magma reservoir. Three main magma types were involved in the eruption: (1) latite; (2) trachyte; (3) rhyolite. There is abundant evidence of magma mixing with reaction rims of orthopyroxene around olivine and K-feldspar mantling plagioclases and textural features such as banding with fluidal contacts, spherical and ellipsoidal enclaves, and enclaves with cuspate margins. Clocchiati and colleagues consider that the trachytes are hybrids formed by mixing of latite and rhyolite magmas. The eruption started with rhyolitic phreatomagmatic breccias with enclaves of latite magma. This was followed by trachytic then latitic tephras, always showing evidence of magma mixing. The final stage involved rhyolitic magmas. The presence of partially melted metamorphic xenoliths and isotopic variation point to the involvement of wall-rock assimilation. Fluid inclusions in the xenoliths give equilibrium pressures of 30–60 MPa, suggesting a shallow depth of around 1500–2000 m for the upper parts of the magma reservoir. This reservoir was clearly compositionally zoned.

Since 1890 the crater has been in a state of vigorous fumarolic activity within and around the crater (Fig. 5.9), evolving CO_2, H_2S, SO_2, HF, HCl, B and Br gases, and depositing sulphur, ammonium sulphide and sassoline crystals. It is argued that much of the gas owes its origin to saline water below the cone and that the main direct

Fig. 5.9. Fossa crater rim, showing active fumaroles; Lipari and Salina are in the background.

magmatic contribution is heat. Temperatures have varied from typically 100–200 °C, to periods of high temperatures over 600 °C. Clearly, when such temperature rises occur there is concern for the possibility of an impending eruption. Sharp rises in temperature have occurred on several occasions, creating concern. The most recent started in 1987, when the Fossa began to show signs of unrest. Temperatures of the fumaroles started to rise. From that date to 1991 fumarole temperatures in the crater rose from 330 °C to 650 °C. From 1993 to 1995, temperature measurements by Marino Martini, from Florence, showed a significant fall, together with an increase in the amount of steam and CO_2 emitted. This he interpreted as the result of ground water entering the system and dilution of the magmatic component. However, at least one fumarole had a temperature of up to 600 °C in 1995.

Of particular concern was that not only was the temperature rising, but other changes were also taking place. Changes in the chemistry of the gases indicated the influx of fresh magmatic gas supplementing that of the surficial geothermal system: the magmatic system cannot be far below the surface.

Hazard from future eruptions

Not surprisingly, Vulcano has never been as densely populated as the other Eolian islands, for the simple reason that it was recognized as a potentially dangerous place to live, as well as having few natural resources. The reverse is true today. The population of Porto di Levante is enlarging rapidly every year, and there are new hotel complexes on the lava platform round Vulcanello. During the summer season especially, there is a massive tourist population that would have to be evacuated very rapidly in the event of an eruption. The risk in the area between the Fossa and Vulcanello is thus high, both to property and human lives.

There have, during the last few years, been several changes that could be considered as evidence that the conditions are changing and that the next eruption is imminent, but this is far from certain.

The hazards expected from an eruption are several. The most likely eruption will occur within the Fossa Caldera, either on land or at sea. It could be another Vulcanian eruption on land like that of 1888–1890, it could be Surtseyan out to sea, or it could be on land with both Vulcanian and hydromagmatic phases. In the case of an eruption similar to that of 1888–1890, the whole of the Fossa Caldera area would be subject to fall from bombs, lapilli, ash and possibly small, but still dangerous, surges. However, with a more vigorous eruption involving surges, the whole island could be vulnerable to life-threatening events. We have found surge deposits from Fossa eruptions plastered on the walls of the Caldera della Fossa right up to the rim and beyond. It is likely that during the largest eruptions, surges have passed over the Caldera wall and reached the far southern end of the island. No area of the island can be considered safe in the event of an eruption of this type.

From an eruption of the Vulcanian style the main danger is falling material. Thick falls may be expected for almost a kilometre from the crater. Breadcrust bombs 50 cm across may fall at 600 m, and of 15 cm at 1100 m according to the work of Frazzetta and his fellow workers. However, as they point out, the fragments break up on landing, so this may be a minimum value. Also, Mercalli and others reported bombs 50–70 cm across as far away as 1.6 km on the isthmus between the Fossa and Vulcanello.

Other hazards must not be forgotten. Even a small tsunami created by seismic or eruptive activity in the archipelago could affect the populated coastal areas, where many houses and hotels are less than a few metres above sea level. Rock falls or landslides could occur from the steep flanks of the Fossa cone where fumarolic activity is rotting the rocks and erosion is steepening the slopes. This could be a serious problem for property at the foot of the cone and could occur just as a result of seismic activity or a heavy storm. During an eruption, accumulations of ash could develop into lahars, especially if heavy rainfall occurred.

The unseen danger from toxic gases is a serious problem, not only during an eruption, but also between eruptions. There is particular concern about CO_2, which is already known to accumulate in the lower floors of some of the new houses. This is of enough concern, but an increased flux preceding an eruption could occur rapidly and catch inhabitants unawares. Peter Baxter, a physician and epidemiologist from Cambridge, is an expert on the medical effect of volcanoes. He not only emphasizes this problem, but also the high levels of H_2S emitted from the Fossa. Hydrogen sulphide gas is easily recognized by smell in non-toxic concentrations, but in lethal concentrations is not detectable by smell. The hazards of living on a volcano are, thus, not restricted to times of eruptions, but also to periods of repose when the dangers may not be so apparent.

Whatever type of eruption occurs, when it does the whole area of the Fossa Caldera will have to be rapidly evacuated, first the area around the port, and then elsewhere. This will have to be done by sea. Escape to the southern end of the island may be a first resort, but even this may not, eventually, be safe if a large eruption develops.

There is also the possibility of an eruption from Vulcanello, although the cessation of fumarolic activity may suggest that this centre is not in imminent danger of activity. However, new vents could open, the most likely place being on the inferred line of weakness trending through the Fossa and Vulcanello. Only time will tell, but the possibility of an eruption within the next few decades must be considered high.

Places to visit

A walk round the port and nearby beaches is worth while to see the fumaroles, mud pools and bubbling hot springs.

The view from the edge of the Fossa Caldera where it is crossed by the road to the south is well worth a visit, and this can be easily made by walking, or using a taxi or bus to get up there followed by a pleasant walk back into town. Equally easy is a walk to Vulcanello.

A visit to the Fossa cone is possible using the path from the port area. This is a relatively easy climb and crosses sections through the different stages in the growth of the cone. From the top there is a fine panoramic view, and the fumaroles in the crater are spectacular with superb crystal growths. The nested craters formed from successive eruptions can be clearly seen. Descent into them is not advisable owing to accumulations of toxic gases. Care should also be taken on calm days, when high concentrations of gases can accumulate around the fumaroles. The acid gases can cause damage to clothing. Look for breadcrust bombs, but many of the smaller ones have now been removed by visiting volcanologists!

A boat trip round the island is particularly rewarding, as most of the best outcrops are in the sea cliffs. Such trips are available from the port.

For those with more time there are numerous tracks that can be explored, including one to Mt Saraceno and the nearby cliffs, in which there are fine exposures of the older cone of Vulcano.

Notes

Early workers

Several workers contributed to the stratigraphic framework; these include Judd (1888), Cortese & Sabatini (1892), Bergeat (1899) and De Fiore (1922, 1925 and 1926).

Modern stratigraphy

The modern stratigraphy was first described in detail in the classic work of Keller (1980*a*). His stratigraphy is broadly similar that of the later work of De Astis *et al.* (1997*a*,*b*), who described the Piano Caldera fill and the Lentia Complex. Borehole data coupled with surface field data were used to further the stratigraphy by Gioncada & Sbrana (1991).

Sheridan *et al.* (1987) and Gillot *et al.* (1990) have presented several new dates that have helped constrain the stratigraphy.

Calderas

Judd (1888) was the first to recognize the migration of activity NW with time, and the nested caldera structures were depicted in a sketch in his book. Keller (1980*a*) has made a major contribution to our understanding of caldera evolution. Gioncada & Sbrana (1991) suggested that the Fossa Caldera formed incrementally.

Tectonics

Recent work by several Italian workers has attempted to relate the tectonics to the geology of the island. Gioncada & Sbrana (1991), Ventura (1994) and Mazzuolli *et al.* (1995) in particular stressed the role of tectonics and proposed that the caldera formed as the result of tectonic processes rather than engulfment.

The Fossa

Studies of the deposits and interpretations of styles of volcanism have been made by Sheridan *et al.* (1987).

The 1888–1890 eruption

The main and most authoritative account of the eruption was given by Mercalli & Silvestri (1891), together with supplementary accounts by Johnston-Lavis (1888, 1890). The geochemistry of the products has been given by Clocchiati *et al.* (1994)

Petrology and plumbing

Keller (1980*a*) provided details on the petrology of the volcanic rocks of Vulcano, which range from potassic (KS) and high-K calc-alkaline (HKCA) to shoshonite (SHO). Discussion on magmatic processes, in particular magma mixing, was given by De Fino *et al.* (1991). Gioncada & Sbrana (1991), using data from deep drilling in the Fossa Caldera, interpreted the subvolcanic structure. Clocchiati *et al.* (1994) considered the shallow magmatic system based on the 1888–1890 eruption. A synthesis of the petrogenesis of Vulcano was presented by De Astis *et al.* (1997*a*,*b*) together with a model of the evolution of the plumbing system throughout the volcanic history of the island.

Chapter 6. **Stromboli**

Introduction

The island of Stromboli (Plate 6) is the most northerly island in the Eolian archipelago and is one of the best-known volcanoes in the world. Because of its almost continuous explosive activity, recorded over several thousand years, Stromboli has acquired the name of the 'Lighthouse of the Mediterranean'. The island is also the source of the name of one of the mildest forms of explosive volcanism, strombolian activity.

On Stromboli, explosions typically take place every 10–20 minutes or so and have probably been occurring nearly continually for more than 2500 years. Certainly Stromboli was active in the third century BC, as the island is mentioned in Homer's *Odyssey*. From Greek times until at least the seventeenth century AD, Stromboli was known as 'Strongyle' meaning 'round one', possibly related to its form.

Geography and history

Stromboli has been inhabited on and off since Greek times. Archaeological excavations between Scari and Ficogrande have discovered a number of Greek tombs and sarcophagi together with coins, rings and precious masks. These findings indicate that the Greek settlers had a relatively advanced culture on Stromboli. Excavations also indicate Roman settlements of late Imperial times. However, by the Middle Ages, with the decline of the Roman Empire, the Eolian Islands became depopulated. The islands were a refuge for Arab pirates, and during this time Stromboli is thought to have been largely deserted. By the sixteenth century Stromboli began to be repopulated. Initially the economy of the island was based on agriculture. At the end of the nineteenth century the population of the island was around 3000. However, this had reduced to some 400 by the end of the 1980s. Post-war tourism has now produced a seasonal reversal of this trend, with several thousand people being present on any one day during the summer months.

The island has two main settlements (Fig. 6.1). The first, on the NE side of the island, is a combination of several tiny villages in a strip along the northern coast. From east to west the villages are Scari, San Vincenzo, Ficogrande, Piscita and San Bartolo; the total population is less than 400. The second settlement, Ginostra, on the westernmost tip of the island, is virtually isolated by land from the more northerly settlements, and consists of some 30 residents. Both the ferries and the hydrofoils from Naples and Milazzo to the islands call at the jetty at Scari at the eastern end of the northerly string of villages.

Near sea level in the inhabited areas there is cultivated land including vineyards and old olive groves. Higher, there is an area of giant bamboo grass, and above this are blackberries and bracken. Higher still, vegetation is reduced to mosses and lichens, and the last few hundred metres to the top consist of essentially barren lava and tephra

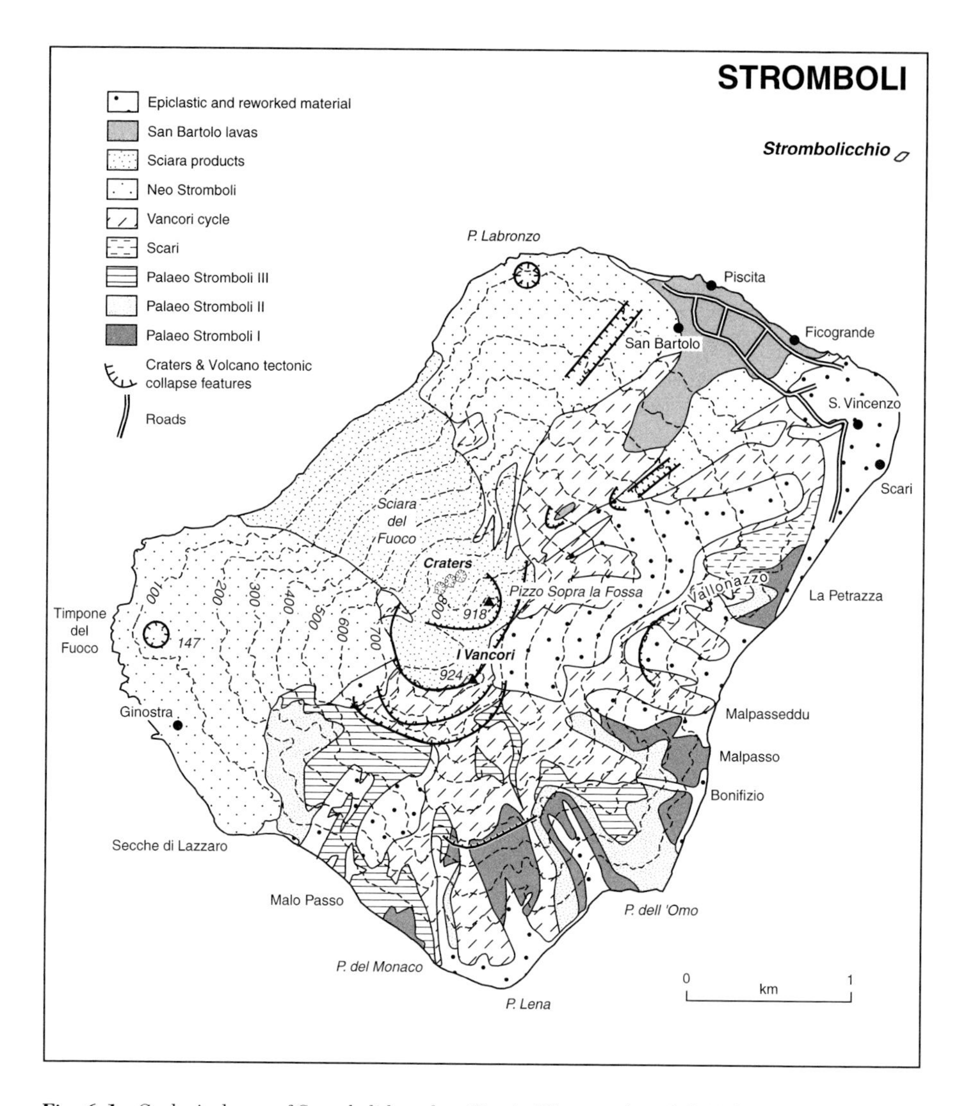

Fig. 6.1. Geological map of Stromboli based on Hornig-Kjarsgaard *et al.* (1993).

(Fig. 6.2). There are roads connecting the villages on the north coast, but none across the island to Ginostra in the south. One overland connection between the two inhabited areas is a poor coastal pathway. A well-trodden pathway leads from Piscita to near the summit at 850 m, where there is a viewing point, Pizzo Sopra la Fossa, overlooking the active vents.

Geomorphology

The island of Stromboli rises to 924 m and at first sight, especially from the south, appears to have a conical form; however, the geomorphology of the volcano is not so

Fig. 6.2. The summit and active craters (A) of Stromboli seen from the lower parts of the ascent route.

simple. It is 5 km × 3 km with the long axis trending NE–SW parallel to the Stromboli–Panarea–Lipari fault system. It is the subaerial top of a large submarine volcano, and bathymetric surveys show that the island is just 4% by area of the whole volcanic edifice. The volcanic construct probably continues for some 2000 m below sea level, giving it a total height of nearly 3000 m, close to the height of Mount Etna. The volcanic neck of Strombolicchio forms an islet some 2 km to the NE of Stromboli. and forms the only subaerial part of a submarine platform that extends between it and the main island; the sea between the main island and Strombolicchio is only 20 m or so deep.

The most obvious morphological feature on the island is the Sciara del Fuoco, the literal translation being 'scar of fire' (Fig. 6.3). Many volcanologists have discussed the origin of the Sciara del Fuoco, with early ideas centred around an explosion having 'blown away' a portion of the cone, followed by partial filling from the subsequent activity. It is now generally accepted that it is a partially filled sector collapse depression that lies on the NW side of the volcano, and was given as an example of such by Howell Williams in his memoir on calderas published in 1941. The Sciara del Fuoco continues below sea level to a depth of around 1700 m. The structure is probably fault controlled, related to the regional tectonics, and is the youngest of a series of collapse structures on the NW side of the island that have occurred in the last 13 ka. Scars on the southeastern flank of the island testify to the instability of the flanks of this volcano. The volcano flanks below sea level are steep, which promotes instability.

The Sciara del Fuoco owes its present-day appearance to the volcanic activity that occurs in the depression at its head. The currently active craters are all located within the confines of the depression and both lavas and pyroclastic deposits, apart from the

Fig. 6.3. Sciara del Fuoco seen from the north, Stromboli. Salina and Filicudi are visible in the distance.

largest explosions, are all contained within it. Although the majority of the material entering the Sciara del Fuoco is pyroclastic, studies have shown that it is the addition of new material as lava flows that actually causes growth of the slopes of the Sciara del Fuoco outwards to the NW.

Present-day activity at Stromboli does not take place from the summit of the volcano, but occurs from a series of vents nearly 200 m lower at 750 m a.s.l. to the NW within the Sciara del Fuoco on what is termed the 'crater terrace' (Plate 7). Typically there are three active craters, although several active vents occur within each of these craters. Interestingly, three craters appear to have been in existence for several centuries, for in 1768 Sir William Hamilton pointed out that three craters had been present at Stromboli for at least 150 years. The US volcanologist, Fred Bullard, during his visits to Stromboli in the 1950s, also reported that there were three main active craters. Studies in the 1990s have revealed some morphological changes in the craters, with hornitos and spatter ramparts being built and then destroyed probably by larger explosions.

Early volcanological studies

The regular, persistent activity of Stromboli has attracted visitors, and captured the imagination of travellers and students of volcanism, for a long time. Seventeenth-century volcanologists made observations at Stromboli and described the explosive activity. One such was the Abbé Lazzaro Spallanzani, who is famous for his melting experiments to explain the causes of volcanic activity. Guy Dolomieu also went to Stromboli in the 18th century and made important observations that helped him to formulate his ideas about volcanism. Observations of the activity at that time describe perfectly the strombolian activity that is taking place today. We quote from the Prussian geologist, M. Hoffmann, who visited Stromboli in 1828 and, with a companion holding his legs, peered over the craters. This is what he saw: 'Three active mouths were seen at the bottom of the crater. The principal one in the middle, was about 200 feet in diameter, was only fuming slightly and numerous yellow incrustations of sulphur coat the walls of its chimney. Close by this mouth is another, somewhat nearer the precipice, only 20 feet wide, in which I could see the play of the column of liquid lava, which at intervals poised itself at a level. This lava did not look like a burning mass vomiting flames, but as glossy as molten metal. Like iron issuing from the smelting furnace, or silver at the bottom of a crucible.

This melted mass rose and fell—evidently urged by the powerful tension of elastic vapours pressing it upwards from beneath; it was easy to perceive the balance of effect between the weight of the molten masses and the pressure of the steam which resisted them. The surface rose and fell rhythmically: there was a peculiar sound, like the crackling of air from bellows entering the door of a furnace. A bubble of white vapour issued at each crack, raising the lava, which fell down again immediately after its escape. These bubbles of vapour dragged to the surface of the lava red-hot cinders, which danced and tossed by invisible hands in rhythmic sport above the brink of the opening.

This play, so regular and attractive, was interrupted, every quarter of an hour or so by more tumultuous movements. The mass of whirling vapour then rested motionless for a moment—even making a jerking motion of return, as if inhaled by the crater, from the bottom of which the lava rose more strongly as if to encounter it. Then the ground trembles, and the wall of the crater starts bending. It was quite an earthquake. The mouth of the crater uttered a loud rolling bellow, which was followed by an immense bubble of vapour, bursting at the surface of the lava with a loud thundering report. The whole surface of the lava reduced to glowing splinters, was then tossed into the air.

The heat struck our faces forcibly; while a flaming sheaf rose right into the air, and fell back in a shower all around. Some bombs ascended to a height of about 1200 feet, and in passing over our heads described parabolas of fire. Immediately after such an eruption, the lava withdrew to the bottom of the chimney, which then yawned black and gaping. But erelong there was seen a re-ascending the shining mirror of the surface of lava, which then recommenced the rhythmic play of its ordinary less violent bubblings.'

Historical activity

The term strombolian activity was coined by Professor Guiseppe Mercalli, who was also responsible for vulcanian activity being named after Vulcano. The persistent 'normal' activity at Stromboli is characterized by brief explosions each of which lasts only up to a few tens of seconds. Jets formed by these explosions are generally up to 300 m in height and incandescent pyroclastic material falls back on and around the crater on ballistic trajectories.

Although Stromboli is one of the most persistently active volcanoes in the world, its activity is not completely uniform, and variations in the magnitude and style of activity do occur. At intervals, activity steps up producing larger explosions and sometimes lavas. The last major lava flow occurred in 1985, when lava reached the sea at the base of the Sciara del Fuoco. Lava flows are erupted on average every 4 years.

The occasional larger paroxysmal events, which affect the whole island, present a real, although relatively rare, hazard at Stromboli. Such paroxysms can involve ejection of large ballistic blocks to a distance of 2.5 km from the crater. Several paroxysmal events occurred in 1998 and 1999. These recent events involved an initial explosion followed by an eruption column that generated extensive scoria fall. A major component of the product of these explosions is vesicular pumice that is compositionally distinct from the typical scoria of strombolian activity.

Particularly violent eruptive events occurred in 1919 and 1930. Both of these produced ballistic material, which caused extensive damage to the villages of San Vicenzo and Ginostra some 3 and 2.5 km from the crater, respectively. Tsunamis were also generated during these vigorous events. There has not been such an event for more than 50 years. Following large eruptive events, pauses in activity sometimes occur for as long as 1 or 2 years.

The eruption in 1930 was perhaps the most devastating eruption to have occurred in historical times on Stromboli. As far as can be ascertained there were no observed precursory signs to this explosive event. Initial explosions occurred at 08.10 on 11 September, but caused only light tephra fall on the SW side of the island. At 09.52, after an hour and a half of normal activity, two particularly violent explosions occurred that threw huge blocks of the old volcano over the northern and SW parts of the island. Extensive damage from these blocks occurred in Ginostra and the Semaforo Labronzo (the lighthouse) was destroyed. These 'vent clearing' type explosions were immediately followed by incandescent tephra fall over much of the summit region.

The Italian volcanologist Giuseppe Imbo reported that from Sicily an eruption column at least 4 km high could be observed to last for around 30 minutes. Substantial fallback of this tephra outside of the confines of the Sciara del Fuoco caused the generation of what were described as hot avalanches or 'pseudo flows', that were essentially small pyroclastic flows. Four fishermen in a boat off the northern coast of the island were killed as parts of these flows swept out as pyroclastic surges over the sea.

Observations of the crater region by Alfred Rittmann before and after the 1930 eruption show that the whole crater terrace was significantly lowered in height. Much of the destroyed crater region was probably ejected in the initial explosions at 09.52. New active craters quickly established themselves following the event.

During both the 1919 and 1930 events a tsunami about 2 m high was formed that killed at least one person and caused extensive damage on the coast.

Lava flows were extruded at numerous times in the 1950s and 1960s but had apparently become subordinate to explosive activity towards the end of the 20th century. The last two major effusive events to send lava flows down the Sciara del Fuoco to the sea occurred in 1975 and in 1985–1986. Descriptions of the 1985–1986 event state that it began with powerful explosions that sent a column of material 2 km above the summit of the volcano. These explosions have been interpreted as being hydromagmatic. Small pyroclastic flows were also observed. A lava flow appeared from a vent at 680 m altitude and built a small peninsula jutting into the sea. The lava flow continued until April 1986 when again powerful, possibly hydromagmatic, explosions terminated the eruption.

Since the mid-1980s activity has been extremely well documented. This detailed documentation has revealed that over the last decade there have been several much larger explosions every year. Typically, fallout of incandescent scoria showers the whole of the summit region and ignites vegetation on the upper slopes of the volcano.

Prehistoric geological history

The oldest dated rocks of Stromboli volcano form the volcanic neck of Strombolicchio with an age of *c.* 200 ka BP. The majority of the island was, however, probably formed in the last 100 ka (Fig. 6.4).

The evolution of Stromboli over the last 100 ka has been divided into seven stages. Each of these stages is geochemically distinct. The periods are, in chronological order with the oldest first: Palaeostromboli I, II and III, Scari, Vancori, Neostromboli and Recent Stromboli (Sciara). Three of these periods, Palaeostromboli 1, Vancori and Neostromboli, had caldera or sector collapses associated with them, generally occurring at the end of the time period. Typically, these collapse events heralded the onset of a change in chemical composition of magma.

Following Strombolicchio, the oldest products exposed are those of Palaeostromboli 1, and dating indicates age ranges of 100–64 ka BP. This early activity was predominantly effusive, forming andesitic lava flows that are now exposed in the SW edge of the island. A phase of extensive explosive activity followed, including convecting eruption columns that generated a number of lapilli fall beds. Surge deposits also occur and might indicate phreatomagmatic activity; and there are interbedded lahar deposits.

Effusive activity resumed before the end of this period. Before the onset of the next phase, Palaeostromboli II, a volcano-tectonic collapse occurred and initial lava flows of Palaeostromboli II filled the collapse depression on the SE part of the cone. Eruption of lava flows predominated for the rest of this period although there are scoria fall deposits interbedded between some of the flows.

The Paleostromboli III deposits are mainly concentrated on the southern sector of the island and are absent on the east. The earliest activity was explosive together with remobilization of tephra to form lahars. At about 35 ka BP many thin lavas, distinctive because of the presence of biotite, were erupted, followed by more effusive and explosive activity.

A relatively prolonged phase of explosive activity formed what is known as the Scari sequence, which consists of up to 50 m of pyroclastic deposits. Interestingly, only one thin lava flow occurs in the middle of the sequence. Although numerous scoria fall beds make up the sequence, about 2 m from the base of the Scari sequence a distinctive white, fine-grained trachytic ash layer between 25 and 30 cm thick occurs. This has

Ka			Composition	Products
	Recent Stromboli		Shosh, HK Calc-alk	Sciara lavas Fosseta lava Pizzo sopra la Fossa tuff cone San Bartolo lavas
10	Neostromboli	C	(K) Lc-shosh	Secche Lazzaro pyroclastics related to formation of Sciara del Fuoco monotonous shoshonitic lavas
20	Vancori	C C	Potassic (K) Shosh (SHO)	Predominantly lavas. Distinctive vulcanian pyroclastic breccias. Frontone welded breccia associated with collapse?
30	Scari		Trans to shosh	Up to 50 m of pyroclastics deposits Upper pt - scoria fall overlain by surges Lower pt - scoria fall layers Ischia Green tuff tephra layer
40 50	Paleostromboli III		HK calc-alk to shosh (HKCA-SHO)	Cavoni pyroclastics Aghiastro lavas & pyroclastics Upper Rina lavas Middle Rina biotite bearing lavas Vallone di Rina - malo passo pyroclastics -Lahars interbedded with scoria fall
60	Paleostromboli II		Calc-alk (CA)	Omo lava flows (6 or 7 lava flows) interbedded scoria fall deposits Rina Lava flows fill collapse structure
70 80 90	Paleostromboli I	C	HK calc-alk (HKCA)	High K andesite lava flows Petrazza pyroclastic series >40m fall interbedded with minor surge & flow Andesite lava flows at Petrazza, Malpasso, Bonifizio & Barbara
100 200	Strombolicchio		Calc-alk (CA)	

Fig. 6.4. Chronological chart of Stromboli mainly based on Hornig-Kjarsgaard *et al.* (1993). C indicates caldera collapse.

been interpreted as the distal ash fall from explosive eruptions on Ischia island some 300 km to the north. Stratigraphically the Scari products overlap with the overlying Vancori products as indicated by relative age ranges. Workers indicate that Scari products could also be interpreted as part of Palaeostromboli III. If the age of the Ischia ash is 55 ka BP then it may be that the Palaeostromboli III and Scari sequences were broadly contemporaneous.

The Vancori period, between 25 and 13 ka, probably saw the volcano reach its greatest height. In addition, the products include trachytes and latites, some of the most evolved products on the island. Lava effusion predominated during the Vancori period, but distinctive pyroclastic deposits also occur, especially partially welded fall deposits. Explosive activity became more important toward the end of the Vancori sequence, as a number of coarse lithic breccias occur that are thought to be the product of powerful vulcanian-type explosions. One of the uppermost of these is known as the Frontone breccia, which differs from the others in that it contains juvenile material. Collapse of the west and NW part of the summit cone occurred at the end of this phase and it is possible that this can be correlated with the Frontone breccias.

The activity of the Neostromboli period is represented by thick monotonous sequences of shoshonitic lavas that occur on the NW and SW flanks of Stromboli. They are exposed in the walls of the Sciara dell Fuoco. The higher Vancori summit has protected the eastern flank from Neostromboli lava flows.

A clue to the origin of the Sciara del Fuoco is given by the tephra layers that overlie lavas of the Neostromboli period, which occurred between 13 and 5 ka. These deposits are relatively fine-grained ash-rich fallout layers containing abundant accretionary lapilli and vesiculated tuff textures. Debris flow deposits are interbedded with the ash fall layers.

The Recent Stromboli phase represents activity from the present Sciara centre. The deposits have been divided into four parts as indicated in Fig. 6.4.

Petrology

The volcanic rocks of Stromboli belong to four series: the calc-alkaline (CA), high-K calc-alkaline (HKCA), shoshonitic (SHO) and potassic (K) series (Fig. 6.5). There is a broad general trend of the erupted products becoming more potassic with time, and the latter part of the Recent Stromboli period has been characterized by the eruption of shoshonitic basalts. The younger part of Stromboli's history involved eruption predominantly of products belonging to the SHO and K series; the exposed part of the earlier history of the volcano is made up mainly of lavas of the CA and HKCA series.

The CA series is composed of basaltic andesites with plagioclase and clinopyroxene phenocrysts and microphenocrysts of orthopyroxene. Sr-isotope values range from 0.70500 to 0.70538. Basalts are subordinate in the HKCA series, which is made up mainly of high-K basaltic andesites and high-K andesites. These lavas are silica oversaturated with rare phenocrysts of biotite and amphibole. Sr-isotope values range around 0.70633. The SHO series are similar in their rock types and Sr-isotope ratios to the HKCA series, although recent lavas have rather higher values of up to 0.70660. Lavas of the K series are distinctive in that leucite is present in the groundmass or as microphenocrysts. The Sr-isotope ratios of the K series are the highest on Stromboli (0.70660–0.70757).

The variability in the geochemistry and isotopic composition of the volcanic products of Stromboli has led workers such as Ellam and colleagues to argue for the involvement of a heterogeneous source region involving input from subducted oceanic crust and marine sediments and a ocean island type mantle wedge, which has been variably enriched with volatile constituents such as Sr and K.

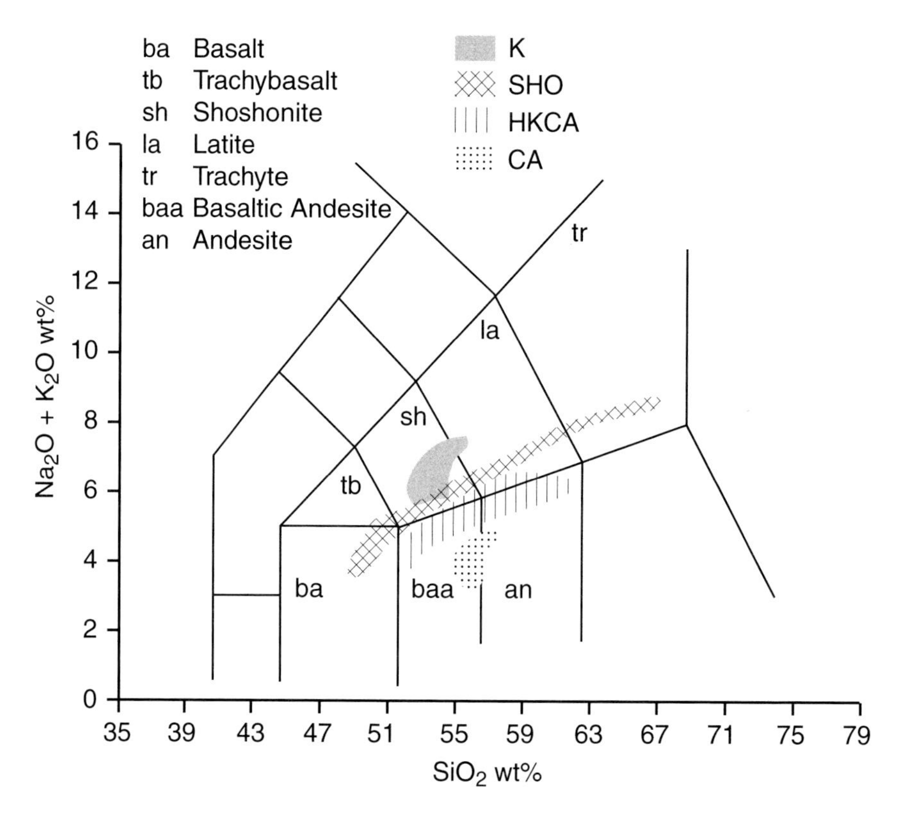

Fig. 6.5. TAS plot for the compositions of rocks from Stromboli: K, potassic series; SHO, shoshonitic series; HKCA, high-potassium calc-alkaline series; CA, calc-alkaline series (adapted from Francalanci *et al.* 1993).

The chemical variation of the HKCA and SHO series can be largely accounted for by fractional crystallization. The variable isotope ratios of some of the more evolved HKCA and SHO magmas are considered to have resulted from mixing with more mafic CA and K series magmas, respectively. Further evidence of mixing is provided by the presence of banded pumice. The mixing episode between SHO and K series magmas occurred towards the end of the Vancori activity and is marked by a progressive increase in Sr content of lavas with time. This reflects the transition to the eruption of the K series products of the Neostromboli sequence, which follows the Vancori period. These K series rocks have a Sr-isotope signature that suggests there has been interaction between the magma and crustal rocks.

The Vancori collapse event around 13 ka BP was associated with a change in the petrology of the erupted products. Francalanci and colleagues argue that the collapse led to a reduction in high-level storage in the plumbing system. Subsequent to this event magmas rose directly from the deep-seated system to the surface. This has led to the eruption of more mafic lavas.

Geophysical studies

Various geophysical techniques are, or have been, in use on Stromboli. Far and away the most extensive of these are seismic studies that have been made for about a century. Guiseppe Mercalli was one of the first to make crude seismological investigations using early seismometers. Mercalli noted ripples on the surface of the mercury of the seismometers a few seconds before strombolian explosions. These precursory signals were later interpreted by Tazieff and coworkers as being related to the change of height of the magma column in the vent. The waveform of the explosion shocks varies between the active craters. The source of the seismic waves related to the explosions lies just to the north of the active craters, rather than directly below them.

As well as discrete seismic events related to the strombolian explosions, continuous seismic signals also occur at Stromboli. Such continuous seismic signals are known as volcanic tremor. Volcanic tremor is considered to have an origin in pressure fluctuations caused by non-steady fluid flow of magma and/or gas within the volcano. Studies indicate that the tremor source is less than 300–400 m below the active craters and in addition that it does not originate from a single point source. Spectral analysis of the tremor shows maxima between 2 and 4 Hz, although more recent studies using broadband seismometers reveal strong amplitudes below 1 Hz. Spectra are also strongly time dependent, with higher amplitudes experienced during intense activity when magma is higher in the column, and smaller average values occurring during mild deep-seated explosions and when magma is at a lower level in the system.

Hazard

The major hazard at Stromboli is falling tephra from the larger explosions. Such explosions occur about once or twice a year and can threaten the population with falling lapilli and blocks. Closer to the vent these may be incandescent and cause fires. Although rare, small pyroclastic flows can form and settlements such as Piscita and San Bartolo have been hit in the past. Most such flows may be contained within the Sciara.

Tsunami were associated with at least five eruptions in the twentieth century, probably all associated with earthquakes or entry of pyroclastic flows into the sea. We have seen that the island's flanks are prone to instability. A collapse involving say 1 or 2 km^3 could generate waves of between 10 and 40 m height and would reach most of the island's shores within 5 minutes. No hazard analysis can ignore the possibility of such a rare event.

In recent years the number of tourists visiting Stromboli has increased dramatically. Many of these tourists come specifically to climb the volcano and observe the activity at night, and for several months of the year rarely a night goes by without people sleeping at the summit. As a consequence people are often at the summit of the volcano when these larger explosions occur.

A particularly large explosion in 1993 showered the summit with 'cow-pat' bombs up to 2 m in diameter. People sleeping at the summit were struck by some of these incandescent scoria fragments. However, it is worth bearing in mind that more people fall and injure themselves in the ensuing panic than are hurt by actual impact from the flying debris.

Places to visit

A climb to Pizzo Sopra la Fossa above the active craters is the main aim of most visitors, geological or otherwise, to the island. Unless the volcano has changed its habits since this was written, you are virtually guaranteed a fine view of strombolian explosions, assuming there is no cloud. The viewing platform at Pizzo Sopra la Fossa is formed by pyroclastic deposits related to explosive activity that formed a crude tuff cone.

A sunset trip is recommended to view the activity first in daylight and then at dusk and in night-time to have the full effect of this splendid phenomenon. Many visitors spend the night there, some taking sleeping bags. We recommend that for night-time visits you do not sleep up there, or use sleeping bags. An occasional large explosion could catch you out, and it is not easy to take avoiding action against bombs while swathed in a bag!

A boat trip from Piscita to Ginostra provides views of the Sciara, but check it takes the anticlockwise route.

To the south of the village of Scari, where the aliscafi and ferryboats dock, and up to Vallonazzo are a series of good exposures through the Scari sequence and the distinctive white 'Ischia' Tephra can be identified.

Lavas on the beach at Piscita and east to Ficogrande are the San Bartolo lavas which form some of the youngest lavas on Stromboli outside the Sciara del Fuoco. The morphology of the lava channel can still be seen behind the church of San Bartolo leading up toward the volcano.

The type locality of Secche Lazzaro pyroclastic deposits, lahars interbedded with accretionary lapilli-bearing ashes thought to be associated with the formation of the Sciara del Fuoco at the end of the Neostromboli phase, is exposed on the southern coast of Stromboli SE of Ginostra.

Notes

General

The general geography of the island has been covered by King (1973) and briefly in the *Rough Guide* (Andrews & Brown 1999). Scarth (1999) has a chapter on eruptions on Stromboli. See also Natale (1997).

Volcanic activity

Williams (1941) first explained the origin of the Sciara by gravitational collapse. Its form, including the submarine extension, has been described by Ramagnoli *et al.* (1993). Sector collapse has been discussed by Tibaldi (2001).

The quotation from Hoffman is taken from Anon. (1867). Particularly notable eruptive activity, both effusive and explosive, in 1915 was described by Perret (1916). The great eruption of 1930 was described in detail by Rittmann (1931), and also by Imbo (1928). Bullard (1954) also made observations during his visits there. Several excellent websites (including Boris Behncke's 'Cradle of Volcanology': http://boris.vulcanoetna.com/Italiahome.html) have particularly detailed accounts of the activity since that period. More recently, Blackburn *et al.* (1976) have described the mechanism of strombolian activity. They pointed out that the large quantities of gas expelled during strombolian explosions represent large bubbles or clusters of bubbles that began to form at depth and grew by coalescence as the magma rose in the conduit. De Fino *et al.* (1988) described the eruption of 1985–1986. Giberti *et al.* (1992) showed, on the basis of thermal degassing modelling, that some form of magma chamber exists at a depth of a few hundred metres.

A thematic volume of *Acta Vulcanologica* devoted to Stromboli was published in 1993 and includes several important papers describing volcanological aspects of the volcano.

Stratigraphy

A geological map of the island has been produced by Rosi (1980) together with a text, and more recently by Keller *et al.* (1993).

Hornig-Kjarsgaard *et al.* (1993) described the stratigraphy of the volcano over the last 100 ka and recognized four major periods. They also further subdivided the stratigraphy into several smaller subunits. Gillot & Keller (1993) provided radiometric dating. Pasquare *et al.* (1993) discussed the structure and geological evolution, emphasizing both sector and caldera collapses.

Ramagnoli *et al.* (1993) and Kokelaar & Ramagnoli (1995) described the nature of the Sciara del Fuoco and its submarine extension, and showed that it is composed mainly of lava and that most of the products of strombolian activity are rapidly transported into the sea. Following Williams (1941), a study by Bertagnini & Landi (1996) has related the Sciara del Fuoco to the Secche Lazzaro pyroclastic deposits. Rosi *et al.* (2000) used dating of pyroclastic sequences to propose that the persistent activity that occurs today began between the third and seventh century AD, later than thought by previous workers.

Petrology

The petrology of Stromboli has been discussed by Francalanci & Santo (1993) and Ellam *et al.* (1998).

Geophysics

There have been numerous recent papers concerning seismological aspects of Stromboli and its activity; for example, those by Dreier *et al.* (1994), Falsaperla *et al.* (1994, 1998), Neuberg *et al.* (1994) and Carniel & Iacop (1996). For a review of geomorphological studies on Stromboli, see Falsaperla & Schick (1993).

Hazard

A hazard assessment for the island has been provided by Barberi *et al.* (1993*b*). Tinti *et al.* (2000) have investigated the nature of tsunamis caused by sector collapse.

Chapter 7. **Lipari and other Eolian Islands**

Of the remaining five inhabited islands of the Eolian archipelago, Lipari, Salina, Filicudi, Alicudi and Panarea (Fig. 5.1), only Lipari has been volcanically active during historical times. Nevertheless, Salina and Panarea have fumaroles both on land and, just offshore, attesting to at least remnant heat from below. Between them the islands show a range of composition and styles of activity.

Geography and history

Lipari, the largest island in the archipelago, has been at the centre of human activity on the islands through historical time. The earliest settlers on the island were in Neolithic times and there is abundant archaeological evidence for their presence on all of the Eolian Islands, except Vulcano, from the middle of the fourth millennium BC to the end of the third. Obsidian from Lipari became a precious commodity for the production of sharp implements. Export of obsidian was widespread during this time, and it has been found on islands in the Mediterranean hundreds of miles away, on Sicily and as far away as Malta.

Bronze Age activity was also high on the islands, as evidenced by the remains of several villages. The first known settlement on Lipari was in 3500 BC.

Greek colonization followed in 580 BC, two centuries after it began on Sicily, and thrived on Lipari. The initial Greek population was terrorized by Etruscan pirates, then in 397 BC the Carthaginians captured Lipari. Hannibal stayed on the island for several months in 269 BC, and it is alleged he visited the hot mud pools on Vulcano for his health.

Roman dominion followed in 251 BC and Lipari developed as a strategic naval base protecting important trade routes. The Romans also recognized the therapeutic powers of the hot springs. The islands were widely developed and even on the tiny islet of Basiluzzo off Panarea there are the remains of a Roman villa, as well as a submerged boathouse testifying to a net sinking of the island during the last two millennia.

With the decline of the Roman Empire and the loss of its navy at Lipari, the islands became virtually unprotected. The Muslims took Lipari in AD 836 and the island became virtually depopulated. The Norman nobles Robert and Roger Guiscard were responsible for building the church of S. Bartholomew and a Benedictine monastery. Piratical raids continued and in the mid-sixteenth century the infamous Khair-ed-din Barbarossa, known as Redbeard, took Lipari, and its inhabitants were forced into slavery.

All the islands then suffered from almost total depopulation until expansion occurred again under the Spanish in the sixteenth century. From then on there was a steady increase in population. The sixteenth-century walled citadel was used as a prison between 1889 and 1915, and again later by Mussolini; for a short time after the Second World War ex-Fascists, including Mussolini's daughter, were imprisoned there.

Population of the islands reached a peak in the early twentieth century with over 20 000 inhabitants; since then the resident population has diminished, although less so on Lipari owing to the rapidly expanded tourist industry. As on Vulcano and Stromboli, the summer population is greatly enlarged by an influx of tourists. As a result, the infrastructure of the islands has improved to the benefit of the residents, although during the tourist season it is stretched to the limits.

As there were no regular marine links with the Sicilian mainland until the mid-nineteenth century, the islanders were forced to be highly self-sufficient. The population was supported by labour-intensive agriculture. As the population increased, so did agriculture, and terracing was extended to higher and steeper slopes. Fishing was also important.

Better transport links in the early twentieth century reduced this self-sufficiency and mainland produce undermined local crops. Local water, collected in cisterns from rainwater, has ceased to be sufficient and tankers bring water in the summer months. Good communications also improved exports including wine, especially the famous malvasia wine, and, for a time, pumice. Emigration increased, leading to abandoned agricultural land which is now replaced by scrub.

The islands are only publicly accessible by boat, and there are both conventional vessels and the much faster hydrofoils (*aliscafi*) from ports on Sicily and the mainland, although not all services run in the winter months.

Lipari

When viewed from the west the morphology of Lipari is dominated by three broad volcanic structures, Monte Chirica in the north, Monte St. Angelo in the central part of the island, and in the south the smaller Monte Guardia lava domes (Fig. 7.1). In the east and NE, the products formed during the historical activity dominate the landscape and include the Forgia Vecchia obsidian flow, the Monte Pilato pumice cone and, on the most NW point, the Rocche Rosse obsidian flow (Figs 7.2–7.4).

Lipari has a long history of volcanism. The oldest dated rocks are 223 ka BP. Throughout Lipari's geological history volcanism has not occurred at a regular rate, and phases of activity have been punctuated by long periods of quiescence.

The geology of Lipari has been divided into four periods of activity. However, compositionally, the stratigraphy can be divided in two, the older products being basaltic to andesitic and those in the two youngest periods mostly rhyolitic.

The oldest rocks on the island (Fig. 7.5) are submarine pillow lavas, hyaloclastites and lava–pyroclastic cone complexes, which crop out on the northern and western side of the island. The Monte Rosa centres, that separate Lipari town from Canneto village on the eastern side of the island, were also formed during this first period. Several small

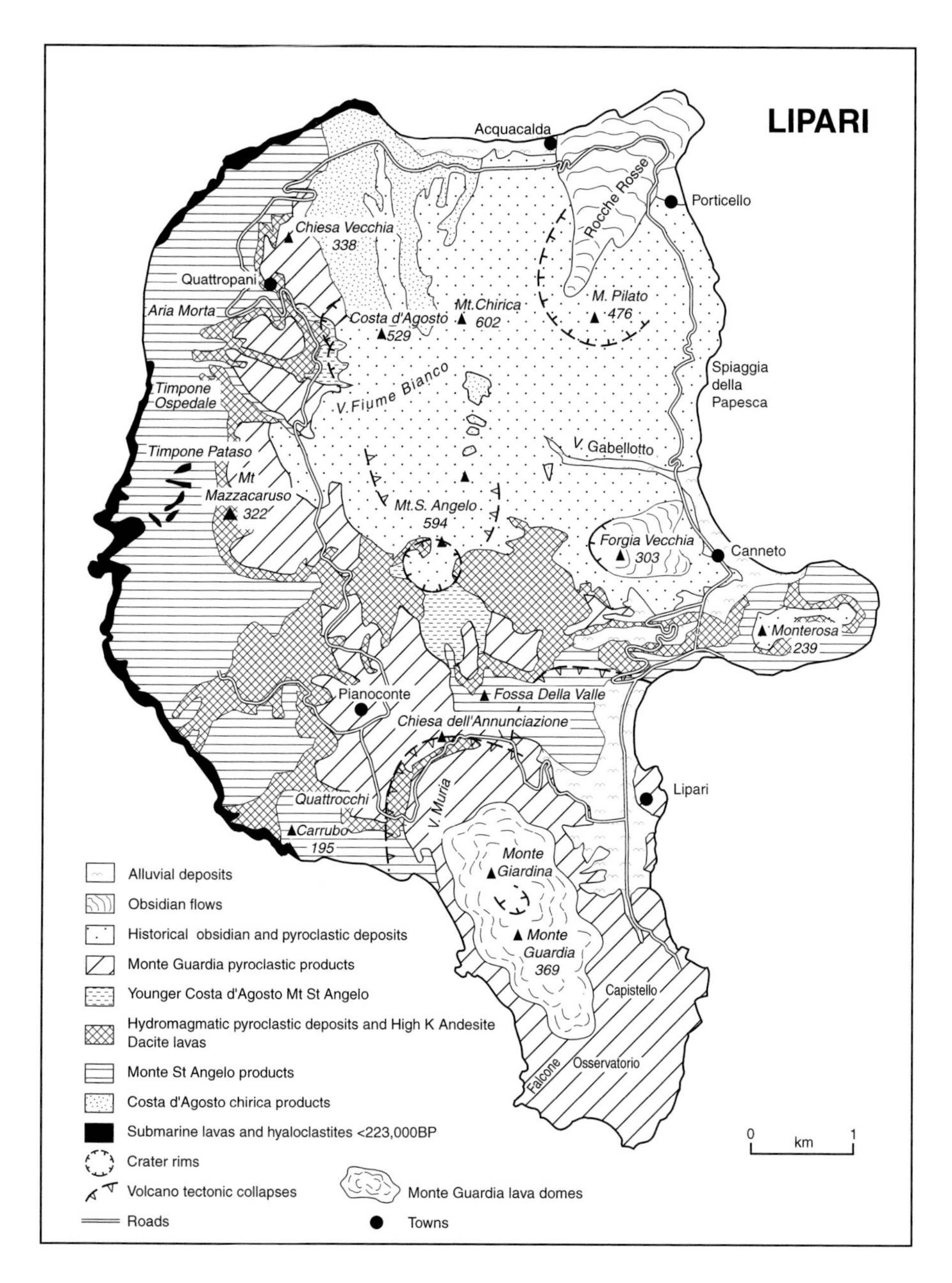

Fig. 7.1. Geological map of Lipari (modified after De Rosa *et al.* 1985).

stratovolcanoes may also be identified on the NW side of the island. These include from north to south: Chiesa Vecchia, Aria Morta, Timpone Ospedale, Timpone Pataso, Timpone Mazzacaruso and Timpone Carrubo.

The second period of activity involved the development of the volcanic edifices of Monte Chirica–Costa d'Agosto in the northern part of Lipari, and Monte St. Angelo in the

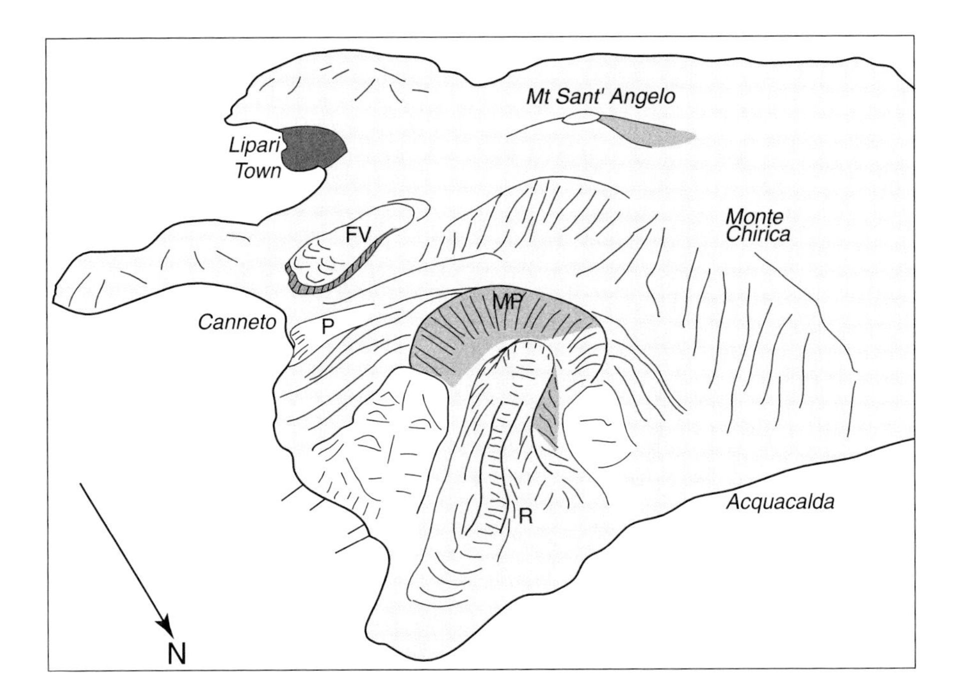

Fig. 7.2. Sketch of Lipari from the air looking south. In the foreground the Roche Rosse obsidian flow (R) breaches the Monte Pilato pumice cone (MP). Immediately to the south the Forgia Vecchia (FV) obsidian flow extends east. The Pomiciazzo obsidian flow is indicated by (P).

Fig. 7.3. The Rocche Rosse obsidian showing folded layers typical of this flow.

Fig. 7.4. Close-up of the Rocche Rosse flow. Note the devitrified layers and lenses. Coin for scale.

central part of the island. The two volcanoes developed broadly contemporaneously and radiometric dates of 150 and 127 ka BP have been obtained from them. Monte St. Angelo has a central crater and a well-preserved morphology. Three main stages of activity have been identified at Monte St. Angelo: (1) early hydromagmatic activity followed by high-K andesitic lavas; (2) explosive activity with production of lahars; (3) production of massive welded pyroclastic deposits and a small lava in the summit region.

From 92 to 42 ka BP the island appears to have been in a state of volcanic rest. The marine platform at 40 m on the west and NW coast may have been cut at this time. Beach deposits consist of coarse, well-rounded pebbles and boulders.

There is a distinctive tephra layer dated at 55 ka BP on Lipari as well as on several of the other Eolian Islands, including Filicudi, Panarea, Salina and Stromboli. This tephra was correlated by Jörg Keller with an eruption on Ischia and may be termed the Ischia Tephra. On Lipari it is a useful horizon to determine the boundary between the second and third periods of activity.

The third period of activity on Lipari after this long gap in eruptive activity consists of the production of rhyolitic domes, a distinct change in composition from the earlier activity. The Monte Guardia centre that followed opened with explosive activity. A pyroclastic sequence built up with a thickness of many tens of metres in proximal locations (e.g. quarries in the Capistello region). It probably represents a single eruption that took place sometime between 20.3 and 22.48 ka BP. The Monte Guardia rocks consist of a complex sequence of lithic and pumice breccias, and interbedded surge and pumice fall

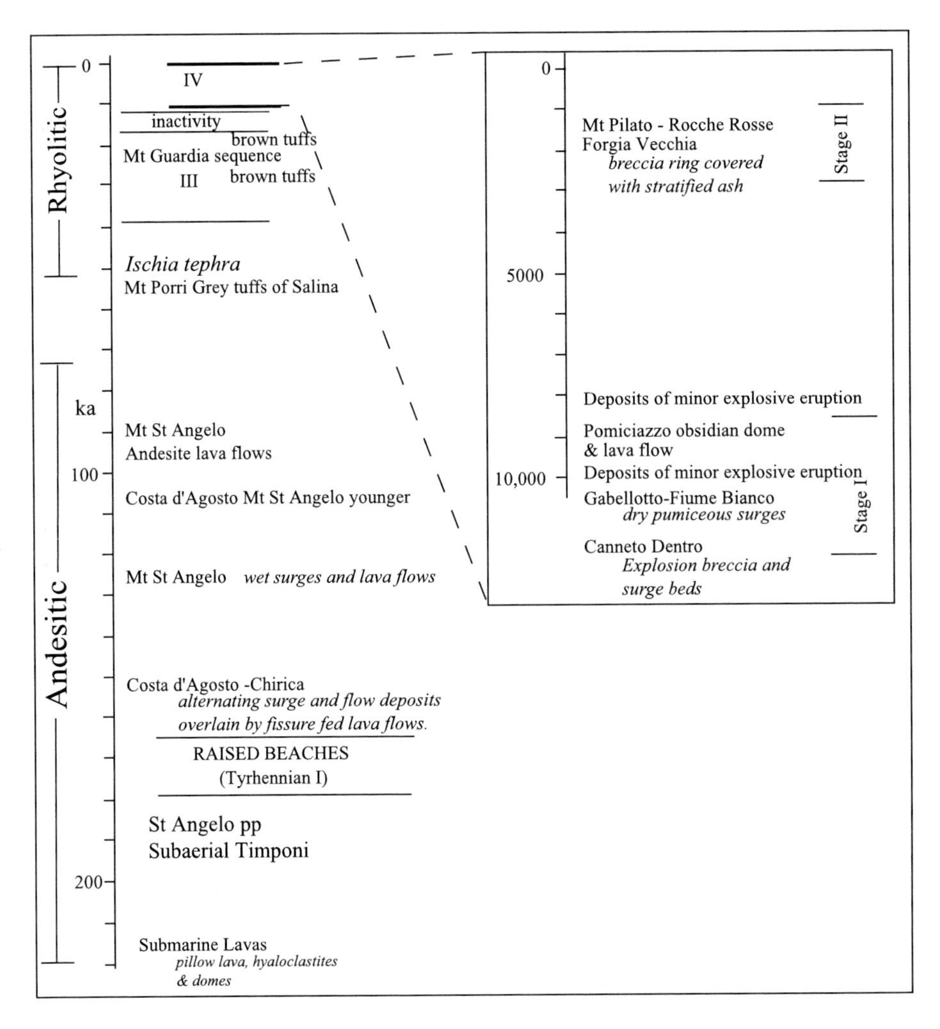

Fig. 7.5. Chronological chart of Lipari volcano (based on Frazzetta 1998; Pichler 1980*b*; De Rosa *et al.* 1985).

layers (Fig. 7.6). Accretionary lapilli-bearing ash layers are also present. These deposits were generally distributed to the NE by the prevailing winds. Detailed studies of these deposits reveal that they record the changing physical nature of surge clouds as sedimentation occurred during the course of their runout. The Castello di Lipari lava dome on which the old part of Lipari town is built was formed during this third period. Domes of Monte Guardia, Giardina, Falcone and Capistello occurred within the third period of activity (Fig. 7.7).

At a number of horizons, both underlying and overlying the Mt. Guardia sequence, are conspicuous, relatively fine-grained deposits of what have been termed 'Brown Tuffs'. These Brown Tuffs are not restricted to any one stratigraphic horizon and have an extremely widespread distribution, occurring on the islands of Filicudi, Panarea and Salina, and on the Milazzo peninsula of northern Sicily. They were initially interpreted

Fig. 7.6. Sandwave surge deposits of the Monte Guardia formation, exposed in the Valle de Muria. Flow was from right to left. The layers below the hammer are fallout.

Fig. 7.7. The Monte Guardia lava domes viewed from the east.

simply as 'tuffloess' the distal products of large explosive eruptions or windblown tephra deposits. Rather than mantling the pre-existing topography, however, they show a valley-filling aspect and have since been interpreted as the deposits of pyroclastic flows formed from hydromagmatic eruptions. Owing to their shoshonitic petrological affinity, workers on these deposits have inferred them to come from eruptions on Vulcano, in particular submarine eruptions from a proto-Vulcanello.

The fourth and last period of activity includes those eruptions that took place in the last 15 ka. During this period there were three distinct cycles considered to represent separate eruptions. Interbedded tephra between the rocks of the main cycles indicate additional eruptions of smaller magnitude. Each cycle started with explosive activity and was terminated with the extrusion of silicic lava.

In the oldest of the cycles the Cannetto Dentro explosion breccia cone was built up first, followed by ash fall and surges, and finally an obsidian lava flow. The source is buried by later deposits.

This was followed by the Gabellotto Fiume Bianco eruption, which mainly formed coarse pumiceous pyroclastic surge deposits. The Gabellotto Fiume Bianco surges were channelled to the east and west by the pre-existing topography, and followed a valley that runs roughly east–west between Mt. St. Angelo and Mt. Chirica. Deposits formed by these surges show alternating thick (up to 1 m) coarse pumiceous layers capped by thin ash beds. They contain spectacular large-wavelength sandwave structures (Fig. 7.8) and metre-sized bombs which are well exposed in quarries in the northwestern part of the island. This eruption was terminated by the Pomiciazzo obsidian lava flow on the NE side of the island. This has been fission-track dated at between 11.4 and 8.6 ka BP. Evidence found by Keller indicates that the most widely distributed obsidian artefacts in the Mediterranean were derived from this lava flow during Neolithic times.

Fig. 7.8. Gabellotto Fiume Bianco pyroclastic surge deposits exposed in a small quarry east of Quattropane. Flow direction was from the left. The sequence shown is 8 m thick.

On top of the Gabellotto Fiume Bianco deposits is a palaeosol of, on average, 1 m thickness which contains obsidian and ceramic Neolithic artefacts, and represents a period of volcanic almost complete quiescence of some 9000 years.

The last eruption cycle on Lipari took place between the sixth and eighth centuries AD on the NW side of the island. Initially, the pumice cone of Monte Pilato formed on top of the Pomiciazzo flow, and at about the same time another vent opened in the Pirrera area to produce the Forgia Vecchia flow. This obsidian flow extends east, terminating just above the village of Canneto. Explosive activity occurred before extrusion of the lava, forming a coarse pumice breccia in a broad ring. The upper part of the breccia is bedded and composed of thin layers of alternating ash and lapilli. Some of these ash layers thicken to the north of the Forgia Vecchia crater, suggesting a source from Monte Pilato. On this basis, the two centres have been interpreted to have been broadly contemporaneous or at least overlapped in time with one another.

Exposures (Plate 8) through the Monte Pilato pumice cone today reveal a variety of pyroclastic deposits, which are up to 150 m thick in the walls of the cone. The base of the sequence comprises pumice lapilli beds and bombs with ballistic impact horizons. Higher in the sequence massive pumiceous deposits and sandwave beds are interbedded with pumice lapilli fallout.

Tephra from this initial explosive activity was widespread, and reached at least as far as Vulcano and almost certainly further afield. The island was covered with a thin ash layer that covers the remains of a Greek city and Roman coins of the fifth century AD.

A second eruption with less violent explosive activity followed. After the explosive phase, the thick Rocche Rosse obsidian block lava erupted through a breach in the northern rim of the new cone and flowed 1.5 km to the NW (Fig. 7.2). The surface of the flow has well-developed ogives (arcuate surface ridges) and talus margins, which are best seen from the air. The flow is probably several tens of metres thick and is typical of silicic flows that were erupted with a high effective viscosity.

Salina

The morphology of the island of Salina (Fig. 7.9) is dominated by the twin cones of Monte Fossa delle Felci (962 m) and Monte dei Porri (800 m). It is these two cones that gave the island its former name 'Didyme', meaning twin. In addition, on the western side of the island is the impressive Pollara crater, which is open to the sea. Volcanic activity at Salina began around 500 ka BP and continued until about 13 ka BP. Broadly, the activity can be divided in two based on the presence of erosional marine terraces or raised beaches occurring on several terrace levels. These raised beaches are dated at a minimum of 100 ka BP.

The earliest activity of the island is represented by three volcanoes; Capo, Rivi and Corvo. All three of these centres involved the eruption of mainly high-alumina basalts. Substantial erosion since then has caused heavy dissection exposing dyke complexes representing the hearts of these volcanoes.

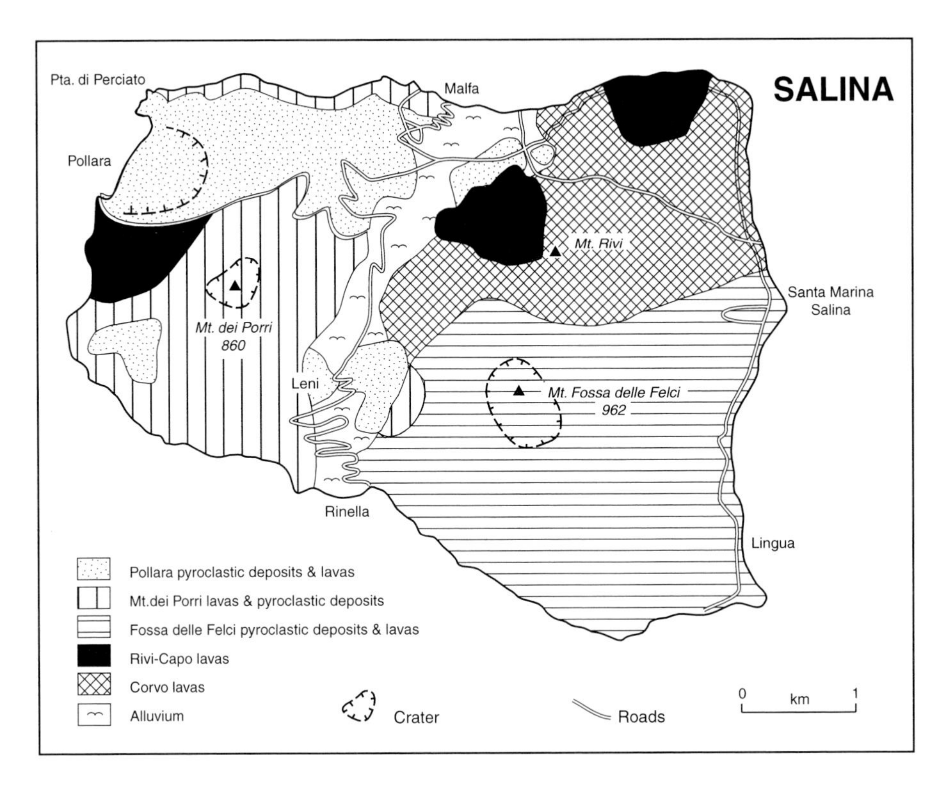

Fig. 7.9. Geological map of Salina (based on Calanchi *et al.* 1996, 1999).

The Fossa delle Felci cone was the last to be formed before marine erosion and it has not been dissected as heavily as the others. Products of this cone range from basalt to dacite and four separate units have been identified: an initial cinder cone, the south coast dacites, the Favarolo series, and andesitic lavas at Fossa delle Felci. The so-called Favarolo series consists of three units: a basal white pumice breccia, a middle layer of tuff breccia containing breadcrust bombs and spatter rags up to several metres diameter, and an upper agglutinate layer. The whole sequence is locally more than 50 m thick and lavas are intercalated with it to the west.

Following the formation of the raised marine terraces, volcanic activity at Salina was restricted to two other centres, Monte dei Porri and the Pollara centre. Interleaved between the products of these two centres are a number of horizons of brown tuff, which probably correlate with those found on Lipari and Vulcano. In addition, the distinctive Ischia Tephra was first identified on Salina. The brown tuffs probably put an upper age limit on the Porri activity at around 60 ka BP. Activity of the Monte Porri centre is represented by two pyroclastic deposits and is capped by a sequence of andesitic lava flows. The most important products of the Porri centre are a sequence of deposits known as Grey Porri Tuffs (GPT), which represent a period of intense explosive activity. Indeed, Keller and others have identified these GPTs on Lipari and Panarea, respectively 10 and 20 km distant. On Salina the GPTs are composed of fallout layers interbedded with chaotic deposits interpreted as lahars. Pyroclastic surge deposits also occur within the grey tuff sequence, and it has been proposed that some of these surges overtopped the over 900 m high cone of Fossa delle Felci.

The most recent activity on the island of Salina took place from the Pollara centre situated on the west side of the island (Fig. 7.9). Dacite lava flows form the initial products; however, explosive activity predominates, with pumice breccias overlain by white lapilli fall and surge deposits. Two pyroclastic deposits are separated from one another by more Brown Tuff, and radiocarbon dating of charcoal at the base of the uppermost white pumices yields an age of around 13 ka BP for this unit, which is the youngest on Salina.

Panarea

The island of Panarea (Fig. 7.10) is the smallest inhabited island in the Eolian archipelago, being only 3.3 km^2 in area and rising to 421 m. It has good soils on the eastern side and it has three hamlets, S. Pietro, Ditella and Drauto. There is a well of potable water, but most of the water was from cisterns that collected rainwater, and is now from water ships.

Several small islets lie between 2 and 3 km east of Panarea and include: Lisca Bianca, Bottaro, Lisca Nera, Dattilo and Panarelli. A larger islet, Basiluzzo, sits isolated 3 km to the NE of Panarea. All of the islets together with Panarea itself are part of a larger submarine edifice. These islets have been interpreted as the remnants of a rim of a crater 1 km × 1.5 km in size. Intense fumarolic activity occurs today from submarine parts of these islets, which are still subsiding, as indicated by Roman ruins that are at present 14 m below sea level. Tectonically, Panarea is connected with Stromboli on a NE–SW lineament and there are suggestions that the two magma systems were at times coeval.

The volcanic significance of the geomorphology of Panarea is, unlike that of many of the other Eolian Islands, not immediately obvious. The island has steep cliffs on the northern and western sides that are considered to be of either tectonic or erosive origin. All along the gentler southern and eastern margins of the island at least three levels of raised beaches can be identified, at heights of 100, 50 and 30 m. Some workers have assigned each of these raised beaches to separate interstadial time periods. These studies do not, however, take into account any localized uplift, or indeed subsidence, that may have occurred on the island, and caution is required in correlating the raised beach levels with elsewhere. Nevertheless, recent studies place an age range of 120–60 ka BP on the raised beaches.

Geophysical studies have revealed a positive gravity anomaly, unique within the Eolian Islands, just to the east of Panarea. This has been interpreted as the expression of a partly submerged caldera structure (3 km × 2 km). The steep NE-facing scarps on the northern part of Panarea could be part of the rim of this structure. The southeastern rim may be represented by Panarelli, where lava centres have been dated at 130 ka BP, which may approximate the age of the caldera. The islets are formed by lavas that range in composition from andesite to dacite and are also of a similar age The gravity anomaly is considered to be caused by an intrusive basaltic body at depth.

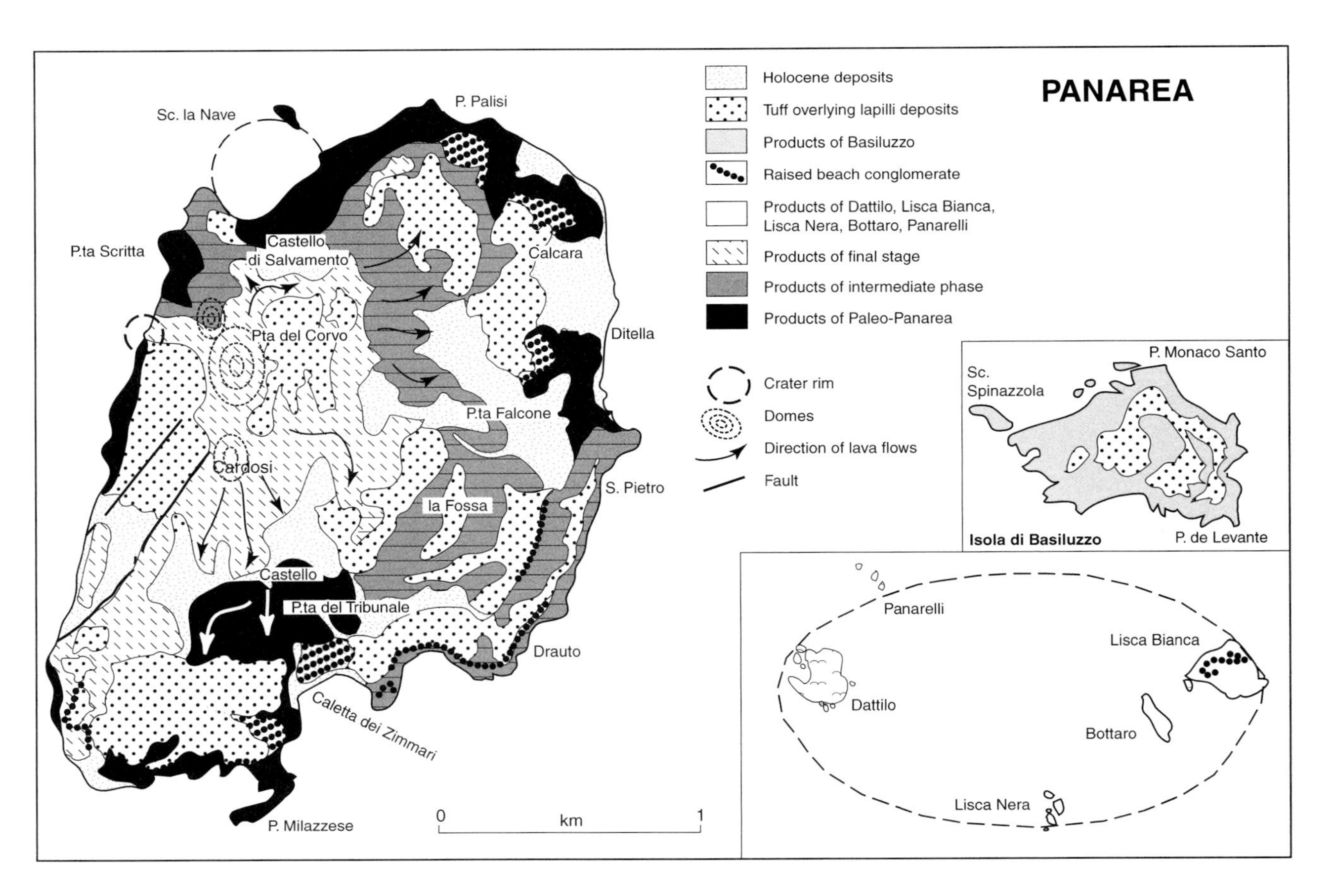

Fig. 7.10. Geological map of Panarea (based on Calanchi *et al.* 1996).

Recent radiometric dating has clarified the geological history of the island, indicating that volcanic activity at Panarea ranged from more than 200 ka BP to younger than 40 ka. Dating of dredged samples from the submarine edifice of Panarea have yielded dates of 780 ka BP. Activity has been mainly effusive in the form of lava domes and flows. Only minor quantities of pyroclastic material are preserved.

The geological history of Panarea may be divided into three main periods. The initial one is known as 'Palaeo-Panarea', and is characterized by the extrusion of lava flows and domes that range from andesites to dacites in the north and west of Panarea island. Andesitic lava flows associated with some minor pyroclastic activity occurred in the southern part of the island. The final period of activity of 'Palaeo-Panarea' formed the two prominent spinose dacitic domes of Punta del Tribunale and Castello. This initial period of activity probably occurred more than 130 ka ago.

The second period of activity includes the production of lava domes of andesite to dacite composition and subordinate lava flows, mainly from the central part of the island. Andesitic domes and lava flows associated with Punta Cardosi were formed during this period. The islets of Lisca Bianca, Bottaro, Lisca Nera, Dattilo and Panarelli formed during this second period and probably between 130 and 124 ka BP. This second phase of activity was terminated by explosive activity of dacite to andesite lapilli tuff of Soldata. The raised beach deposits divide the second phase with the third and last stage.

During the last phase of activity, thick dacitic lava domes were emplaced in the NW region of the island and numerous andesite lava flows were erupted that flowed largely to the south. The rhyolite lava dome of Basiluzzo has been dated at about 54 ka BP.

Towards the end of the last phase strombolian activity, thought to be located in the region of the islets, generated basaltic to basaltic andesite scoria lapilli. Brown tuff is the youngest pyroclastic deposit of Panarea; however, this unit is thought to be derived from another of the islands.

Filicudi

Filicudi, or Phenicusa as it was previously known to the Greeks, is probably the oldest island of the Eolian archipelago, with rocks that range in age from over 1 Ma to 40 ka BP.

The island is 'teardrop' shaped and is elongate in a NW–SE direction (Fig. 7.11), probably reflecting the regional tectonic trend. A distinct peninsula juts out to the SE, formed by the connection of the Capo Graziano lava dome with the main part of the island. Archaeological excavations on Capo Graziano indicate that there was a thriving Early Bronze age settlement on Filicudi.

As on many of the other islands, a number of raised beaches occur on Filicudi. These occur at three distinct levels that may relate to different sea levels at various times, the youngest of which is probably around 100 ka old.

The main volcanic centre of the island is that of Fossa Felci, which forms the highest point on the island (774 m). Other edifices, now eroded away by wave action, are

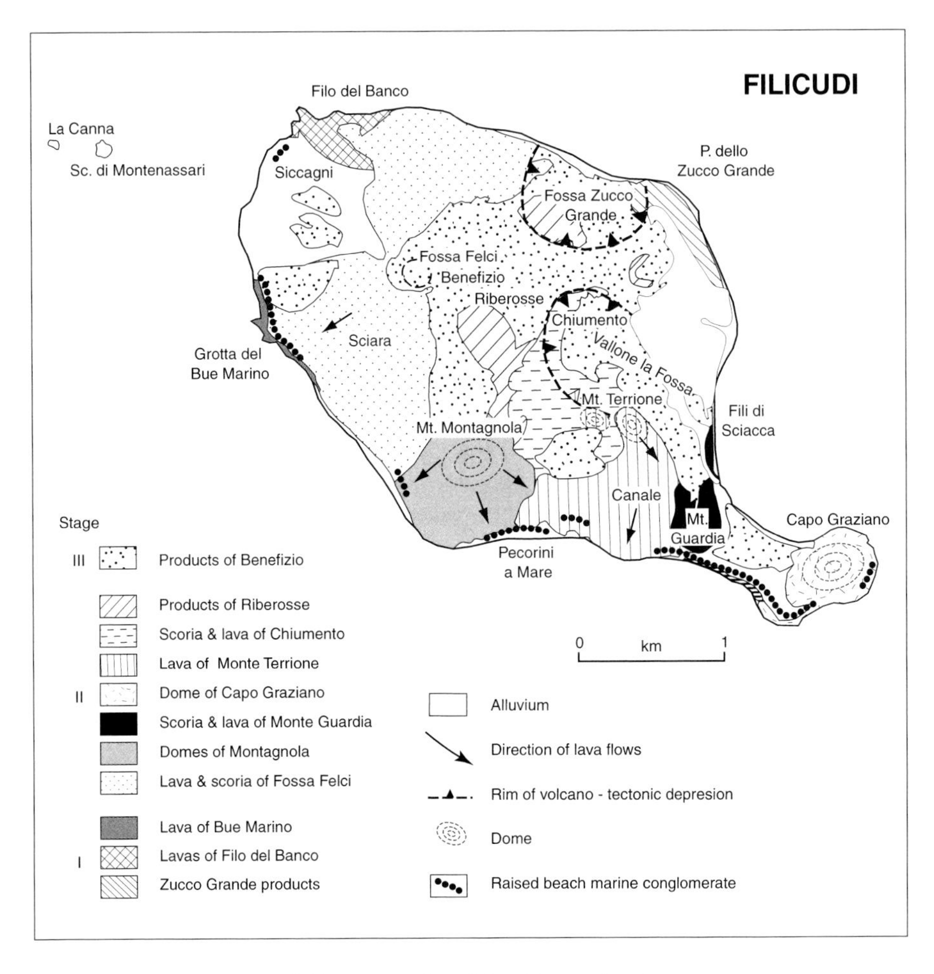

Fig. 7.11. Geological map of Filicudi (based on Calanchi *et al.* 1996).

represented by off-shore stacks such as La Canna, a volcanic neck off the NW tip of the island.

The activity on Filicudi has been divided into four stratigraphic periods. The first and oldest is represented by the Zucco Grande Formation, dated at 1.02 Ma, and consists of pyroclastic rocks overlain by lavas of basaltic andesite composition. The aspect of this sequence indicates that they were derived from an edifice centred just to the north of the present-day island; a part of the Zucco Grande crater is still preserved.

Two formations form the second phase, the Filo del Banco Formation, which crops out on the NW part of the island (dated at 390 ka BP), and the Bue Marino Formation, which occurs to the west. Both these units are composed mainly of basaltic lava flows.

The third period of activity is related to the building of the Fossa Felci edifice and a number of other distinct units. The oldest products are basaltic and basaltic andesite lavas and high-K andesite pyroclastic deposits that are sometimes referred to as the Sciara products. These crop out mainly on the SW part of the island. Monte Montagnola, a morphologically well-preserved, exogenous lava dome, sits on the southern flank of Fossa Felci and clearly overlies the Sciara products.

Monte Chiumento was built to the east of Fossa Felci, and this edifice is now truncated by a horseshoe-shaped depression that is open to the SE. This centre was constructed from the products of alternating effusive and explosive activity of basaltic andesite composition, the deposits of which are termed the Monte Palmieri formation. The Monte Guardia products are thick scoria fall deposits and some thin pyroclastic surge deposits interbedded with subordinate lava flows.

Domes of the Monte Terrione Formation sit astride the south and NW rim of the Monte Chiumento structure and overlie the Monte Guardia products. Lava flows related to at least two distinct phases of activity occurred from Monte Terrione. The uppermost of the Canale lava flows forms a prominent ridge that extends from Monte Terrione south to the coast, and spectacular columnar jointing occurs in one of these flows exposed at the coast.

The fourth period, which represents the final activity of Filicudi, is thought to have occurred from the Fossa Felci edifice, but may have been penecontemporaneous with the basaltic and basaltic andesites of La Canna to the NW of the island and occurred around 40 ka BP. The activity was explosive and is represented by andesite pumiceous pyroclastic deposits, termed the Benefizio Formation.

Alicudi

Alicudi (Fig. 7.12) is the westernmost of the Eolian Islands and also one of the smallest. It was formerly known as Ericusa after the heather that grows on the island. Alicudi has a population of around 100, almost all of whom live in houses that cling to the SW side of the island. There is only one road on the island, which runs the few hundred metres from the port to the main hotel. The rest of the island is a network of steep cobbled footpaths.

Alicudi was probably initially inhabited in the sixth and seventh centuries BC. In addition, fragments of Roman pottery have been found in the region of the port. During the Middle Ages, this remote island was particularly prone to piratical activity. Dwellings were built on the slopes above the coast to afford protection, and it is thought that the women took refuge at the Timpone delle Femmine, one of the highest and most impregnable parts of the island, during attacks.

Morphologically, Alicudi initially appears as a relatively simple, steep-sided cone. A closer look reveals a more complex structure with two possible collapse structures, both of which appear to be open to the south. Submarine investigations to the south of the island have revealed chaotic deposits that could be debris avalanche deposits associated with sector collapse. Between each of these collapses volcanic activity filled the

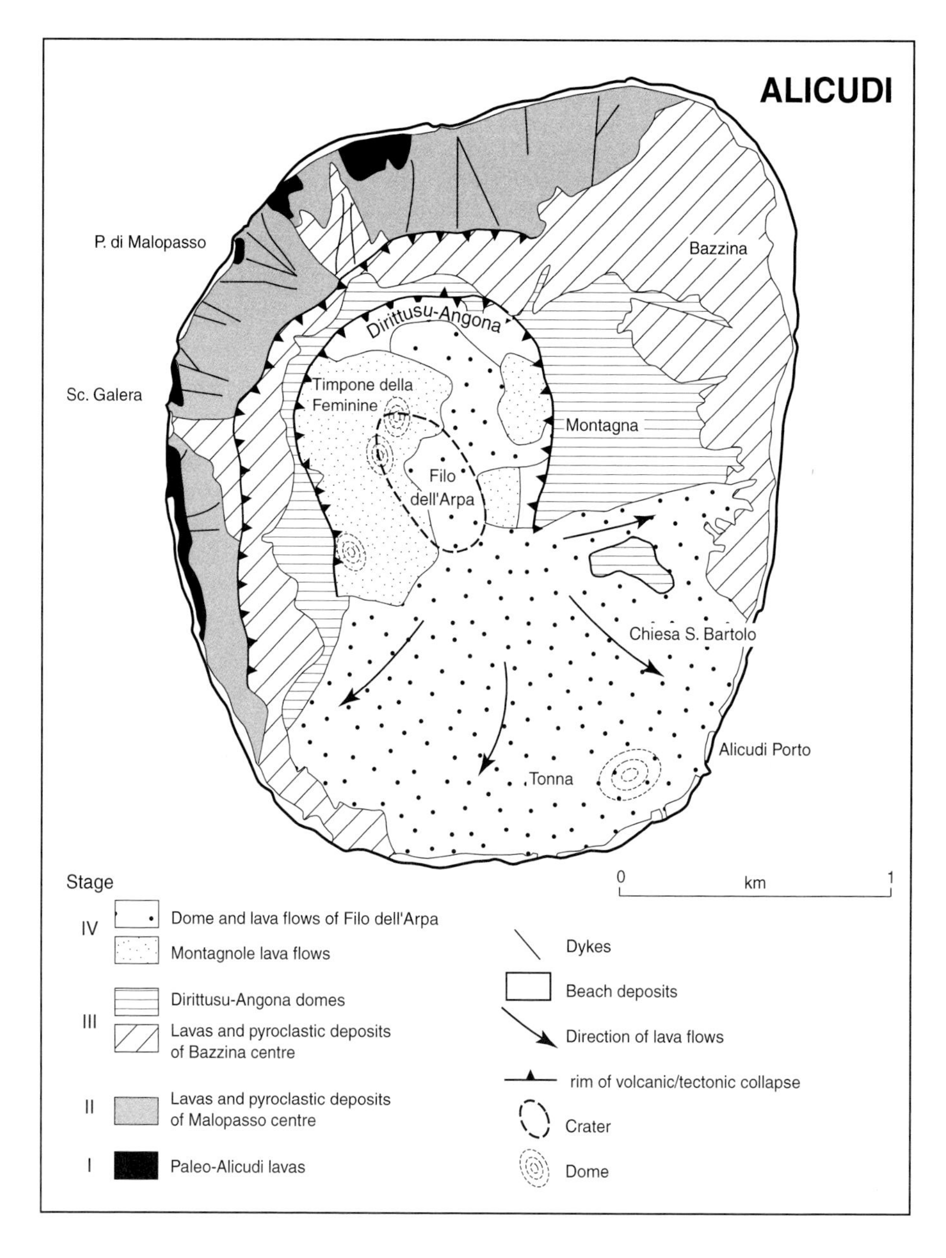

Fig. 7.12. Geological map of Alicudi (based on Manetti *et al.* 1995)

depressions and rebuilt the cone. Radiometric ages for rocks on Alicudi range from 90 to 28 ka BP.

The initial activity of Alicudi is represented by the Galera sequence, consisting of thin basaltic lavas alternating with scoria and ash deposits, some of which are deposits of pyroclastic flows. This material constructed the first part of a stratocone. Overlying this and forming the second part of the cone is the Malopasso sequence, which comprises alternations of lavas and pyroclastic deposits ranging from basaltic to basaltic andesite in composition. The Malopasso sequence is cut by collapse of the volcanic edifice. Both the Galera and Malopasso units have been cut by radial dykes ranging in composition from basalt to andesite. Xenoliths include biotite gneisses derived from the crystalline Calabrides of the underlying continental crust. Today the remnants of this cone are well exposed on the NW side of the island.

A hiatus in activity followed collapse of the edifice. Activity resumed at about 55 ka BP to form the Bazzina sequence within the collapse structure. The products are again alternating basaltic and basaltic andesite lavas and pyroclastic deposits. The increase in pyroclastic rocks towards the top of this sequence indicates that explosive activity became more prevalent toward the end of the Bazzina phase. The end of the Bazzina phase was marked by a second major collapse event. This forms the prominent collapse structure, the Dirittusu caldera, that is clearly visible from the east today. The andesite lava domes of Dirittusu–Angona were extruded along the rim of this collapse structure.

The final activity on the island is represented by the Montagnole lavas and Filo dell'Arpa exogenous lava domes. The Montagnole lavas are characterized by a series of at least four separate plagiophyric high-K andesitic lava flows, which flowed to the SE and south. These lavas have been dated at the relatively young age of 28 ka BP.

Hazard and risk

Hazard is not the same for each of these islands, nor is the risk. The islands that have erupted more evolved magmas present the greatest hazard, as they can produce the more violent explosive activity. Thus the greatest hazard is at Lipari, Panarea and possibly Salina. Alicudi and Filicudi, if they are still active, are most likely to produce lavas and accompanying limited ash fall. Lipari is particularly at risk because of its higher resident population, and like Vulcano, it has a large summer population of tourists. In the event of an eruption, any required evacuation would have to be by sea. In the summer months this would be a herculean task.

Places to visit

Lipari

A drive around the island provides a good introduction to the geology of Lipari. Travelling north from Lipari town the centres of Monte Rosa are visible to the east (right) before going through the tunnel under them. On exiting the tunnel one travels down through the village of Canneto. To the west (left) above the village is the historical obsidian flow of Forgia Vecchia, A detour west up to Lami affords excellent views of the sequence of Gabellotto Fiume Bianco pyroclastic deposits to the south across the gorge. Toward the north end of Canneto the road begins to ascend over the Pomiciazzo obsidian flow. This obsidian flow is exposed on the roadside in small outcrops underlying the Monte Pilato tephra. Better exposures can be viewed on the beach of Papesca. About

1 km further along the road, the famous pumice quarries of Porticello begin. Many of the disused quarries show excellent sections through the Pilato products. Permission must be sought to enter the working quarries at Porticello. Just past the turning down to Porticello and continuing along the main road one encounters the impressive Rocche Rosse obsidian flow. Small unofficial quarries into the obsidian expose flow banding and intricate folds and contortions of the obsidian.

As the road swings round the northeastern end of the island it then drops down to Acquacalda (hot water). On the hairpin bends the road cuts through the entire thickness of the obsidian flow. After Aquacalda the road rises up towards Quattropani. A right turn down a track before Quattropani leads to the kaolin quarries that have been exploited since Roman times. On the way a number of deep valleys are passed that cut through lavas of the early Mt. Chirica activity. About 1 km after Quattropani the small hamlet of Chirica Rasa a track due east leads to the Vallone Fiume Bianco, where used and disused quarries reveal superb exposures through the Gabellotto Fiume Bianco deposits.

South through Pianoconte the viewpoint of Quattrocchi (four eyes) is reached, where there are excellent views of the Mt. Guardia domes and Vulcano beyond, with Etna seen in the distance in clear weather. On the road back into Lipari town there are a number of small exposures of Mt. Guardia pyroclastic deposits, which include imbricated breccias. The Valle Muria, reached from a small road leading south 200 m east of Quattrocchi, has good exposures of Mt. Guardia products.

South from Lipari town towards the southern margin of the island in the Capistello region are quarries through thick sequences of Mt. Guardia pyroclastic deposits; other smaller exposures of the same deposits are accessible at the roadside. The road eventually leads to the volcano observatory, where there are excellent views across to Vulcano.

Salina

Perhaps one of the most spectacular places to visit on Salina is the remains of the 13 ka Pollara crater on the western side of the island. The road from Malfa winds round the northern flank of Monte dei Porri and many exposures of the white pumiceous pyroclastic deposits, derived from the second eruptive phase, of the Pollara crater are visible on the sides of this road. The base of the crater is now filled by reworked material, interpreted as being lacustrine, that has accumulated in the crater and is visible along the shoreline. A track leads down from the road to Punta di Perciato, a natural arch cut into the dacite lava that forms the first cycle of Pollara activity.

Walks to the summit of Fossa delle Felci and Monte dei Porri are strenuous but worth while for the amazing panoramas viewed from the summit.

Excellent field relations of the older products are visible from the sea off the eastern side of the island, and views of the marine conglomerate raised beaches, often continuous for many hundreds of metres, are visible. The conglomerate often rests, sometimes unconformably, on the older products (those of Rivi and Corvo volcanoes), whereas the Fossa delle Felci products underlie the raised beaches.

Panarea

Walks along the SE coast of the island from the port to Punta Milazzese are worth while and afford good views of the two dacitic 'spines' of Punta del Tribunale (lower) and Castello (higher). Near Drauto bay, rounded boulders of raised beach deposits are visible in the track, testifying to the previous sea level in the past. Where the path comes down to the sea at Caletta dei Zimmari and after crossing the beach there is a promontory that is part of an andesitic lava flow that has extended from Castello and has become brecciated where it has made contact with the water. Further round to bay is the lava flow that forms Punta Milazzese on which the Bronze Age settlement was located. Some dykes in this region display spectacular columnar jointing arranged perpendicular to the margins.

Filicudi

Mt. Guardia products are seen in the roadside south of the port. These exposures show thick proximal scoria deposits interbedded with thin fine-grained hydromagmatic fall and surge deposits. Lava flows also occur within the sequence. There is a raised beach deposit near the port.

Alicudi

On approaching the island of Alicudi clear lava flow morphologies are visible in the region of the port with good levees and channel structures. These lavas belong to the Montagnole phase dated at 28 ka BP. A visit to Alicudi involves a strenuous climb up through the houses on the SE flank. Continuing upwards the path passes exposures of scoria fall deposits and eventually leads into the Diruttusu caldera. Dirittusu–Angona lava domes fringe the flat caldera plain. Above this are the lava domes of Filo dell'Arpa, the highest point of the island.

Notes

Lipari

Pichler (1980*a*) produced the first geological map of Lipari. This was followed by his description of the geology (Pichler 1980*b*). Following this, Crisci *et al.* (1981) described in detail one eruption: the Monte Guardia sequence. More recent studies of this sequence by Collella & Hiscott (1997) generated discussion on several aspects of its origin. Crisci *et al.* (1983) also described the origin of 'brown tuffs' that occur throughout the Eolian Islands. The detailed stratigraphy of the last 10 ka on Lipari was described by Cortese *et al.* (1986) and the Gabellotto Fiume Bianco deposits, a sequence of dry pumiceous pyroclastic surges, were interpreted by Frazzetta *et al.* (1989), who also provided a summary of the geological history of the island (Frazzetta 1998).

Dellino & La Volpe (1995, 1996) used various techniques to study the eruptive and emplacement mechanisms of the historical Monte Pilato deposits.

Salina

A geological map of the island was published by Keller (1980*b*), including a memoir chapter. Barca & Ventura (1991) described the tectonic evolution of the island. Calanchi *et al.* (1993) described field and petrological characteristics of the Lower Pollara pyroclastic deposits, which were formed by eruptions between 24 and 13 ka ago.

Panarea

Initial geological mapping of the island was carried out by Romano (1973). Calanchi *et al.* (1996, 1999) described the tectonic and volcanological evolution of the island. Gabbianelli *et al.* (1990, 1993) discuss the geological evolution of the island and the submarine surroundings.

Alicudi

A geological map of the island by Villari & Nappi (1975) was followed by a memoir chapter (Villari 1980*a*). A more recent geological map and summary of the stratigraphy were provided by Manetti *et al.* (1995*a*,*b*). The petrology has been described by Peccerillo *et al.* (1988, 1993) and Peccerillo & Wu (1992).

Filicudi

A geological map of the island was produced by Villari (1980*b*) together with a memoir chapter (Villari 1980*c*). A more recent geological map and summary of the stratigraphy were provided by Manetti *et al.* (1995*c*). Radiometric dates have been provided by Santo *et al.* (1995). Francalanci & Santo (1993) and Santo (2000) have described the petrological evolution of the island.

Chapter 8. **Mount Etna**

Mount Etna is distinctly different from the other volcanoes in southern Italy, and indeed the whole of the Mediterranean region when all its major characteristics are taken into account. First, it is large, with a basal diameter of some 40 km, a height of over 3300 m and a volume of over 500 km^3. Second, it is in a state of almost continuous activity with the central conduit open to magma supply. Records suggest that it has behaved in this way throughout historical time and probably for much longer. Vesuvius had a similar situation between 1631 and 1944, and Stromboli has been in this state throughout history. Third, Etna has a different composition from most other major volcanoes in southern Italy. The main bulk of Etna consists of rocks of the Alkali Basalt Series, with tholeiitic basalts at the base of the pile.

Morphologically, Mount Etna is also distinctive (Plate 9), and does not fit any of the classical volcano textbook types. It is not a typical shield volcano, nor is it strictly a composite cone. The lower slopes are just a few degrees, but at about 1800 m there is a break in slope and the flanks steepen to about 20° or more. The construct has been truncated in the past by at least two calderas that later became filled with lava. The steeper part of the mountain probably results from being built up by frequent short flows from the summit, whereas the shallow outer slopes are the result of much less frequent long flows. At the top there is a summit cone rising from about 3100 m, together with two subsidiary cones. However, the morphology of the summit constantly changes, and any description of the summit will be out of date by the time this book is read.

Etna is one of the best sites in the world to study active volcanism and the evolution of a basaltic volcano. Throughout historical times Etna has had two forms of eruptive activity: the almost continuous activity at the summit, termed by Alfred Rittmann *persistent activity*; and *flank eruptions*, which occur every few years or so. Not only does it have a high frequency of effusive activity, but accessibility is relatively good, with a network of roads and tracks covering most of the mountain apart from the Valle del Bove, which is a remote, deep amphitheatre-shaped sector collapse scar cut into the eastern flank. There are also driveable private tracks, suitable only for field vehicles, leading to the summit cone on both the north and south sides of the mountain.

History

In Classical times, Sicily was considered to be the centre of European civilization. It was a lush island ripe for colonization by the peoples of the surrounding Mediterranean countries, and from elsewhere. Its history has always been diverse, with frequent changes of rule as new invaders took over. Despite continued domination from outside, the island people have retained their Sicilian character.

It is known from cave paintings that Sicily was already inhabited in Late Palaeolithic times, perhaps 20 ka ago. Neolithic traditions were introduced in the fourth millennium BC. Metal working came to Sicily around 3000 BC with copper followed by bronze about a thousand years later. Bronze Age settlements are known on Etna; for example, at the foot of the mountain on the remote NW side, where there are springs issuing from between lava and the underlying sediments.

By the time the Hellenic colonization of the island started early in the first millennium BC, previous invaders, probably from the Iberian peninsula, had established a race called the Sicels by the Greeks, hence the name Sicily. The new colonials from Greece rapidly built settlements on the fertile coast at the foot of Etna. The earliest of these were Naxos, near the Sicel settlement at Tauromenion, now the tourist town of Taormina, and Katane, or Catania as it later became known. Greek colonization grew rapidly, especially in eastern Sicily, and within 135 years there were settlements round much of the coast and inland to the east. In the Etna region, Greeks and Sicels appear to have initially lived peaceably side by side, the latter often living in hilltop strongholds. However, it appears that intermarriage and persecution forced the Sicels to move inland, and this greatly reduced their influence.

On the other hand, the influence of the Greeks was profound in architecture, arts and science. The philosopher Empedocles lived on Etna and studied its activity; the Greek temple at Taormina, with its wonderful view of Etna, has been described by the historians Finley, Mack Smith and Duggan as 'one of the most breathtaking sites anywhere in the world'.

Phoenicians from Carthage also established colonies in Sicily as well as developing strong trading links with the island. They made little attempt to take over land, but established safe ports from which to trade.

The conquest of Sicily by Rome began in 264 BC and by 210 BC the whole island had been conquered. Sicily was known as the 'Granary of Rome', and its produce was used to feed the Roman army. The prosperity of Sicily was drained for a time until it began to benefit from the might of the Empire. The Romans ruled for seven centuries and left fine buildings; for example, in Catania. The Sicilian–Greek vernacular was lost and replaced by Latin.

After raids by the Vandals and Ostrogoths, Sicily became incorporated into the Byzantine Empire for some 300 years until the Saracen invasion, which took place between AD 827 and AD 878, ending with the capture of Syracuse. The island began to prosper again and new crops were introduced, such as sugar cane, cotton and lemons; but within a century and a half Arab Sicily was in decline. Nevertheless, it took many bloody battles for the professional soldiers of the Norman army to gain Sicily, which they finally achieved in 1091. In the Etna region the Arabic influence is still seen in some of the place names such as Mongibello (an old name for Etna), Linguaglossa and Aci Castello, each hybrids of two names meaning the same thing, one Arabic and the other Latin. The visitor to Etna will notice that most souvenir shops have large puppets for sale. These are normally in the form of crusaders in their armour. Puppet shows were at one time a major form of entertainment, and the common tale told in these shows was about the 'heroic' deeds of the Normans against the so-called infidel.

The Normans' strength was in their efficient organizational skills. They recognized that they had captured a superior civilization and worked to provide the infrastructure to allow science, art, poetry and architecture to flourish. The distinct Norman keeps in the Etnean towns of Adrano and Paterno (the latter standing atop an old, eroded volcanic plug) are striking evidence of the power of the Normans (Fig. 8.1). Once again, Sicily was at a peak in civilization. But in less than a hundred years the country was again in decline, and in 1194 came under Swabian rule, owing to a royal marriage.

Sicily was not physically invaded again until Garibaldi, but it did change hands many times; first to the French for 14 years, then to the Spaniards for 300 years. A great deal of architecture dates from this Baroque period. Much of Catania was rebuilt in this time following the 1693 earthquake, which did a great deal of damage. By the Treaty of the Hague in 1720, Sicily passed briefly into Austrian hands, but was soon to become part of the Kingdom of the Two Sicilies under Bourbon rule from Naples (see Chapter 2).

It was near the end of Bourbon rule that Napoleon invaded Naples after Lord Nelson had evacuated the royal family to Palermo, the Sicilian capital. Nelson's claim to fame on

Fig. 8.1. The Norman keep at Adrano.

Etna is that he was created Duke of Bronte, Bronte being a small, remote town, then (and until recently) little changed since medieval times, on the lower NW flanks of the volcano. He was presented with the Castello Maniace, a Norman castle later changed to a fortified country mansion complete with chapel. There is no evidence that he ever went there, but, before his untimely death, he had planned to retire to the castle with his mistress Emma Hamilton.

For nine years from 1806 it was Britain's turn to run Sicily as a strategic base against Napoleon. A subsidy was paid to the Sicilians and the island was protected by more than 17 000 soldiers. A British-style parliament was set up only to be removed, not surprisingly, when the Bourbons came back to power.

The next event of note was a series of uprisings and revolts in Sicily resulting in Garibaldi and the red-shirted Thousand landing on the island, defeating the Bourbons first in Sicily and then on the mainland, and marching on to create a unified Italy in 1860. Sicily did not change a great deal from that time until the Allied invasion in 1943. One change was the influence of Mussolini as a fascist dictator. He preserved buildings of antiquity, originated the Corpo Forestale (Forestry Commission), and played a key, but controversial, part in the management of the response to the 1928 eruption that destroyed the town of Mascali.

The last invasion of Sicily was by the Allied troops in 1943. After a successful campaign in North Africa, British and Commonwealth troops were joined by US troops to drive the Germans out of Sicily. After an initial battle on the Plain of Catania, General Patton of the US Army led his army north to Palermo with no resistance from the Germans, who left, and virtually none from the Italians. He set up a new government there with, some argue, an established US Mafia base. His British counterpart, General Montgomery, had the task of taking eastern Sicily, and that involved Etna. Most of his troops went up the Simeto River (Fig. 8.2) to Randazzo and then round the northern flanks of Etna to Messina. A small group of Montgomery's troops were sent to clear the coastal route to Messina. Railway and road tunnels below Taormina were destroyed to prevent German soldiers from doubling back and attacking from the rear. Patton and Montgomery met in Messina to cross the Straits to the mainland and continue their offensive through Italy.

There have been immense changes in the Etna region since the Second World War, most of them in the last two decades. Peasant dress has largely been replaced by more fashionable clothes. Towns, such as Nicolosi, now have supermarkets and boutiques, as well as many smart restaurants. The once common calls of the charcoal burners in the woods are no longer heard, and donkeys carrying agricultural produce from the fields have been replaced by motorized vehicles. Large numbers of smart houses have been built on the volcano's flanks, many as second homes where families escape from the summer heat of the coastal towns to the fresher atmosphere at higher altitudes.

Geography

Not only is there a considerable difference in temperature between that at sea level and at the summit; also, the amount of precipitation increases with altitude. The summit

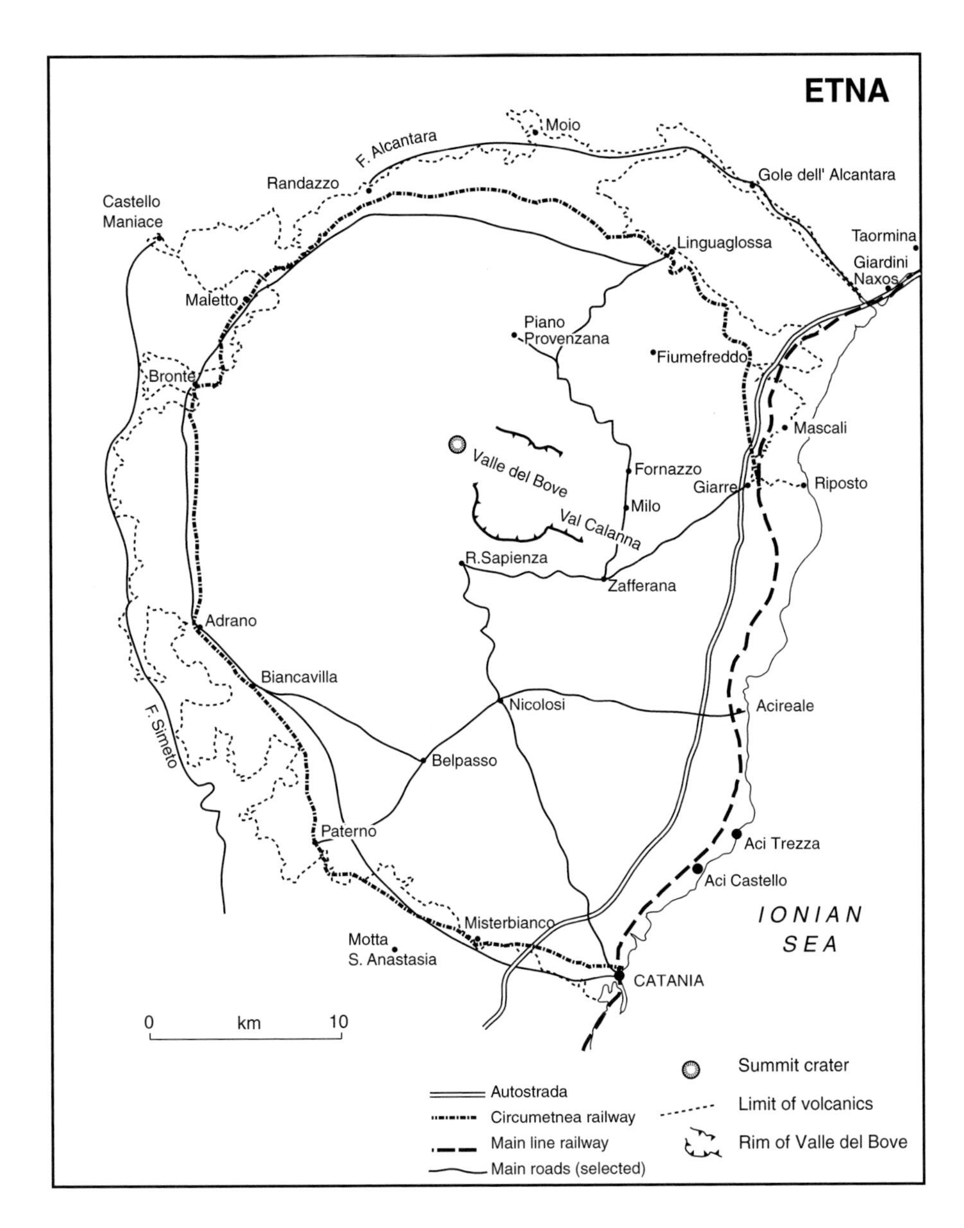

Fig. 8.2. Map of Mount Etna showing towns, roads and railways.

region is often in cloud, and even when the mountain is clear elsewhere, the Valle del Bove tends to fill with cloud as the day progresses.

Vegetation also changes with altitude. Below about 1000 m the ground is mainly under cultivation. Above this is the so-called wooded zone, although much of the forested area has been lost to agriculture, lava flows and exploitation for timber. However, considerable replanting has taken place in the last hundred years. Above about 2000 m, the vegetation becomes scrub grading up into the barren upper parts of the volcano.

Agriculture is important on the rich soils, and the main crops are cereals, grapes, citrus fruits, and pistachio and hazel nuts. Traditionally, farmers did not live on their land, but in small towns (known technically as *agrotowns*) for their safety. Some have to travel several kilometres to work on the land.

Etna provides a major water resource. The volcano attracts considerable rainfall and snow cover in the summit region during the winter months. The average mean annual rainfall is 850 mm with a marked seasonal distribution, there being little rain during the summer months. There is also geographical variation, with the east flank being wetter, with in excess of 1200 mm mean annual rainfall in the higher regions. There is no permanent surface water on Etna because the volcanic pile has high porosity and permeability. Most of the water passes down through the interbedded tephra and lavas to a main aquifer at the base of the volcano above the sedimentary basement. There is a 75% infiltration of rainwater on Etna, much higher than on other basaltic volcanoes such as Hawaii. As a consequence there are only a few springs on the upper slopes, where perched aquifers have formed, for instance behind a dyke in the Valle dei Zappini on the southern outer slopes of the Valle del Bove above Monte Monaco. The lack of surface water and high-level aquifers on Etna means that much of the supply of water in these rural areas came from *cisterne* fed by runoff from the roofs of stone shelters.

The basal aquifer feeds major springs round the periphery of the volcano. The springs at Fiumefreddo on the NE margin of Etna have the highest discharge in Sicily with an output of $2000\ l\ s^{-1}$. The flow of ground water is controlled by the palaeotopography buried by the lavas of the volcanic edifice, and it is likely that these springs are situated at the end of palaeovalleys. Springs from the volcano feed the Simeto and Alcantara rivers, which are unusual in Sicily in that they maintain flow throughout the summer drought. Use of the available water has contributed to the prosperous agriculture on the flanks of Etna, with development of complex irrigation systems. Ground water is exploited by means of galleries that have been dug into the volcanic pile; for instance, above Bronte, where there is a gallery 200 m long, and in the Valle del Bove, where there was one 400 m long. Access to the Valle del Bove gallery was covered by lava during the 1991–1993 eruption, destroying a supply of water for the town of Zafferana. Near the foot of the volcano wells have also been drilled to extract water from the aquifer.

There is no evidence of a hydrothermal system on Etna and this may reflect the lack of any substantive high-level magma reservoir. The temperature of ground water is less than 25° and typically only slightly higher than environmental temperatures. The high flux of CO_2 through the volcanic pile has led to some of the ground waters being carbonated, particularly on the lower SW flank. In addition to the CO_2-rich spring waters there are a number of mud volcanoes near Paterno. These mud volcanoes discharge methane as well as CO_2 and, indeed, there is a commercial field exploiting methane near Bronte.

Industry, based in Catania, has continued to expand during the past few decades. Of considerable importance to the economy is tourism. In the summer there are those looking for the sun and places of interest to visit, including the summit of Etna; and in the winter, there is skiing on the upper slopes of the mountain above 1700 m.

Communications

Catania is served by a busy international airport. The Sicilian autostrada (Fig. 8.2) links Messina, Catania and Palermo, the three principal cities of Sicily. The autostrada has many access points to the network of roads on Etna. An important road, the Via Etnea, goes north from Catania through the town of Nicolosi, to the highest point on the volcano accessible on a tarmac road at about 1900 m. From here a cable-car (Funivia) and four-wheel-drive vehicles take tourists to near the summit area of the volcano and in winter to the ski areas. However, in July 2001 the top station of the cable-car was put out of action by an eruption. The flanks of the volcano are well supplied with many roads of varying quality below about 1000 m, and on the north side private cars can reach a ski area, La Provenzana, at 1700 m (Fig. 8.2). Four-wheel-drive vehicles can also reach the summit on the northern side from here.

Etna is served by a main line railway from Naples, Rome and the north. This line runs along the coast to Catania, and then on to Siracusa and Palermo. There was a branch line just north of Etna running to Randazzo, a town at the NW foot of the volcano, but this has now been closed and replaced by a bus service from Taormina. Small towns round the perimeter of the volcano are served by a narrow-gauge railway known as the *Circumetnea*. This was opened in 1895 and consists of a 113 km long loop starting at Riposto and ending in Catania. It does not run along the coastal part of Etna's flank. All the lines have been cut by lavas during flank eruptions. The *Circumetnea* was cut in 1923 just west of Linguaglossa, and again in 1928 when both this and the main line were overrun by lava. On the latter occasion the lava ran down a gorge under the narrow gauge-line, destroying the bridge, but filling the gorge to the brim and obviating the need for a new bridge! In 1981 both the *Circumetnea* and the main line to Randazzo were cut just east of that town.

Development of scientific ideas

As a volcano that has been in an almost constant state of eruption throughout a long history of human occupation, it is interesting to investigate how the understanding of volcanic activity has changed through time.

For the majority of Greeks and Romans who settled near Etna, the eruptions and earthquakes could be explained by acts of the gods expressed as myths. The driving force of the volcano was the Greek god Hephaestus (later Vulcan to the Romans), the son of Zeus and Hera. Born a cripple, his mother threw him to Earth. Here he learnt his craft as a worker in metal. He worked under several Mediterranean volcanoes, eventually establishing his base under Etna and making weapons and items of beauty for the gods. In his work he was assisted by the one-eyed Cyclops, made famous by Homer's *Odyssey*, in which Odysseus and his men are captured by the Cyclops and trapped with him in a cave, almost certainly inspired by the many lava tubes on Etna. They escaped and as they sailed away, the Cyclops hurled stones at their ship, and these were preserved, tradition has it, as the rocks off the shore at Aci Trezza called the Isola Cyclopi.

Even better known is the beautiful wife of Hephaestus, Aphrodite (or Venus to the Romans): but that is another story!

One man stood out in his attempt to understand Etna. The Greek philosopher, Empedocles (*c.* 492–432 BC), is reputed to have argued that to understand the volcano it is necessary to observe the phenomena, hence the *empirical* method. He spent much time at the summit observing activity, and some claim he eventually lost his life by falling into the central crater; others wrote that he was exiled to Greece and died of natural causes. Later, the Roman philosopher, Lucretius, following Aristotle (384–322 BC) published a poem in which he states that Etna is hollow inside and contains wind that, raging furiously, melted the rocks and carried them to the surface.

Records of flank activity and earthquakes became more reliable from the fourteenth century AD onwards, but were seen and remembered as portents of evil. Little advance was made in understanding the volcano after this until the eighteenth century. The developing idea that an aim of science was to classify and bring order to the Universe led to improved observations of Etnean activity. This was particularly true of the massive 1669 eruption, the lavas of which invaded part of Catania. A key observer of this eruption was Giovanni Alfonso Borelli, a polymath who not only described the eruption, but recognized that the source of the lava was associated with the summit crater. In the 18th century a detailed description of the volcano and its activity was made by Canon Recupero; it was he who accompanied Sir William Hamilton during his studies of Etna.

Etna became a focus of attention during the 'craters of elevation' debate as described in Chapter 1. The French geologist, Elie de Beaumont, a meticulous field geologist, went to Etna and concluded that lavas making up the mountain were originally erupted on a flat surface and were then uplifted by pressure from below. His arguments were based on the uniform thickness over long distances of lavas exposed in the Valle del Bove cliffs, implying shallow slopes of emplacement.

Charles Lyell, as part of his effort to formulate the structure of the science of geology, visited Etna in 1824, 1857 and 1858. He had rejected the idea of 'craters of elevation' in 1830, but continued to examine Etna to test his views. In an amazingly perceptive monograph, he demonstrated that the arguments of de Beaumont did not follow and that all the observations supported a constructional mechanism. Today we might argue that injection of magma does uplift the edifice, but this is small compared with build-up by fresh lavas and tephra. The monograph by Lyell is a wonderful review of all the questions that still might be asked about the volcano, apart from those related to geochemistry, which was not a well-developed research field at the time.

Considerable advances in our knowledge of Etna were made in the nineteenth century by the Gemmellaro brothers, Giuseppe, Gaetano, Mario and Carlo. Between them they mapped the volcano, studied the Valle del Bove, maintained regular monitoring of activity and speculated on the volcanic phenomena. Later in the century, Orazio Silvestri continued the observations of activity, and following him the tradition was maintained into the twentieth century by Professors Ricco, Ponte, Imbo and Cucuzza-Silvestri.

By 1970 it was time to produce a new geological map of Etna to replace preceding ones such as that of Sartorius von Waltershausen produced in the nineteenth century and those of the Italian Geological Survey. Alfred Rittmann had the vision to recognize this, and set up a team of Italian and British geologists to carry out the fieldwork that was the basis of a map published in 1979. This map provided the framework for future work on the volcano.

Studies of Etna and its activity continue to contribute to our understanding of how volcanoes work. Italian and international teams and individuals have, for example, set up geophysical and geochemical monitoring programmes, continued with geological mapping and petrology, and studied both active and historical flow fields to further our understanding of how they are emplaced.

Geological setting

Etna lies close to the boundary between the colliding African and Eurasian plates. There is no consensus about exactly where this boundary lies, but there is a clear geological distinction between the plates. The Apennine–Maghrebian thrust-sheet belt forms the southern margin of the overriding European plate, whereas to the south the African plate is relatively undeformed, and is represented by the Iblean platform of flat-lying, predominantly carbonate sediments (Figs 1.2 and 1.3).

Sicily is characterized by complex geological relationships. It is something of an enigma that from the summit of Etna it is possible to see the Eolian Islands in the Tyrrhenian Sea to the north. The Eolian Islands are the products of subduction zone magmatism associated with consumption of oceanic lithosphere in a NW direction from the Ionian Sea. In contrast, the largely basaltic edifice of Etna has many of the petrological characteristics of a within-plate ocean island volcano. Trying to identify a sensible model that can reconcile two such contrasting tectonic environments in close spatial proximity has confounded tectonic interpretation of the region.

It has been argued recently that the basaltic magmatism of Etna is related to a roll-back motion of the subducted Ionian slab. The calk-alkaline magmatism of the Eolian Islands is associated with the subduction of this slab. About 700–500 ka BP the slab became decoupled from under Calabria and began to sink. The Calabrian lithosphere rebounded upwards, allowing mantle material to flow into the gap that was opened up. As the slab sank deeper there was sideways and upwards flow of mantle material from under the African plate. Decompression of this upwelling mantle material led, it is argued, to partial melting generating the basaltic magmas of Etna.

Etna lies at the intersection of three main fault systems: these are NNE–SSW (the Messina Fault), ENE–WSW and ESE–WSW. These fundamental fracture systems in the basement play an important role in the ascent of magma, and the distribution of vents on the flanks of Etna reflects this tectonic control. The volcano is situated in a zone of active uplift of about 1 mm a^{-1}. That this uplift has been active throughout much of the history of the volcano is demonstrated by the fine sequence of river terraces in the Simeto valley. These terraces provide a valuable stratigraphic record. Lavas spreading out over the flood plain were successively uplifted. Thus, the highest terraces preserve the oldest lavas in places nearly 1000 m above sea level.

Lavas

Lava textures

Lava surface textures have traditionally been classified into three main types: pahoehoe, aa and blocky. Basaltic lavas normally have pahoehoe or aa textures (Plates 10 and 11), aa being the classic form for historical flows on Etna. These two flow textures take their names from the Hawaiian language, a'ā and pāhoehoe; the Polynesian settlers gave onomatopoeic names to these two different lava forms. Rough lava is difficult to walk on, especially with bare feet, hence a'ā; the smooth pāhoehoe is kinder to the feet, thus a soft name. The distinction between these two forms is not always so clear cut, at least on Etna.

Aa shows a number of forms, usually related to distance from vent. As a crust starts to develop, spinose protuberances develop; but as the crust thickens, differential movement breaks it up to give a cover of small clinkers. Continued cooling further from the vent creates a thicker crust; this breaks to larger blocks, which may become rounded owing to attrition during flow. Near the snout of the flow, squeeze-outs of material from the interior of the flow may form spines.

Pahoehoe surfaces consist of smooth glassy sheets (although with age the glass breaks down), hackly sheets, ropes and bulbous toes. These surfaces are essentially smooth; but on many pahoehoe flows on Etna, the relatively smooth slabs have been fractured and tipped up to varying degrees, giving areas on the flow that are rather rough, although still much easier to walk on than fresh aa.

Although Etna has a reputation for aa flow fields, there are pahoehoe fields. In addition, a considerable amount of pahoehoe forms from ephemeral boccas on aa flows in the more proximal regions. These are usually associated with tumuli.

Flow fields and lava transport

As an eruption proceeds, typically more than one lava lobe is generated, forming a lava flow field consisting of several flows. Flow fields on Etna show a variety of planimetric forms. The majority are either long compared with their width and consist of relatively few flows, or broad compared with their length and the result of a complex history of flow development. In general, the first type forms during an eruption of short duration, usually less than 1 week. The second type is characteristic of eruptions that last several weeks, months or occasionally years. The factors that control the development of a flow field are complex.

It was studies of Etnean eruptions that led George Walker to conclude in the early 1970s that effusion rate was a critical factor in determining the maximum length that a flow field can achieve. The higher the effusion rate, the further the flow may travel. This is because the flow front stops when it reaches a critical effective viscosity controlled to a large extent by cooling. Thus the faster the flow travels the further it will reach from the vent before cooling reduces the effective viscosity sufficiently for the flow front to be halted. In reality, the question of flow field length is more complicated than this as there are other factors, but effusion rate appears to be the most critical.

Lava is normally transported from the vent to flow snout in either a channel or a tube. Channels (Fig. 8.3) are formed when the margins of the flow have cooled sufficiently to form levees on either side of the flowing lava. Close to the vent the levees can be progressively built up by overflows that may have either clinkery aa or pahoehoe surfaces, or both. Further downslope the outer levee surfaces are typically aa. Channels range in size from a metre or so across to tens of metres, and have depths of similar dimensions. Channels become apparent as depressions only when they drain, as a result of either a drop in supply rate or increased speed of lava further downslope. The level of the lava flowing in the channel may fluctuate depending on the balance between supply and passage of lava down the channel. Repeated changes in lava level may lead to a succession of lava veneers on the inner levee walls.

With time, cooling may cause a stationary crust over the channel, giving rise to a tube within which the lava continues to flow. The level of lava in the tube may fluctuate, and a hollow tube forms only if lava drains from it. Benches within the tube may form representing different levels of flow, and lava stalactites can form on the roof as flow level drops. Flows that are within a lava tube, rather than a channel, are insulated and can travel further before cooling occurs and thus be longer. Tubes are normally associated with pahoehoe flows, but are a common feature of aa flows on Etna. They are often marked at the surface by tumuli and ephemeral boccas.

Fig. 8.3. View from the air of flows from the 1983 eruption of Etna. Well-developed surface channels are seen, together with two skylights of a lava tube to right.

Flank eruptions

A flank eruption could occur almost anywhere on Etna (Plate 12). Indeed, in prehistoric times a few eruptions have taken place on the edge of the edifice, notably near the towns of Bronte, Moio and Linguaglossa. Nevertheless, during historical times most eruptions have occurred from well-defined zones on the mountain marked by clusters of vents (Fig. 8.4). The highest density of vents is on the NE Rift, which forms a spine down the flank of the volcano. This rift swings south through the summit and continues in a less striking form down the southern flank. Eruptions most commonly occur in association with these two rifts. A fracture belt running roughly ENE from the summit also gives rise to a high-density cluster of eruption sites. Two clusters that have had less frequent activity lie on the west and SE flanks. Eruptions from vents on the south side of the mountain threaten this highly populated area.

Eruptive vents during historical time have been of two types: cinder cones resulting from relatively gas-rich magma, and fissure vents lined by spatter ramparts and hornitos from gas-depleted magma. We consider gas-rich magmas to have been tapped from the main conduit by dykes at depths of several kilometres before exsolution of H_2O; whereas dykes propagated from shallower depths do so without the exsolved volatiles, which escape up the central conduit leaving a gas-poor magma that moves laterally along dykes to erupt on the flanks.

Flank eruptions can produce both aa and pahoehoe type flows, the latter normally forming from the longer duration eruptions. Effusion rates are typically at their highest in the early part of an eruption forming aa, but with continued activity effusion rates decrease, facilitating the formation of pahoehoe surface textures as well as aa.

Persistent activity

The summit of Etna is in a state of almost continuous activity, implying an open conduit to the summit area. Activity at the summit was termed persistent activity by Alfred Rittmann. It has several forms broadly divided into cinder cone activity and lava flows, and pit collapse and intra-pit activity. Documentation of persistent activity has generally not been as good over most of the recorded history of the volcano compared with that of flank eruptions. Because summit activity did not normally threaten the local inhabitants it was more of a spectacle, and only the extreme spectacles tended to receive systematic recording.

The present summit cone started to build up in the eighteenth century and a 500 m diameter Central Crater became well established. At the foot of the cone on the NE side is the NE Crater (Fig. 8.5), a cinder cone that began life in 1911 and continued to grow in height and produce a huge fan of lavas below it.

Effusive activity filled the Summit Crater, and a deep pit formed on the NE side known as the Voragine or 'Chasm'. This pit clearly represents a long-standing open conduit connected to the volcano's feeding system. More recently, another pit has opened, known as the Bocca Nuova (Fig. 8.6).

The Bocca Nuova has had a history of repeated filling by lava followed by collapse and has throughout its history continued to enlarge its perimeter. This pit provides a

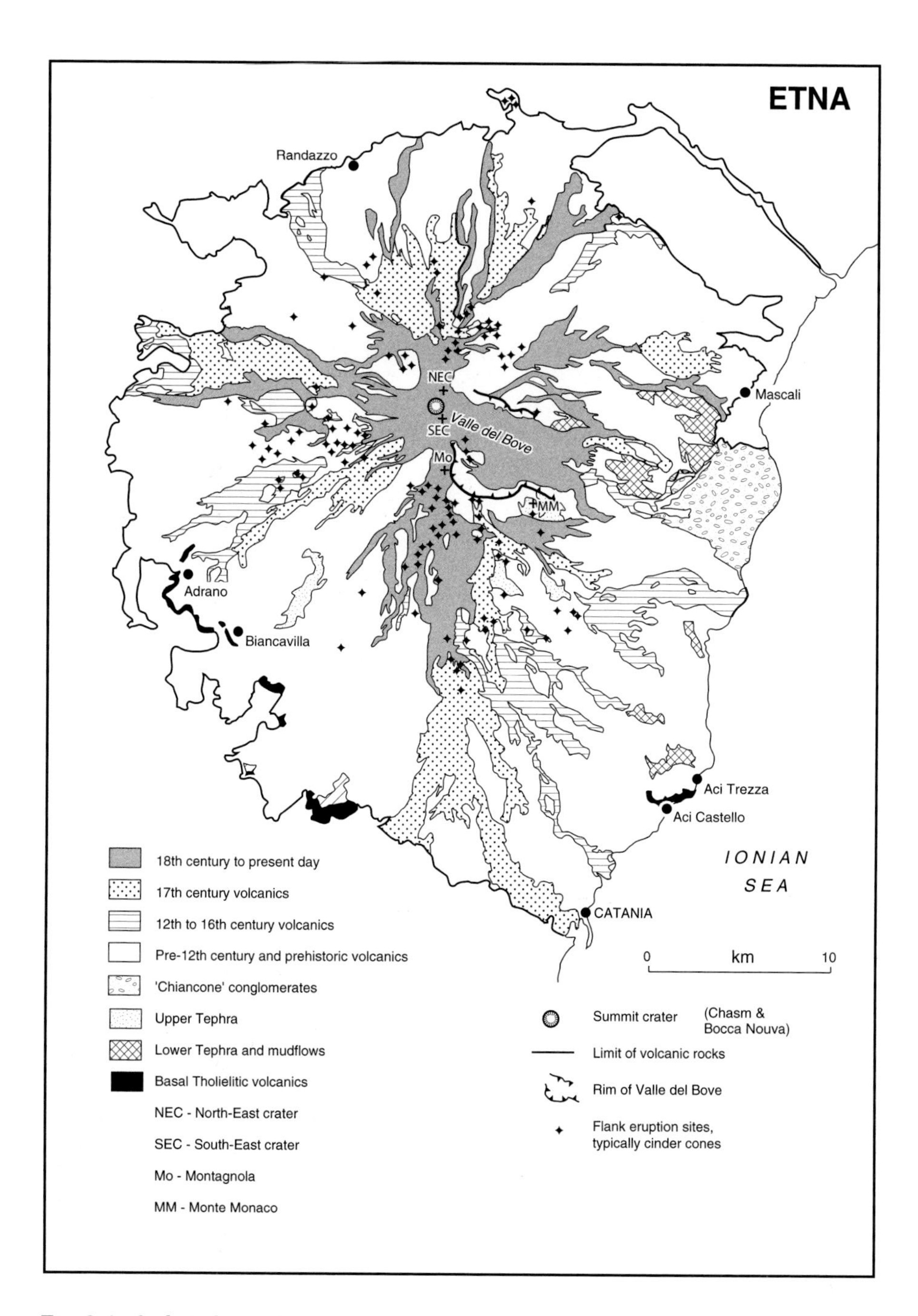

Fig. 8.4. Geological map of Mount Etna.

Fig. 8.5. NE Crater of Etna.

Fig. 8.6. Summit pits of Etna from the air. The Bocca Nuova is in the foreground, and the Chasm in the background. Picture taken in 1985.

remarkable record of the life of such a feature from birth. The first collapse occurred in 1968, when an 8 m diameter hole appeared without warning at the foot of the west flank of the summit cone. Until sometime during the winter of 1969–1970 it emitted gas at high pressure and a temperature of about 1000 °C. Occasionally it would explode, throwing out small fragments of wall rock.

Fortunately, it was winter when the first major collapse occurred, and no one was at the summit. Early in 1970 the Bocca Nuova enlarged to about 100 m across and 300 m deep, with vertical, unstable walls. It gave off a continuous white plume, which became tinged brown by ash particles when small collapses took place on the floor of the pit. Collapses round the rim increased its maximum diameter some 300 m when the wall between it and the Chasm collapsed in 2000.

When the walls were not collapsing, high-pressure gas emissions were common from small vents, or strombolian activity occurred from one or more vents on the floor of the pit. Lava effusion could rapidly decrease the depth by several hundred metres, sometimes filling it completely. Only when the depth was shallow could bombs fall outside the pit. During the summer of 1999, however, metre-sized bombs reached several hundred metres from the lip, hitting a dirt track.

A new explosive vent started during the 1971 flank eruption at the site that was to become the SE Crater (Fig. 8.7). The main cone-building phase of the SE Crater began in 1978. It has built up from a number of eruptions some of which, after initial explosive and/or effusive activity from the cone, migrated down fissures into the Valle del Bove.

The normal summit explosive activity is strombolian (Plate 13), and, until recently, fire fountaining has been a rare phenomenon, at least during the twentieth century. In 1998–2000 fire fountaining events lasting up to about 20 minutes became common from

Fig. 8.7. SE Crater of Mount Etna seen from the air in 2001. The summit craters are to the right. (Photograph courtesy of Maria Carmen Solana.)

the SE Crater (Plate 14). Fountaining is normally up to some 1000 m, with a much higher convective column delivering a centimetre or so of tephra on villages downwind. These vigorous explosive events can be unexpected, but during 2000 were heralded by effusive activity from the sides and foot of the cone. Then a pulse of gas-rich magma rose into the upper conduit, giving a dramatic fire fountain; some bombs were white hot, indicating surface temperatures of 1150 °C or more.

Activity at the summit tends to diminish during and after a flank eruption, which diverts magma from the central conduit in the upper part of the volcano. Depending on the magnitude of the flank eruption, incandescent magma is not normally seen again at the summit until months or years later, although gas emission and collapsing continues. After the 1991–1993 eruption fresh magma appeared in the summit craters in 1995 and eventually all four of the centres at the summit contained fresh magma. This was unprecedented in the last 50 years.

Volcanic history

How the volcano started: the Basal Volcanics (<500 ka to 1500 ka BP)

Etna was born around 300–400 ka ago in an area that was then a gulf on the eastern shores of present-day Sicily. Within the gulf, marine clays were being deposited; these are now named the *Argille Marnose Azzurre*. The palaeo-Simeto river drained into this gulf, which had a coastline situated between the present towns of Paterno and Motta Santa Anastasia. The first activity involved the eruption of tholeiitic basalts, part of the Basal Volcanics (Fig. 8.8). To the east, they erupted under shallow-water conditions and also formed near-surface intrusions within the unconsolidated marine muds, whereas to the west they were subaerial and formed extensive pahoehoe lavas in the Simeto valley.

The submarine deposits are at present exposed along the coast between Aci Castello and Aci Trezza and inland towards Ficarazzi. At Aci Castello there is a classic exposure of pillow lavas below the Norman castle (Fig. 8.9). Associated with the pillows are crudely stratified hyaloclastite breccias. The stratification together with the boundary between the hyaloclastites and the pillows is subvertical. The form of the pillows tends to indicate that the rocks of this outcrop have been tilted from their original subhorizontal attitude at emplacement. Thus the hyaloclastite stratification and the boundary between that and the pillows may have been originally horizontal. Andrea Borgia has suggested that this was caused by horizontal deformation of the basal sediments by gravitational sliding of the whole Etna edifice. However, the effect appears to be only local.

At Aci Trezza, 1.5 km to the north, there is no such deformation, but there are examples here of tholeiites that have intruded into the clays of the Pleistocene *Argille Marnose Azzurre*. The clays above the basalts are thermally metamorphosed, indicating that the magma burrowed into the marine muds. In places we can see where the magma broke through the sea floor to give deposits similar to those at Aci Castello, but with horizontal stratification.

Along the SW periphery of the volcano, tholeiitic lavas belonging to the Basal Volcanics are also exposed between the towns of Paterno and Adrano (Fig. 8.10). These basalts,

(a)

age	units	CC	centres	composition	R.S.T.S	volcaniclastics
0						
	Recent Mongibello	C	present centre Piano	mainly hawaiites		Upper Tephra Chiancone Milo Lahars Biancavilla igs
10		C	Belvedere/ Leone			
20			Vavalaci/Ellittico other small basic centres	hawaiites, mugearites mugearites, benmoreites, trachytes	T3	Lower tephra
Ka 30						
40	Ancient Mongibello					
		C?				
50	Trifoglietto					
60						

(b)

age	units	cc	centres	compositions	R.S.T.S
0	Mongibello				
	Trifoglietto	C	Trifoglietto II	basic mugearites	
100		C		mugearites	
	pre-Trifoglietto		Calanna, Tardaria	mainly hawaiites	T4
200			Motta S. Anastasia Paterno	tholeiitic basalts alkali basalt	← T6
Ka			Simeto Basalts	tholeiitic basalts	← T7
300	Basal Volcanics				
400					
500			AciCastello/ Aci Trezza	tholeiitic basalts	

Fig. 8.8. Stratigraphy of Etna. (**a**) More detailed version of (**b**) for the last 60 ka. CC, caldera collapse; R.S.T.S., River Simeto Terrace Sequence.

Fig. 8.9. Pillow lavas at Aci Castello. Note person for scale.

Fig. 8.10. View of the Simeto valley from Adrano showing the terrace capped by columnar jointed tholeiitic lavas to the right of the picture.

which crop out on the highest terrace of the Simeto River, were erupted under subaerial conditions to form sheets of lava with pahoehoe surfaces. This terrace, capped by the tholeiitic lava, dominates the Simeto River valley in this region and forms the flat-lying ground on which the towns of Adrano, Biancavilla and Santa Maria di Licodia are built (Fig. 8.10). These lavas have been dated at about 300 ka BP.

The town of Paterno lies alongside an old eroded cone surmounted by a Norman castle and monastery. The lava in this cone is a distinctive alkali basalt, which has been dated by the K/Ar method at about 170 ka BP. David Chester and Angus Duncan, in their work on the river terraces of the Simeto, found clasts of the distinctive alkali basalt of the Paterno cone in the gravels of Terrace 6 (second highest) and, therefore, the cone was erupted between the formation of the upper two terraces.

At Motta Santa Anastasia, a town to the east of Paterno, there is a plug of tholeiitic basalt intruded into the Terrace 6. This is the youngest identified activity of the Basal Volcanics.

The ancient alkalic centres (150–100 ka BP)

The older products of the main massif of Etna have been largely obscured by younger materials. Old volcanic rocks of alkalic affinity are exposed in the Valle di Calanna and as inliers near Piedimonte. Tephra, lahar deposits and hawaiite lava flows exposed in the fault scarps at S. Catarina and Santa Tecla near Acireale also belong to this early phase of alkalic activity. Monte Calanna is the eroded remnant of an ancient volcanic centre composed of mildly alkaline products typical of the activity of Mount Etna up to the present day. Old volcanic rocks have been identified on the northern wall of the Valle del Bove and are also relicts of ancient alkalic centres.

In the Simeto valley river terrace sequence the first evidence of volcanic rocks after the Basal Volcanics is a hawaiite lava that caps the gravels of Terrace 4, and clasts of hawaiite occur within the gravel itself. This terrace has not been dated but is older than 30 ka and may be contemporaneous with activity from one of the ancient alkalic centres.

The Trifoglietto Phase (100–40 ka BP)

Charles Lyell in the 19th century described how some of the sequences exposed in the southern and western walls of the Valle del Bove did not dip away from the current summit area but appear to be part of a construct whose centre lay somewhere in the centre of the Valle del Bove itself. This centre is called the Trifoglietto volcano and was mapped by J. Klerkx. In the late 1970s Bill McGuire mapped the southern wall of the Valle del Bove and in his reconstruction estimated that the Trifoglietto cone reached a height of between 2500 and 2600 m. The early activity of Trifoglietto was largely phreatomagmatic and explosive, building up a thick sequence of scoria with thin interbedded lava flows.

This was followed by more effusive activity that built up a pile of lavas, which Bill McGuire subdivided into three groups: the lowest group with a thickness of 140 m, composed of mugearite lavas, the middle at 400 m, and made up mainly of basic mugearites, and the upper 125 m with distinctive feldspar-phyric basic mugearites. Much of the Trifoglietto volcano has been lost in the excavation of the Valle del Bove but the unconformable relationship with younger centres is exposed in the southern and western walls of the Valle del Bove.

The Mongibello Phase (40 ka to present)

Following Trifoglietto was the development of a new centre, the Ellittico volcano. The profile of the Ellittico edifice is still clearly visible on the upper NNW flanks of Etna. In the southern wall of the Valle del Bove the main construct overlapping the Trifoglietto volcano is the Vavalaci centre, which is built up on its SW flank. Smaller centres are also present such as Cuvighghiuni, located beneath Montagnola (and probably part of it), made up mainly of pyroclastic material, and the Giannicola unit located on the western wall below La Cisternazza. The Ellittico Centre to the north has a similar composition and may be of the same age. The Ellittico edifice was eventually truncated by a caldera collapse at around 15 ka BP; this caldera-forming event is taken as the boundary between the Ancient and Recent Mongibello units.

A pumice layer at the top of the Ellittico sequence, the Portella Giumenta unit, is correlated with the trachytic Biancavilla ignimbrite, dated at 15 ka, which was emplaced on the lower SW flanks of the volcano. This would place the Biancavilla ignimbrite as a possible product of the collapse of the Ellittico caldera.

Pyroclastic deposits that are exposed on the eastern flank of Etna have been correlated with this period of activity. On the NE flank, the Lower Tephra comprise massive yellow–brown ash beds, which are considered to be of phreatomagmatic origin intercalated with lapilli beds. The lapilli horizons are crystal rich and contain kaersutite typical of the Trifoglietto phase of activity. However, a radiocarbon date gives an age of around 26 ka, which would place these deposits in the Ancient Mongibello unit, possibly associated with the Ellittico centre.

The Recent Mongibello unit includes all products from the formation of the Ellittico caldera to the present day. Initial activity involved infilling of the Ellittico caldera with flat-lying lavas exposed in the Val del Leone. It may be that the flat-lying lavas of Belvedere exposed on the upper western wall of the Valle del Bove belong to the same phase of activity.

A major event during the Recent Mongibello was the formation of the Valle del Bove, the horseshoe-shaped scar incised into the eastern flank of Etna (Fig. 8.11). It is our view that this formed as a result of gravitational sector collapse of the unsupported eastern flank of the volcanic construct. Below the mouth of the Valle del Bove is a sequence of debris flow deposits which we previously termed the Milo Lahars and attributed to the Trifoglietto volcano. Climatic conditions around 8 ka BP are well constrained by palaeoenvironmental data, and show conditions both warmer and wetter than those of today; just the conditions to favour processes of gravity-induced mass wasting. Sonia Calvari and coworkers have subsequently identified debris avalanche materials and consider them to be products of the formation of the Valle del Bove. We would accept this as a sensible interpretation. The Chiancone, a fan of alluvial material that forms a feature along the coast south of Giarre, we interpret as being derived from reworking of the debris avalanche material from the Valle del Bove. The Chiancone alluvial fan has a date of around 5 ka BP.

Fig. 8.11. The Valle del Bove, Etna.

Since the formation of the Valle del Bove, Etna has been dominated by basaltic activity with the eruption of mainly hawaiite lavas. Periodically, however, there have been phases of more vigorous explosive activity generating considerable falls of lapilli and ash on the flanks of the volcano. Some have argued that a large eruption occurred in about 1500 BC and that as a result the local tribes were forced to leave and move to the west of Sicily.

There are many undated lavas with relatively well-preserved surface textures that could have formed just before and during the early times of human occupation. These indicate that the present style of activity on the volcano goes back to well beyond historical times, and probably back to when the Valle del Bove formed.

Historical activity

The Greeks apparently recorded only eruptions that directly affected them; in other words, eruptions that affected the coastal areas. The first was probably in 693 BC when lavas entered the new town of Catania, and was famous for a noble act by two brothers, who, according to legend, carried their parents away from the invading lavas. The next lava to reach the coast was in 425–424 BC, when a flow entered the sea at Ognina north of Catania. In 396 BC a lava prevented the Carthaginian general Himileo from marching his troops along the coast just north of Acireale.

In 122 BC, during Roman rule, there was a violent eruption that deposited more than 15 cm of tephra on Catania and caused considerable structural damage, so much so that no taxes were levied on the inhabitants by Rome for 10 years as a form of compensation. The last of the major Roman eruptions was in AD 252–253, when lavas from near Nicolosi again threatened Catania but stopped just short of the town.

Eruptions continued to be reported, but it was not until the Normans that there was a start to more regular, but still vague, documentation. In 1169 there was a major catastrophe when a violent earthquake caused part of the summit to collapse, and it is said that 15 000 perished in Catania, and a tsunami engulfed Messina.

Lava reached the coast again in 1381, just north of Catania, and from then on we appear to have a continuous record of flank activity and the more obvious summit events. From these records it is possible to recognize several phases of activity, which represent different plumbing conditions. During the seventeenth century there was a marked increase, by a factor of about six, in the overall production rate of the volcano. In addition, eruptions tended to be of exceptionally large magnitude, some involving more than 1 km^3 of lava. The lavas, although of similar composition to other historical ones on Etna, have a distinctive petrography in that they contain large phenocrysts of plagioclase giving a texture known locally as *cicirara*, the local name for chick peas. This texture implies some high-level storage of magma to allow the crystals to grow, but not long enough for the magma to evolve.

The longest eruption during this period was that of 1614–1624 on the north flank erupted from the NE Rift. This eruption formed an extensive flow field, most of which has a pahoehoe texture. The flows are tube fed. The flow field is distinctive in having mega-tumuli some 2 km across and 200 m high formed by pressure build-up in tubes arching the roofs; and lava terraces interpreted as large perched lava ponds. A similar, but smaller, 17th-century flow field was formed on the west flank in 1651–1653.

A large channel-fed aa flow field was formed on the north flank from a cinder cone, Monte Nero, on the NE Rift in 1646–1647; but the largest aa flow field was formed in the famous eruption of 1669 on the South Rift. The eruption lasted 4 months, and produced some 1 km^3 of lava and probably as much again of tephra.

The first signs of an eruption were a series of earthquakes that began on 25 February. These became progressively stronger, putting great fear into the people, especially in the village of Nicolosi, which was worst hit. By 10 March buildings were falling and many inhabitants of Nicolosi left the village and camped in the fields. Next day the mountain was split by a 2 m wide fissure, which started near the summit and extended 12 km southward to just above Nicolosi. Vents opened at the bottom end of the fissure, first explosively and then later in the day lava poured from the end of the fissure. As lava advanced down the mountain villages were successively overwhelmed. The flow front reached the walls of Catania on 14 April. As the town started to be invaded the inhabitants removed valuables, and attempted to protect the town by building barriers, some of which may have been successful, but many were not. An attempt to divert the flow was made by breaching the levee to the channel feeding the flow front entering Catania. This might have been successful if others threatened by the newly diverted flow had allowed the work to continue.

Lava ceased to flow into Catania on 8 May and the eruption stopped on 11 July. By that time the cinder cone, Monti Rossi, over the vent, had grown to a height of 250 m, ash blanketed like snow a wide area around, a dozen or so villages had been destroyed and nearly 30 000 people were homeless. The only people who died did so at the hands of plunderers or were executed by the authorities as robbers.

After 1669, Etna went into a period of relative quiet for 86 years, although an earthquake in 1693 killed between 60 000 and 100 000 people. Summit activity continued during this time with a few small flows, and there were two small eruptions in the Valle del Bove. Then in 1755 regular flank eruptions began again with normal basalt typical of most historical lavas. This style of eruptive activity has continued to the present time, although there has been some evidence that since about 1980 the volcano's output has increased.

Examples of recent flank eruptions

1971

The eruption of 1971 followed a long gap in flank activity since the previous one of 1951, although continuous effusion of lava from the NE Crater had been taking place since 1966. It started high on the volcano at the foot of the summit cone and as the eruption developed new vents opened progressively downslope associated with en echelon fissures.

The first activity began on 5 April and by 8 May three cinder cones had built up by strombolian activity close to the Volcano Observatory, which was eventually buried by lavas erupted from the foot of one of the cones. The upper part of the Funivia was also destroyed; the lower part was reopened after the eruption, later to be destroyed in two more eruptions.

The lavas produced had aa textures and spread down the southern side of the volcano, eventually reaching just over 3 km from the vent area. As the flow field developed, the main channelled source from the cone known as the Observatory Vent roofed over to form a tube, which further downslope gave rise to a distributary system of tubes feeding ephemeral boccas. Thus, in the later part of this phase of the eruption, much of the lava transport was underground in tubes, over which, in places, tumuli developed.

Next a succession of fissures opened northeastwards across the head wall of the Valle del Bove, emitting small lavas. On 11 May the fissure system crossed to the north wall of the Valle del Bove, and vents opened on the outer slopes of the Valle, producing lava that flowed down the eastern flank towards Fornazzo. Fortunately, a deep valley, Cava Grande, at the north end of the village directed the lava from the town, saving all but a few houses.

In contrast to the first phase at the upper vents, the magma from the last two phases was gas depleted and there was no strombolian activity, only lava spattering to give low ramparts along the eruptive fissures.

The 1971 flank eruption provides an example of a shallow dyke complex transporting magma from the central conduit to the flank of the volcano. Explosive activity from the eruption occurred only from vents close to the central conduit, and when the dyke extended away from the summit, this transported degassed magma. Neverthless, degassing from the ascending magma continued from an explosion crater on the SE side of the summit cone. This was later to become the site of the SE Crater.

1974

The next eruption, 3 years later, was very different both in style and plumbing. In late January, a red glow was seen on the western flank. Strombolian activity built up a cinder cone in the pine forest at an altitude of 1600 m (Plate 12). The cone built rapidly and at first, small boccas around the foot of the cone formed several small flows, one of which was thick and sluggish, probably formed by highly degassed magma that was more viscous than the other flows. Then, 10 days after the eruption began, strombolian activity temporarily ceased, and a new bocca opened on the south side of the cone. This was to produce the longest flow of the eruption. The eruption appeared to stop after a short phase of vulcanian explosions on 17 February. However, 22 days later a new vent opened just to the west and another cinder cone built up. This was breached on the downslope side, emitting a thick viscous lava. The whole eruption finished on 29 March.

Although of similar hawaiitic composition to most historical lavas of Etna, the 1974 lavas are distinctive in not containing plagioclase phenocrysts. They are also slightly more mafic. This implies that the magma was a fresh batch rising directly from depth with no high-level connection with the central conduit. Plagioclase phenocrysts are indicative of low-pressure crystallization, and the lack of them here suggests an unusually rapid rise of the magma from depth.

1981

Just as the flank eruptions of 1971 and 1974 were different from one another, that of 1981 was different again. On 17 March a fissure opened on the northern side of the mountain, a relatively rare place for eruptions. Fire fountains developed with small lava effusions. Within hours a NNE-trending fissure system had propagated downslope with lava being erupted from several stretches of the system. At 1800 m a larger flow than those from the fissure higher up was discharged with effusion rates of about 180 $m^3 s^{-1}$. A sheet of lava moved down the volcano, covering 5 km in 4 hours. Rapid evacuation of many threatened houses was carried out. Some houses were destroyed or isolated, and two railway lines as well as the main roads out of Randazzo to the east were cut; all this within 10½ hours of the start of the eruption. The flow finally stopped in the floor of the Alcantara valley just west of Randazzo on the third day of the eruption.

Although the main flow did not threaten Randazzo, another fissure opened during the eruption directly above the town. Fortunately for the inhabitants, the flow stopped 2 km from the town. Mild activity from this vent continued until 23 February when the eruption stopped.

From this narrative we see that this was a short-lived, high effusion rate eruption with a relatively long flow that was emplaced at a rate much higher than is normal on Etna. It therefore posed a greater threat to communities in its path as there was little time for evacuation and no time for intervention.

The final length of the flow was not governed by effusion rate, but by the fact that the supply of magma ceased before it had travelled as far as the effusion rate predicted.

1983

The 1983 eruption began on 28 March and lasted for 131 days. A fissure opened between 2450 and 2250 m on the south flank. Lava was erupted for the duration of the eruption from the lowest part of the fissure system. In addition, an explosion crater opened beyond the top of the fissure system. Between the explosion crater and the effusive part of the fissure system fractures developed and faulting destroyed a tourist building known as the Piccolo Rifugio.

During the first few days of the eruption in the zone below the Piccolo Rifugio explosions threw out blebs of lava that built hornitos on top of the fissure. Below the hornitos lava emerged from the fissure and poured down the steep slope above the Sapienza tourist complex and base station of the Funivia. The main flow passed the main tourist centre on its western side, but destroyed two restaurants and a house. The flow front progressively cut sections of the road from Nicolosi. The flow not only lengthened but branched, producing a complex channelled aa flow field. A small breakout from the channel above the Sapienza produced a flow that surrounded the Rifugio and banked up against the Funivia base station. The flow field reached its maximum length 42 days into the eruption. From this time it appears that the effusion rate began to decline.

Meanwhile the channel below the vent was progressively roofing over to form a tube system that extended at least 6 km (Fig. 8.3). Once the maximum length was achieved, most of the activity was from ephemeral vents around the 1800 m level fed from the lava tube system. Myriads of small flows were erupted mainly from small centres marked by tumuli. A high percentage of these flows have pahoehoe textures including ropes, smooth sheets and toes. The result of this activity, which occupied some half of the duration of the eruption, was to produce a large fan of lava extending down to about 1700 m.

A fissure opened up again in 1985 close to that of 1983, following a paroxysmal episode at the SE Crater. Lavas again poured down the steep slope above the Sapienza region, but the eruption was short lived and no damage was done. Unfortunately, from a volcanological point of view, most of the vent areas for both the 1983 and 1985 eruptions have been bulldozed away to build a new ski-lift and ski runs.

1991–1993

The largest magnitude flank eruption on Etna since 1669 began on 14 December 1991. It was to produce some 235×10^6 m^3 of lava over a period of 473 days and presented a perceived threat to the town of Zafferana. Fortunately, all of the lava was contained within the Valle del Bove and Val Calanna.

The eruption was heralded by hundreds of small earthquakes. Early December saw an increase in magmatic activity at both the Bocca Nuova and SE Crater, and early on 14 December a system of fissures opened progressively downslope to the SE on the wall of the Valle del Bove. Lava erupted onto the floor of the Valle and had extended to 5 km from the vents into the Val Calanna by the end of the year. Explosive activity at the vents by this time had diminished, and it stopped altogether by mid-January 1992.

The flow front looked menacingly close to Zafferana, although there is debate as to whether the town was really in danger. Nevertheless, an earth dam was erected at the lower end of the Val Calanna to contain any further lava. The flow field continued to enlarge across the Valle del Bove and to fill the Val Calanna behind the dam. This barrier was finally overtopped by lava on 7 April. Three new barriers were built, but they too were overwhelmed.

Fear that the flow could still enter Zafferana led to the testing of other methods of diversion. By this time a tube system was developing. Two attacks were made on the main lava feeding artery. The tube was blocked by dropping slabs of concrete into a skylight in the tube, and it was dynamited to divert the flow near the vent. After June 1992 all new lava went into thickening the upper part of the flow field, probably as a result of a lower effusion rate. We shall never know if the attempts to prevent lava entering Zafferana were effective or not: for those who suffered the loss of property on the outskirts of town, they were not.

2001 (July–August)

Just showing us that it is in a constant state of change, Etna produced one of the most spectacular and unusual flank eruptions for at least a century (Plates 10, 15 and 16) as we were completing the manuscript for this book. Before the eruption started, there had been a series of explosive events from the SE Crater together with lava effusion. After a particularly violent episode on 13 July there was an intense seismic crisis, which lasted for 2 days. Following this crisis there was further strong eruptive activity at the SE Crater 17 July; a fracture then propagated southwards, emitting lava and strombolian explosions. By the evening of 17 July a new eruptive fissure had opened some 3 km south of the SE Crater at the northern foot of Monte Montagnola. Another seismic swarm on 18 July accompanied the opening of another eruptive fissure at about 2100 m, 600–700 m NE of the Funivia–Sapienza tourist area. A small cinder cone built up by strombolian activity and a lava sheet poured south down the mountain. Although heading in the direction of the town of Nicolosi, flow front advance became very slow at about 6 km from the vent when it encountered almost level ground.

On 20 July another effusive vent opened at the head of the Valle del Bove. At this stage lava effusion was occurring at vents over an altitude range of some 900 m. The most violent explosive activity was from the Montagnola vent area, where a substantial cinder cone was built up by strombolian explosions and fire fountaining. Some of the explosive activity, especially during 23–24 July, showed characteristics of phreatomagmatic explosions, with tall fingers of black ash shooting up hundreds of metres (Plate 15). Areas on the SE flanks of the volcano received steady falls of ash and lapilli. Catania also received falls of fine ash and the airport was closed several times during the eruption.

By 25 July lava from the Montagnola vents had reached the Funivia–Sapienza tourist area and energetic efforts were made to divert the lava; the flows passed just to the east of the complex, leaving it almost intact, and continued downslope to become a part of the flow field from the 2100 m vents. From about 1 August when lavas destroyed the upper cable-car station, the eruptive activity decreased, and lava ceased to be erupted on 9–10 August.

This spectacular eruption had many unusual characteristics compared with activity over the last few decades. Lava was emitted from vents ranging from the summit region to the flanks simultaneously. Two batches of distinctly different magma were involved. From the vents associated with the SE Crater, a phenocryst-poor magma was involved, suggesting rapid rise from depth, whereas at the Montagnola and 2100 m vents a ‘normal’, more phenocryst-rich magma was erupted. Magma from the lower vent was rich in sedimentary xenoliths, suggesting residence below the base of the volcanic pile; such xenoliths are rare in historical Etnean lavas. Sustained fountaining occurred during part of the eruption, and magma–water interaction was evident, implying a high-level aquifer was being penetrated.

By the time this chapter is read, more activity will almost certainly have occurred.

Petrology

During historic times, which for Etna extend back more than 2000 years, the volcano has erupted lavas of a rather uniform mildly alkaline basaltic composition, strictly hawaiite. The current rapid rate of resurfacing means that much of the surface area of the volcano is covered by these basaltic lavas.

However, examination of the prehistoric volcanic products of Etna reveals a much more varied petrology (Fig. 8.12). The tholeiitic basalts of the Basal Volcanics, the oldest exposed products of Etna, are sub-alkaline and range in composition from olivine-normative to quartz-normative tholeiites. The tholeiitic nature of these early basalts was first documented by Renato Cristofolini, who was a pioneer of modern petrological studies on Etna. The petrography of the tholeiitic basalts is best exemplified by the relatively fresh subaerial lavas exposed on the upper terrace of the Simeto River valley. These basalts are rich in olivine phenocrysts, which are typically rounded and range in composition from Fo_{86} in the olivine-normative basalts exposed near Adrano, to Fo_{74} in the quartz-normative basalts that crop out to the SE near Paterno.

In addition to the abundant olivine, there are occasional phenocrysts of labradorite plagioclase. The groundmass of the tholeiites is relatively coarse grained with a distinctive subophitic texture that probably reflects the relatively slow cooling in the lava sheets, which reach thicknesses of up to 25 m. Pyroxene is abundant in the groundmass and both Ca-rich subcalcic augite and Ca-poor pigeonite occur. Jean-Claude Tanguy has recognized in these lavas a silicic glassy residuum, which ranges in composition from rhyodacite in the olivine-normative basalts to rhyolite in the quartz-normative basalts.

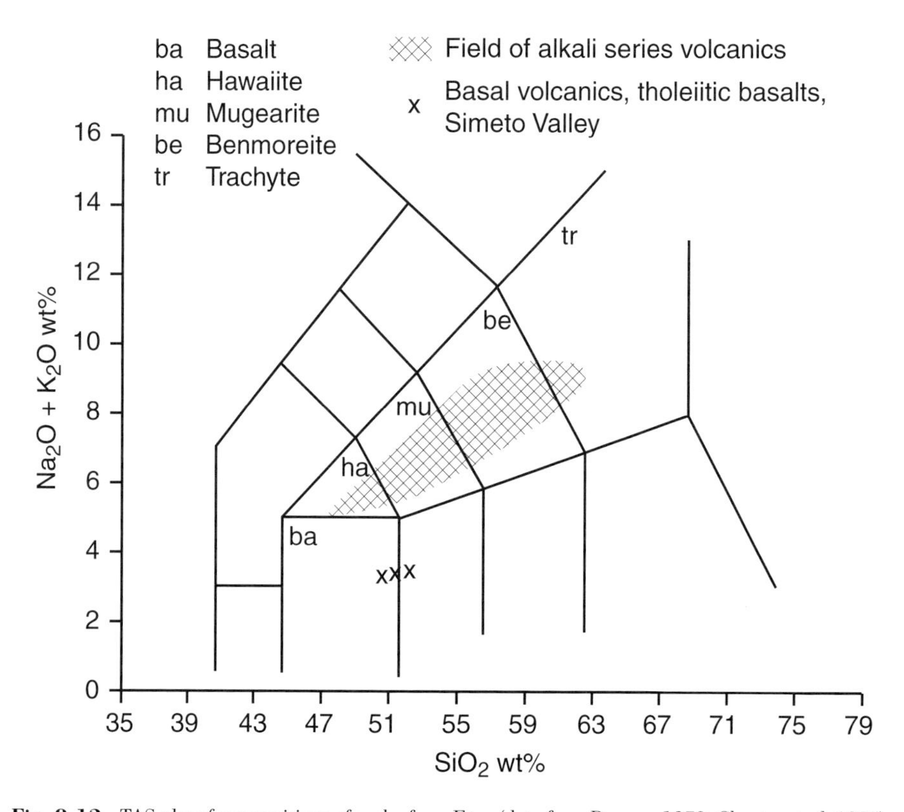

Fig. 8.12. TAS plot of compositions of rocks from Etna (data from Duncan 1978; Chester *et al.* 1985).

The submarine tholeiitic basalts exposed on the east side of the volcano along the coast between Aci Castello and Aci Trezza show evidence of having been modified by late-stage metasomatic activity. The pillow lavas are subalkaline basalts with similar petrography to the tholeiite basalts of the Simeto valley. The intrusive dolerites found near Aci Trezza show clear evidence of disequilibrium, with olivines being replaced by clinopyroxene. Near the margins of the intrusions, in close contact with the marine clays, there are bodies of analcite dolerite and also veins of this material within the body of the intrusion. Maurice Wells and Renato Cristofolini argued that these analcite dolerites resulted from the interaction between penetrating solutions, derived from sea water or wet clays, and the cooling tholeiite basalt magma.

The chemical variation of the tholeiitic basalts plotted on binary plots such as MgO v. SiO_2 do not show correlation with olivine fractionation, the predominant phenocryst phase, and it is thus difficult to account for this variation by low-pressure crystal fractionation. The trace element chemistry does not support deep-seated fractionation of high-pressure phases such as garnet. It is likely, therefore, that the eruption of these tholeiitic basalts was fed by discrete batches of magma rising from depth. The distinctive Sr isotope chemistry of the tholeiitic basalts compared with the Alkalic Series rocks does not support the idea that the tholeiitic magmas were parental to the Alkalic Series lavas. It is likely that these magmas were each derived from different source regions in the mantle. Indeed, the variation within the tholeiitic basalts indicates that they have been derived from a heterogeneous mantle.

The alkali basalt of the Paterno cone, erupted at an early stage in the history of Etna as part of the Basal Volcanics, is also petrographically distinctive, with attractive bottle-green olivine phenocrysts. These olivines are Mg rich (Fo_{86}) and contain high concentrations of Ni, suggestive of a relatively primitive near-primary magma. The $^{87}Sr/^{86}Sr$ value for the Paterno alkali olivine basalt indicates a different mantle source from that of the tholeiitic magmas, and reflects a rather depleted mantle isotope signature.

The main bulk of Etna is constructed of products belonging to a mildly alkaline, trachy-basaltic suite of volcanic rocks. The rock types of the Alkalic Series range from hawaiite, through basic mugearite, mugearite and benmoreite to trachyte.

The basaltic rocks are strongly porphyritic with typically more than 30% by volume phenocrysts. Plagioclase is the dominant phenocryst, with lesser amounts of augite and olivine. Some of the hawaiites, the cicirara, have up to 45% by volume phenocrysts dominated by large plagioclase crystals often 1 cm or more in length. The more evolved rocks contain fewer phenocrysts and some of the benmoreitic and trachytic lavas are virtually aphanitic.

The plagioclase phenocrysts range in composition from An_{80-55} in the hawaiites to An_{70-40} in the trachytic lavas. Anorthoclase and sodic sanidine have been detected by X-ray diffraction in the groundmass of the more evolved rocks. The phenocrysts typically show complex zoning patterns and sieve textures indicative of complex growth histories. In many rocks there is evidence of disequilibrium, which was probably brought about by magma mixing. The clinopyroxenes range from calcic augite to augite but show little evidence of iron enrichment with differentiation. These pyroxene phenocrysts typically show both well-developed oscillatory and sector zoning. The olivine phenocrysts range from Fo_{85-70} core to rim in the hawaiites to Fo_{70-60} in the trachytic lavas. The amphibole kaersutite occurs as a phenocryst in some products of Etna, but in particular in the basic mugearites and mugearites of the pyroclastic sequence and lower lava group of the Trifoglietto volcano. Apatite is found as a microphenocryst in mugearites and benmoreites, and is distinctive in showing brown pseudopleochroism caused by orientated inclusions of magnetite or hematite.

There is a complete range of compositions from hawaiite to trachyte with no evidence for the presence of a Daly Gap (i.e. a scarcity of products of intermediate composition). The chemical variation of the Alkalic Series is broadly similar to that of other mildly alkaline suites and lies between the potassic trend of Gough Island and the more sodic trend of the Skye main lava series.

It has been shown that the chemical variation can be largely explained by low-pressure crystal fractionation of the phenocryst phases with possibly a contribution to alkali depletion by volatile transfer. The trend is somewhat unusual in that it ranges from undersaturated Ne-normative in the hawaiites to oversaturated Hy- and Qz-normative in the more evolved trachytic members. This oversaturated trend could be due to the loss of alkalis through volatile transfer and/or fractionation of titanomagnetite. Only periodically in the history of Etna has sufficiently extensive fractional crystallization occurred to generate the more evolved magma compositions such as mugearite, benmoreite and trachyte. A summary of petrology in relation to the stratigraphic units of Etna is provided in Fig. 8.8.

Gases

Etna is a major site of mantle degassing. It discharges CO_2 from the summit craters at a mean rate of 35 000 tons per day, an order of magnitude greater than that of Kilauea in Hawaii. Indeed, Etna is the largest known non-anthropogenic source of CO_2 in the world. Not only is it pumped from the summit craters, but it leaks out of the flanks of the volcano, particularly along fractures and faults. H_2O is the dominant gas discharged by Etna, at a mean rate of 200 000 tons per day. Much of the water vapour is probably derived from meteoric water that seeps into the volcanic pile. SO_2 is another important product, with a mean output of between 1000 and 12 000 tons per day, but often increases before eruptions.

Seismicity

Seismic activity on Etna occurs mainly at shallow levels, with most hypocentres located at depths of less than 5 km. Earthquakes associated with volcanic phenomena rarely reach magnitude 4, and larger earthquakes are of tectonic origin. Summit or near-summit eruptions are not normally preceded by a seismic crisis. Flank eruptions, however, typically follow periods of increased seismic activity. Before the 1981 eruption there were many small seismic events with a seismic crisis during the day before volcanic activity commenced. In 1983 there were small seismic events for 3 months before the eruption with a 2 day seismic crisis before the onset. The 1991–1993 eruption was preceded by nearly 11 months of continuous seismicity, with a rapid rise in activity for the 24 hours before lava started to erupt. Seismicity declined as the eruption proceeded.

In the period 1865–1980, 892 seismic events of M >2.4 occurred on the eastern flank and 173 on the western flank. The eastern flank is seismically more active and this may relate to the lack of buttressing on this side and gravitational-induced movements to the coast. Deeper earthquakes are more common on the western flank and are associated with the NNW–SSE tectonic trend.

Plumbing

Etna is an ideal site for the study of the internal workings of a basaltic volcano because it is essentially in a state of continuous activity. Direct research into the internal plumbing of Etna effectively began in the 1970s. This followed the major eruption of 1971, which focused volcanological attention on Etna. The geophysical investigation of active basaltic volcanic systems at this time was strongly influenced by the classic work on Kilauea, Hawaii. The ground deformation of Kilauea could be largely explained in terms of the Mogi model with inflation of a shallow reservoir before eruption.

Early studies of ground deformation at Etna were, following the Hawaiian model, very much directed towards monitoring the likely inflation of the volcanic edifice in response to filling of a high-level magma reservoir before eruption. This research, however, showed that unlike the case of Kilauea there was no overall inflation of Etna before flank eruptions. Nevertheless, localized deformation occurred in the area of the vent up to 2 years before the start of an eruption. This was interpreted as resulting from the prior emplacement of magma in a lateral fissure as a dyke some months before the start of the eruption. It would appear that for Etna, therefore, there is no significant high-level storage of magma, and flank eruptions are predominantly fed by magma rising from depth. This is supported by the fact that the flank eruptions of 1971, 1978, 1983 and 1989 were characterized by slightly more mafic magma, which probably represented the ascent of batches of more primitive melt.

There is a marked sectoral control in the nature of flank eruptions on Etna over the last 250 years. The eruptions on the western and northern flanks tend to be of short duration and low volume, and form simple flow fields, whereas those on the eastern and southern flanks are often of long duration and large volume, and form complex flow fields. It is likely that this sectoral control is due to the buttressing effects of the mountains on the western and northern margins of the volcano whereas the lack of support to the east and south will allow eruptive fissures to remain open at lower magma pressures. Tensional movement is evidenced by large steep fault scarps (known as *timpa*) on the eastern flank.

During the last 250 years, there has been a broadly continuous supply of magma into the volcanic edifice. At times the magma is released by persistent activity, with the eruption rate a function of the average input rate. At other times, flank eruptions discharge magma at much higher rates over short periods of time followed by a period of quiescence. The magma seems to be fed into the volcanic system from depth in a series of pulses, giving an overall steady supply rate.

Geophysical techniques have been used to probe the deeper workings of magma supply and storage. Retardation of seismic P waves travelling beneath the volcano can be used to identify the presence of low-velocity bodies such as magma storage regions, a form of seismic 'shadowgraphing'. A group from the University of Cambridge in the late 1970s undertook a detailed seismic refraction survey of Etna for a period of months using P waves generated by tectonic earthquakes in the Mediterranean area and a number of charges set off in the Ionian Sea. They identified a low-velocity zone beneath Etna, which could be modelled as a flattened ellipsoid oriented 15°E at a depth of about 20 km. The velocity reduction was not large enough for a completely molten body and it was estimated that the proportion of melt was about 14%, probably stored in a complex of fissures. This magma storage zone located towards the base of the crust would act as a filter collecting mafic magmas rising from the mantle. These magmas would fractionate, generating less dense melts, which could then rise upwards through the lower-density crustal rocks. This would explain why primitive magmas are typically not erupted by Etna at present.

More recently, a seismic tomography survey of Etna has been carried out under the direction of Alfred Hirn. His work has revealed the presence of a high-velocity region 6 km in depth and 10 km in diameter to the SE of the present summit. This is interpreted as a mafic plutonic complex, which was the subvolcanic system feeding the old volcanic centres now exposed in the Valle del Bove. Low-velocity zones identified round the western margin of this complex at around 6 km depth may represent a magma body feeding the current central conduit of the volcano.

Although there is no evidence for substantial high-level storage of magma on Etna in historical times, the presence of suites of evolved magmas resulting from low-pressure plagioclase fractionation does imply a high-level reservoir at times in the history of the volcano. In addition, caldera collapse implies a reservoir from which magma was removed. The plumbing of Etna has not remained the same throughout its history.

Hazard

The greatest hazard to life on Etna is earthquakes, of both tectonic and volcanic origin. Leaving aside earthquakes, what are the main volcanic hazards? Lavas pose a threat to property, but only rarely to people. Flank eruptions on the lower reaches of the mountain can seriously affect agricultural land and the increasing number of houses. Most at risk are the areas surrounding Catania, where an eruption from a vent below about 1000 m on the southern rift area could threaten this densely populated area. The last such eruption was that of 1669. Fortunately, eruptions in this sector of the volcano have occurred only rarely.

Several factors have been used to identify the vulnerability of different areas on Etna. First, the most likely areas for flank vents are known based on density of previous vents. Frequency of eruption in any area is known based on the historical record. The effusion rate gives a measure of the ultimate length of the flow. There appears to be a progressive decrease in effusion rate with altitude: vents lower on the flanks have the potential to give the highest rates of effusion and thus lava from these vents will travel the furthest.

From any vent site, the probable path of the initial lava flow can be determined based on topography. With these factors it is possible, for example, to assess the risk for any town based on an eruption starting at a given place.

Although most eruptions produce lavas that are relatively slow moving, thus giving time to prepare plans for lava diversion, the occasional one produces relatively fast-moving flows, of the order of hundreds of metres to kilometres per hour. These cause damage too quickly for mitigating activity to be instigated. Examples are the eruptions of 1928 and 1981; in the former case the town of Mascali was completely destroyed, and in the latter many people had to be rapidly evacuated from their homes on the volcano's north flank.

The eruptions of 1928 and 1981 were both from unusual sites for eruptive activity and such maverick activity can be expected in the future. However, the majority of eruptions occur from the rift zones. The frequency of eruptions for each zone can be determined based on historical activity. In addition, as George Walker showed, there is a relation between altitude of vent and maximum length of flow: the higher the vent on the mountain the shorter the maximum length of the lava flow. Thus, from any point within the rift zones, it is possible to determine not only the most likely path, but also the potential maximum length of a flow field (Fig. 8.13).

The first known human intervention to divert a lava took place in 1669, when lavas reached the walls of Catania and started to invade the town. This story is well known and demonstrates that successful diversion may save one area but cause a threat in another. A breach was made in the side of the flow to divert lava from the main channel feeding the flow front entering Catania. The Catania diversion was brought to an end when the folk of Paterno perceived that their town was in line with the newly diverted flow, and drove the men of Catania away from their task.

Diversions were again attempted in 1983 (Fig. 8.14) and 1992. In both cases barriers were built, and efforts were made to breach or block channels and tubes near the source to divert lava from the main feeding system and start a new one further from areas at risk.

Explosive activity from the summit or from flank eruptions can cause significant dispersal of lapilli-sized scoria and ash over crops, roads and villages, and occasionally the airport, causing disruption. As we have seen, extremely violent basaltic explosive activity of sub-plinian character can occur, but is rare.

At present, activity consists of the eruption of hawaiitic basalts, but in the past more evolved magmas, generated in high-level chambers, have produced more explosive activity, including pyroclastic flows and caldera collapse. Such events are less likely, but not impossible under the present regime, but more probable should the plumbing system change to one of a greater volume of high-level storage of magma.

Floods caused by modifications in the water table by intrusive activity have occurred in the past, but do not appear to be common. One other, extremely unlikely, hazard is major failure of the flank as a landslide similar to those that formed the Valle del Bove. It has happened before, and could happen again. It is important that the seaward flank be monitored for rate of sliding, which we know takes place.

Fig. 8.13. Map of hazard from lavas on Etna. The densely stippled zone round the summit shows the potential area of hazard from persistent activity. The lightly stippled zone outside this is the area most likely to produce an eruption. Stippled zones with long arrows are potentially hazardous, and unornamented zones are topographically protected, at least from initial flows from an eruption starting on the expected area of eruption (from Guest & Murray 1979).

Places to visit

A visit to the summit cone area is made easy as it is one of the tourist attractions of Sicily. On the north side jeeps carry tourist to the top via a dirt track that winds its way up the NE Rift from the Piano del Provenzana ski and tourist area (now buried by lavas

Fig. 8.14. Diversion barrier to protect the tourist area at the Rifugio Sapienza, Etna, during the 1983 eruption. Note the dark 1983 lavas banked against the barrier to the left.

from an eruption in 2002). From the south, the cable-car (Funivia) used to go up to about 2500 m, and from then on jeeps continued the journey accompanied by guides; but the eruption of 2001 destroyed that facility. Even in midsummer the weather can be brutal, and warm waterproof clothing may be required. Stout shoes or boots are recommended. For those unfamiliar with the area, it is advisable to stay close to the guides.

It is possible to walk up, either from the base of the Funivia or from the top station. Good views of the Valle del Bove and the stratigraphy, including the Trifoglietto volcano, exposed in the walls are obtained from the cliff top between the upper station of the Funivia and the summit area; walking down this area from the summit zone is worth considering. There are several ways down into the Vale del Bove here, but it is advisable to attempt this only with someone familiar with the routes. Cloud can fill the Valle rapidly and without notice, making navigation difficult in this remote area. People have been killed. Morning is normally the best time to go to the upper part of the volcano and to view the Valle del Bove.

A drive round the volcano's perimeter is highly instructive and gives a picture of the gross morphology of the volcano. A trip on the *circumetnea* railway is also a good way of viewing Etna. However, the top of Etna is often cloud covered and a good day is needed for a circumnavigation of the volcano to be at its most productive. Some of the sites described below could be seen in a day's drive.

The coastal towns of Aci Castello and Aci Trezza are key places to examine the submarine Basal Volcanics. At Aci Castello is one of the type areas for pillow lavas and hyaloclastites, and at Aci Trezza lava intrusions into the marine clays are well exposed on the shore. One place to see the subaerial tholeiitic basalts is on the terrace edge just outside the eastern perimeter of Adrano. The terrace sequence can be seen by continuing down the road into the Simeto valley towards the solar energy plant.

The best outcrop of the 15 ka ignimbrites is on private land in a gorge on the west side of the mountain and cut by the superstrada from Catania near Biancavilla. At Biancavilla the domes of similar composition to the ignimbrites are by the main road to the west of town, where they are being removed by quarrying. In this area, the castle on the ancient centre at Paterno is a fine viewing point.

On the north side of the mountain the eccentric cones of Moio provide good cross-sections through cinder cone deposits. Splendid examples of columnar-jointed basalt are a tourist attraction at Golo dell'Alcantara down-valley from Moio; and this lava may be from one of those cones.

A good viewing point of the upper eastern part of the volcano is at the Rifugio Citelli situated within a cinder cone crater. From here the rim of the Ellittico caldera can be seen on the skyline, as well as the fissure line that fed eruptions in 1928 and 1979. The road to Citelli criss-crosses over the 1928 lava and the eruptive fissure. Good tree moulds are to be found in this lava.

The road from Fornazzo to Citelli climbs an example of a large *timpa* (fault scarp). There is another impressive *timpa* on the coast at Acireale.

A large part of the road from Nicolosi to the Sapienza–Funivia tourist area was replaced after being cut by lavas from the 1983 eruption. This road provides cross-sections of the lava as well as access to excellent examples of aa lava channel phenomena. To the west of the Sapienza tourist complex just above the Cantoniere and Corsaro Albergi are fine examples of tumuli and associated products of secondary ephemeral boccas on the 1983 flow field.

Continuing down from the Sapienza towards Zafferana the road crosses the small graben formed in 1979. This is seen as fractures in a wall on the uphill side of the road. Just below this and above the road is the fissure vent for the 1792 lava. Where the road crosses the flow, it cuts into a lava tube, providing an easy-to-see example of this phenomenon.

Much of the 1792 flow field has a pahoehoe texture and is fed by lava tubes. A good tube to visit was discovered when the road was cut into its roof just above the Monte Monaco picnic area. Access to the 200 m long tube is on the road edge. It shows all the classical features of tubes including roof sags (mind your head!), lava stalagmites, aa and pahoehoe textured flows, lava terraces and rolls on the tube sides. A hard hat and two sources of light for each person are mandatory.

To get away from it all, the *Corpo Forestale* dirt road round the mountain at about 1700 m (high enough for snow except in summer) round the northern and western flanks provides some fantastic volcanic geology. It starts from near the Mareneve tourist complex on the NE side of the volcano on the high road from Fornazzo to Linguaglossa, and goes all the way round the mountain to near the Astrophysical Observatory just below the Sapienza complex (see the map by Touring Club Italiano 1993). It is normally accessible only by foot, so sorties may be made from either end, or the whole route walked with a night's camp halfway.

Highlights of the walk include, from east to west, crossing the NE Rift and associated vents and lavas; the 1614–1624 flow field and the Grota de Lampone, a lava tube in this flow just by the track; and the 1981 eruption fissure area. Approaching from the east there is the 1780 flow and vent area. Whichever way you go there is much to see. The maps mentioned earlier will be needed.

The mud volcanoes are worth a visit. There is one by the sports stadium in Paterno, but the one SE of Paterno (see map by Romano 1991) on a valley side just south of the road is one of the best.

Notes

General

Russell King's book *Sicily* provides a good account of the island, its geography, history, customs and culture (King 1973). As well as King's book, the classic work on the history of Sicily is the three-volume *A History of Sicily* by Finley & Mack-Smith (1968). This has now been abridged by Duggan into one much shorter volume (Finley *et al.* 1986). *The Rough Guide to Sicily* (Andrews & Brown 1999) provides good general information.

Chester *et al.* (1985) covers the geology of Etna and the social effects of volcanic activity at a research level, as well as providing general information on the geography of the area, and its myths and legends. Romano (1982) contains a series of papers on the geology of Etna. The Touring Club Italiano produce a general map of Etna (Anon. 1993), and a geological map containing other eco-tourist information is published by the Club Alpino (Romano 1991). The latter map is based on a geological map prepared for the Italian Geodynamics Project (Romano *et al.* 1979), surveyed by an Anglo-Italian team including two of the authors of this book (J.E.G. and A.M.D.).

At the time of writing, the web page by Boris Behncke (http://boris.vulcanoetna.com/Italiahome.html) provides, in English, up-to-date information on activity. The Istituto Nazionale di Geofisica e Vulcanologia is the official body monitoring Etna and has a website (in Italian): http://www.ct.ingv.it.

Development of scientific ideas

An account of the 'craters of elevation' controversy was given by Macdonald (1972, pp. 34–35) in a brief account of the history of the study of volcanoes. Lyell's *Memoir on Etna* (Lyell 1858) presents his arguments against the theory, based on his observations at Etna. This treatise also provides the best English-language description of knowledge of Etna in the mid-nineteenth century.

The paper that started the idea of non-Newtonian behaviour of lavas on Etna was that by Walker (1967). From Walker's observations, Robson (1967) deduced that lavas behaved as a Bingham plastic. This was confirmed by later rheological measurements in the field (Pinkerton & Sparks 1978). The observation that effusion rate was critical to the maximum achievable length of a lava flow was made by Walker (1973).

The state of understanding of Etna in 1972 was reviewed in a compendium of papers edited by Guest & Skelhorn (1973). Some of the advances made in the following decade were documented by Romano (1982). A research-level account of the knowledge of the Mount Etna in the 1980s was provided by Chester *et al.* (1985).

Lavas and eruptive activity

Detailed field observations of the behaviour and characteristics of both active and dead lavas have been reported by a number of researchers, for example, Pinkerton & Sparks (1976), Guest (1982), Guest *et al.* (1987), Kilburn & Guest (1993) and Calvari & Pinkerton (1999). The role of lava tubes in aa flows has been discussed by Guest *et al.* (1980) and Calvari & Pinkerton (1998, 1999). Guest *et al.* (1984*b*) discussed the large flow field formed during the 1614–1624 eruption; this field is mainly pahoehoe and has exceptionally large tumuli and lava terraces. An informative account of the 1669 eruption was given by Scarth (1999).

Rittmann (1973) made the distinction between persistent and flank activity. Descriptions of the summit and its evolution have been given by Guest (1973), and more recently by Behncke (http://vulcanoetna.com) and Chester *et al.* (1985). Recent flank eruptions have been described by the following: the 1971 eruption by Rittmann *et al.* (1971); the 1974 eruption by Guest *et al.* (1974) and Bottari *et al.* (1975); the 1981 eruption by Cosentino *et al.* (1981) and Guest *et al.* (1987); the 1983 eruption by Frazzetta & Romano (1984) and Guest *et al.* (1987); the 1991–1993 eruption by Calvari *et al.* (1994*a*), Armienti *et al.* (1994) and Patanè *et al.* (1994).

Geological setting

The geological setting of Mount Etna has been described by Grindley (1973), Lentini (1982), Chester *et al.* (1985) and Roure *et al.* (1990). Further information on the regional tectonics of the Etna region is given in Chapter 1.

Stratigraphy

Charles Lyell (1858) in the 19th century, from an analysis of the attitude of the strata exposed in the walls of the Valle del Bove, recognized the existence of an older volcanic edifice centred well to the east of the current summit. Klerkx (1970) mapped the geology exposed in the Valle del Bove and identified the remnants of the oldest visible centre, Calanna. He also identified what he considered to be another ancient centre, Trifoglietto I, exposed in the northern wall, and mapped the major centre, Trifoglietto II, which was the old edifice recognized by Sartorius von Walterhausen and Lyell in the previous century. The status of Trifoglietto I is open to doubt (Chester *et al.* 1985) and may represent a number of smaller centres (see Coltelli *et al.* 1994). Trifoglietto II, the major edifice recognized by Lyell, is now generally referred to as the Trifoglietto volcano (Chester *et al.* 1985). Romano & Sturiale (1975) mapped the geology of Etna Sud (1:25 000 IGM) and McGuire (1982) provided a detailed analysis of the deposits of the Trifoglietto volcano exposed in the southern and western walls of the Valle del Bove. Cristofolini & Lo Giudice (1969) mapped the sequence overlying Trifoglietto and identify a younger centre, which they called Vavalaci, which built up on the western flank of the older volcano. Kieffer (1973) recognized the rim of an old caldera exposed on the north and NW flank of the volcano, which he called the Cratere Ellittico. He considered that this caldera was formed by a major explosive eruption that generated benmoreitic pyroclastic flows including those that emplaced the Biancavilla ignimbrite. The northern side of the Valle del Bove (Etna Nord, 1:25 000 IGM) was mapped by Romano & Guest (1979), who provided a fuller interpretation of this post-Trifoglietto centre, Ellittico.

Summaries of the stratigraphy of Etna have been given by Romano (1982), Chester *et al.* (1985) and Kieffer & Tanguy (1993). One major obstacle to the interpretation of the stratigraphy of Etna following Trifoglietto is that the relationship between the sequence in the northern wall of the Valle del Bove and the sequence exposed in the western and southern walls is obscured by a fan of young lavas and scree. Chester *et al.* (1985) proposed that the Vavalaci centre to the south and the Ellittico centre to the north may be part of the same edifice, but there is no firm field evidence to support this conjecture. The determination of radiometric dates in the 1980s and 1990s provided the first opportunity to relate the stratigraphy to an absolute chronology. Condomines *et al.* (1982) presented ^{230}Th–^{238}U disequilibrium dates, Duncan *et al.* (1984) radiocarbon dates of tephra sequences, and Gillot *et al.* (1994), using K–Ar, pushed the dating back to the earliest activity of Etna. In the 1990s more detailed mapping of both the northern wall (Coltelli *et al.* 1994) and the southwestern wall (Calvari *et al.* 1994*b*) has led to further subdivision of the succession. Dating data currently available, however, do not allow effective correlation between the successions to the north and south of the Valle del Bove and the relationship between the Vavalaci and Ellittico centres remains unresolved.

Tephra, the origin of the Valle del Bove, lahars deposits, debris avalanches deposits and the Chiancone

The origin of the Valle del Bove has caused much controversy. Rittmann (1973), Kieffer (1977) and McGuire (1982) argued that it formed as a result of a major terminal phreatomagmatic eruption of Trifoglietto, and McGuire suggested that the Lower Tephra, a sequence of predominantly phreatomagmatic ashes deposited on the eastern flank, were products of this event. Duncan *et al.* (1984) obtained a radiocarbon date of around 26 ka BP for the Lower Tephra.

Guest *et al.* (1984*a*) proposed that the Valle del Bove was not necessarily related to any volcanic event and formed as a result of gravitational collapses of the unsupported seaward side of the volcano; this mechanism is now generally accepted.

Following the dating work of Gillot *et al.* (1994), it is now recognized that Trifoglietto is mainly older than 60 ka and that the Valle del Bove is a much younger feature. Indeed, the Lower Tephra, which Chester *et al.* (1987) related to Trifoglietto, probably relates to activity of the Ellittico volcano.

Associated with the Lower Tephra are a sequence of debris flow deposits, the Milo Lahars, which we suggested (Guest *et al.* 1984*a*) were contemporaneous; however, we accept the argument of Calvari & Groppelli (1996), who consider that the Milo Lahars are much younger, with a minimum age of about 9 ka. Calvari & Groppelli found some deposits in the Milo Lahars that are suggestive of a debris avalanche origin, and they argued that these deposits are products of the excavation of the Valle del Bove.

The excavation of the Valle del Bove almost certainly occurred incrementally, and Calvari & Groppelli suggested that it was initiated before 10 ka ago as evidenced by the Milo Lahars and debris avalanche. The Chiancone, an alluvial fan that extends offshore south of Giarre, is interpreted to be reworked material derived from the Valle del Bove, and is dated as younger than 7.5 ka. The upper tephra are predominantly khaki ashes, which are considered to be of phreatomagmatic origin (Chester *et al.* 1987), but there are also numerous lapilli horizons, which are products of magmatic strombolian style activity. The Upper Tephra have yielded a number of radiocarbon dates ranging from 2.5 ka to in excess of 6 ka (Kieffer 1979; Guest *et al.* 1984*a*) and it is probable that they are the products of a number of eruptions including the plinian event that caused such damage to Catania in 122 BC (Coltelli *et al.* 1995*a*; Chester *et al.* 2000). It should be noted, however, that there are difficulties in interpreting radiocarbon dates on active volcanoes, especially those such as Etna that degas large volumes of CO_2 (Duncan *et al.* 1984).

The stratigraphy of Holocene explosive eruptions has been given by Coltelli *et al.* (1995*b*).

The evolution of the Simeto river terraces has been described by Chester & Duncan (1979).

Historical activity

Carefully prepared catalogues of historical activity have been prepared by Tanguy (1981) and Romano & Sturiale (1982). The two catalogues are the result of considerable effort using previous compilations (e.g. Sartorius von Waltershausen 1880) and historical documents. There are some differences of opinion between the catalogues, and Chester *et al.* (1985) have tabulated the history of eruptions pointing out where there is controversy. Behnke has maintained this chronology of activity on his website (http://geo.mtu.edu/~boris/ETNA_news.html).

Petrology

General accounts on the petrology of the volcanic products of Etna have been given by Duncan (1978), Tanguy (1978), Cristofolini & Romano (1982), Chester *et al.* (1985), Corsaro & Cristofolini (1996) and Tanguy *et al.* (1997). Specific accounts on the petrology of individual eruptions have been given by the following: for the 1669 eruption by Corsaro *et al.* (1996); for the 1983 eruption by Armienti *et al.* (1984); for the 1991–1993 eruption by Armienti *et al.* (1994). Information on gas discharge by Etna has been given by Allard (1997).

Isotope geochemistry and mantle source regions

Carter & Civetta (1977) and Carter *et al.* (1978) carried out the first work on the isotope geochemistry of the volcanic rocks of Etna. They showed that the tholeiitic basalts of the Basal Volcanics had lower $^{87}Sr/^{86}Sr$ values (0.70314–0.70332) than members of the

Alkalic Series (mean value 0.70352) and that the Paterno alkali basalt had a very depleted signature with a value of 0.70301. They argued that this reflected derivation from magmas from different sources in a heterogeneous mantle. The $^{87}Sr/^{86}Sr$ and $^{143}Nd/^{144}Nd$ values of the Alkalic Series reflect derivation from mantle that has been depleted in LREE, yet the lavas themselves are relatively enriched in LREE. This may reflect a late-stage enrichment event in LREE in the mantle too recent to be reflected in the isotopic signature.

Tanguy (1978), however, argued that all the magmas of Etna are derived by polybaric fractionation from a tholeiitic parental magma. Condomines *et al.* (1995) in study of recent lavas noted the constancy of $^{143}Nd/^{144}Nd$ and $^{3}He/^{4}He$, and suggested that the variation in $^{87}Sr/^{86}Sr$ may be due to crustal contamination. This was supported by Tonarini *et al.* (1995), who showed that in 1989 lavas clinopyroxene phenocrysts are in isotopic disequilibrium with the whole rock, and this they attributed to late-stage contamination by crustal fluids.

Although there may be some interaction between magma and high-level crustal fluids the general view is that the various magma series of Etna were derived from different sources in the mantle. Kamenetsky & Clocchiatti (1996) in a study of spinel mineralogy and melt inclusions argued that the tholeiitic and alkaline series of Etna have distinct parental magmas. Cristofolini *et al.* (1987) in a study of Sr/Nd isotope geochemistry of the 1983 lavas supported the model of Carter and colleagues that different mantle sources have been tapped during the evolution of the volcano.

Geophysics and internal plumbing

Early work on ground deformation was carried out by Wadge (1977) and Murray & Guest (1982), and this did not reveal the presence of a high-level magma reservoir. Analysis of travel times of natural and artificially generated seismic waves led Sharp *et al.* (1980) to identify the presence of a deep-seated magma storage area near the base of the crust.

This information was integrated into other volcanological data to provide an interpretation of the internal plumbing of Etna by Guest & Duncan (1981) and Duncan & Guest (1982). Analysis of historic eruptions has revealed a distinct sectoral control on eruptive behaviour, and Hughes *et al.* (1990) argued that this is due to the southern and eastern flanks of the volcano not being buttressed by mountains. This is supported by the work of McGuire & Pullen (1989) and Rasa *et al.* (1996) regarding the instability of the eastern flank of Etna.

Geophysical monitoring of recent eruptions has allowed further refinement of understanding of the current plumbing of the volcano. Rymer *et al.* (1995) used gravity and ground deformation to monitor magma movements in the dyke system feeding the 1991–1993 eruption. Ferrucci & Patane (1993) interpreted the seismic activity associated with this eruption. Gresta *et al.* (1990) have analysed seismicity (magnitude $M > 2.4$) at Etna for the period 1865–1980; Vinciguerra *et al.* (2001) have investigated seismic patterns associated with flank eruptions during 1981–1996 and Azzaro & Barbano (1996) more generally. Cardaci *et al.* (1993) and Hirn *et al.* (1991) have undertaken seismic tomography analysis of the crust beneath Etna to identify zones of magma storage and ascent.

Hazard

Hazard from lavas has been analysed by Guest & Murray (1979). Possible hazard from slope failure and sector collapse has been highlighted by Murray & Voight (1996). Lava diversion techniques during the 1991–1993 eruption are described by Barbari *et al.* (1993*a*).

Chapter 9. **Other islands: Ischia, Ustica, Linosa, Pantelleria and Graham Island**

Ischia, Pantelleria, and Graham are active volcanoes, whereas Ustica and Linosa have not had volcanic activity in the last 10 ka; but that does not mean they are necessarily extinct.

Ischia

The island of Ischia is part of a line of volcanoes running from Vesuvius to the Ponza Islands (Fig. 1.1). It lies 10 km west of Campi Flegrei and just 5 km west of the island of Procida, which is part of the Campi Flegrei complex. Ischia, less than 10 km across from east to west and 5 km from north to south, is a separate volcano in its own right (Fig. 9.1). The last eruption took place in 1302, but it is still active, with intense fumarole fields and thermal springs, some being the most radioactive in Italy (and advertise themselves as such!). There have been many earthquakes on the island in historical time, and numerous landslides, some fatal.

Ischia's early settlers were severely affected by volcanism. The first Greek colonists in the Naples area settled on the NW promontory of Ischia; the island was then known as Pithecusa. This settlement probably took place in about 770 BC. The settlers were forced to abandon the island owing to the violence of eruptions that were taking place there. It may have been the initial eruptions of Monte Rotaro around 600 BC that caused them to leave. Once on the mainland they founded Cuma on the western edge of the Campi Flegrei volcanic complex, as we saw in Chapter 3. New settlers from the Greek colony of Syracuse in Sicily arrived on the island in the fifth century BC, but they too are thought to have been driven away after only a few years by an eruption that is now the site of Ischia Porto. Greek mythology has the island as the abode of Typhoeus, a monster with a hundred heads, each of which had a terrible voice. He had made war on Zeus, who killed him with a thunderbolt. Typhoeus had his revenge by creating eruptions and earthquakes. Other myths have him buried under Etna.

The island was seized by the Neapolitans in 450 BC, and then in 326 BC by the Romans who called it Aenaria (or Inarime). Augustus swapped it with the Neapolitans for Capri. After being taken by the Saracens and the Pisans it finally returned to Naples. It was sacked by the pirate, Barbarossa, in 1541, and Nelson occupied it for a short time during the Napoleonic wars.

Culturally and historically, Ischia is part of the Campi Flegrei–Naples area. There are a number of coastal towns, and a few inland villages joined by a road that runs round the island. Some are spas with thermal, therapeutic mineral waters. The spas, plus the

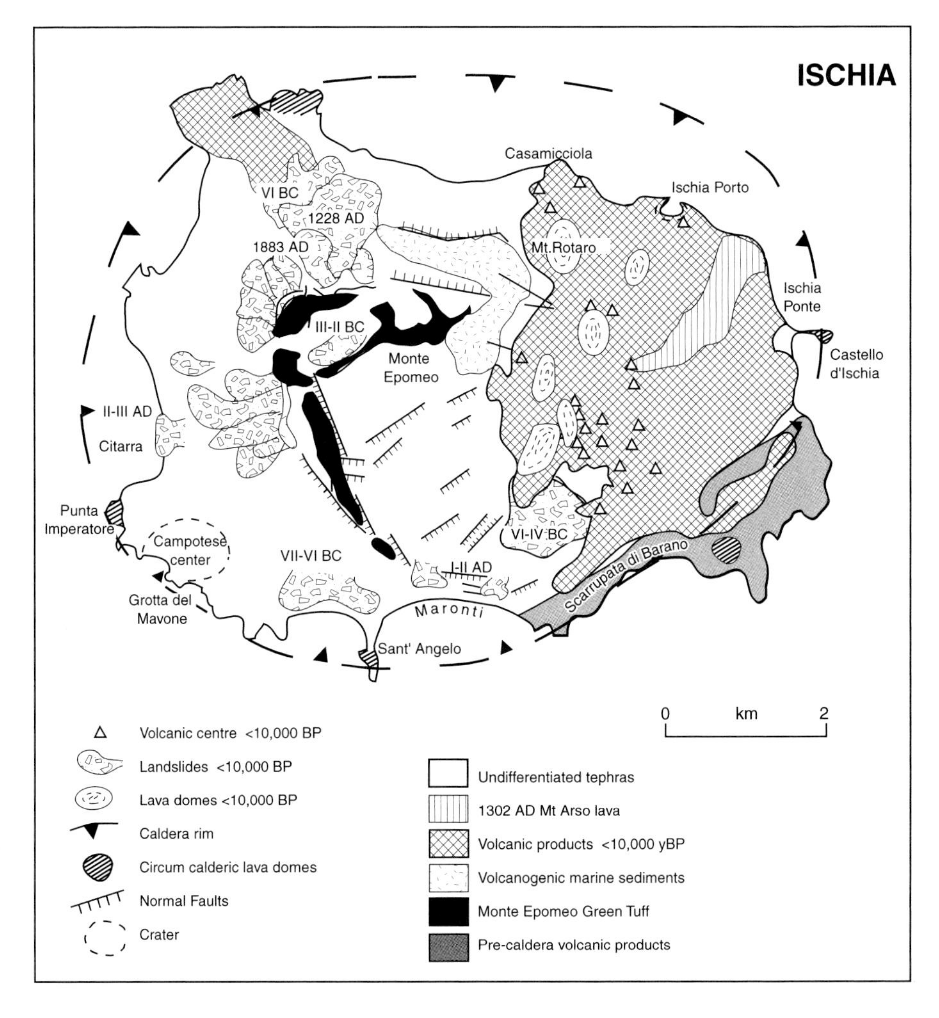

Fig. 9.1. Map of Ischia based on Vezzoli (1988).

beaches and picturesque nature of the island, make it a popular holiday centre, and tourism is key to its prosperity. It is also well known for its wine.

Monte Epomeo, the highest point on Ischia, rises to 787 m and dominates the island's morphology when viewed from any direction. The geomorphology of Monte Epomeo is not one of primary volcanic origin, but tectonic. The presence of marine mollusc shells on Monte Epomeo has been known since early in the nineteenth century. Charles Lyell noted not only that there were shells, but that ones near the summit were recent. This evidence he used to support the view that considerable uplift of the Earth can take place in a relatively short time and that the shells so high above sea level were not the result of Noah's Flood. A hundred years later Alfred Rittmann suggested that Monte Epomeo was a fault-bounded, uplifted block, termed a 'horst'. More modern interpretation is that uplift resulted from resurgence of the caldera floor.

Radiometric dating suggests that rate of uplift may have been as high as 22 mm a^{-1}. Samples of both shells and coral from marine terraces at 57 and 71 m date respectively at about 6000 and 8500 a BP, implying an average rate of uplift of about 9 mm a^{-1}. This lower rate may imply that that uplift is slowing down, or that it has generally been variable. Subsidence has also been reported on the island in historical time and, between 1890 and 1910, there was indeed a net submergence at Porto D'Ischia in the graben east of Monte Epomeo.

The oldest rocks to be dated on the island are around 150 ka, but the edifice is probably considerably older than this (Fig. 9.2). Volcanic products ranging in age from 150 to 74 ka are generally distributed in the SW and SE extremities of the island. Lava domes and flows dominate this early period, and the prominent Castello d'Ischia and Sant' Angelo peninsulas are such domes. Abundant pyroclastic rocks testify to considerable explosive activity. A putative early caldera structure, formed earlier than 130 ka BP and largely concealed by later deposits, is marked by a ring of lava domes.

The most extensive volcanic deposit on Ischia is the Monte Epomeo Green Tuff (MEGT), composed of pyroclastic flow deposits dated at 55 ka BP. The MEGT was the product of a major eruption thought to have been associated with collapse of a 10 km × 8 km caldera. Italian geologists have proposed that the MEGT caldera encloses the majority of the island and cuts the present-day subaerial part only in the NW and SE (Fig. 9.1).

The MEGT crops out over most of Ischia. Two facies can be identified: a proximal welded facies located mainly within the caldera, and a slightly more distal nonwelded facies. The proximal facies is heavily faulted owing to the remarkable resurgence that has taken place. Basal plinian pumice fallout occurs at the base of many of the non-welded outcrops. Some thick exposures of the nonwelded facies have a densely welded obsidian-rich layer up to 3 m thick near the base, for example, at Scarrupata di Barano (Figs 9.1 and 9.2). In other places the base of the sequence is composed of up to 30 m of lithic-rich flow units, as at Sant' Angelo. In places this lithic-rich basal sequence coarsens to become a breccia. The ignimbrite itself is composed of a chaotic sequence of massive flow units interbedded with surge deposits. Locally the surge deposits contain accretionary lapilli, impact sags and thin inversely graded layers.

Deposits of MEGT reach a thickness of between 140 and 400 m inside the caldera, whereas outside it is much thinner at less than 60 m. Tephra fall deposits from this event may also occur outside Ischia, and are up to 40 cm thick on several of the Eolian Islands 300 km to the south, as described in earlier chapters. Indeed, this same fallout deposit forms an important stratigraphic marker in deep-sea sediments across much of the Mediterranean.

Following the MEGT eruption, tuff cones and rings were formed on the western side of the caldera. There is little evidence of intracaldera volcanic activity following the MEGT, which might be evidence to suggest that this collapse was piston–block-like rather than occurring in a piecemeal fashion. Immediately following collapse, the caldera depression was flooded by the sea for an extended period of time and some 200 m of marine sediments were laid down on top of the ignimbrite.

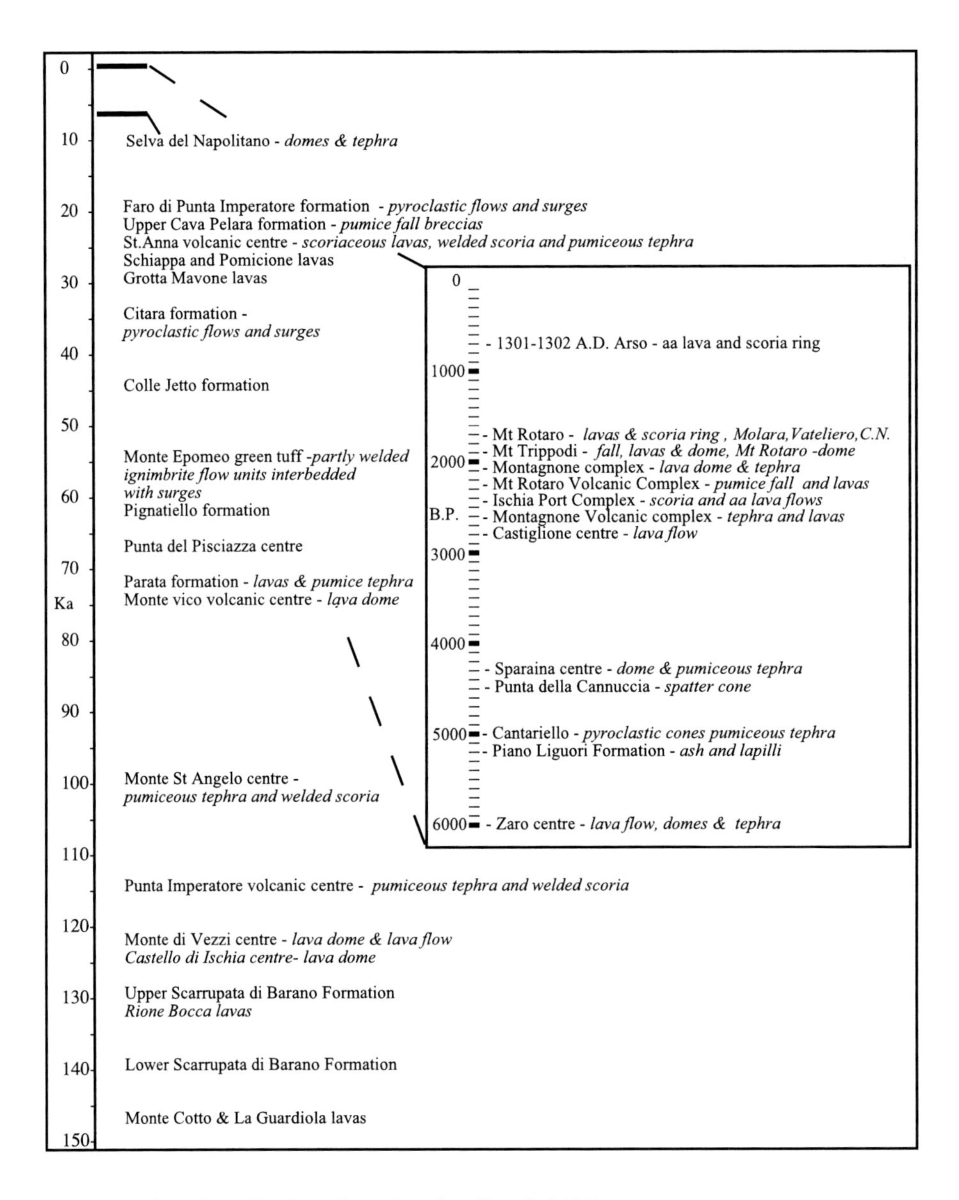

Fig. 9.2. Chronology of Ischia volcano based on Vezzoli (1987).

At some stage after the caldera formed, its floor started to rise, eventually to form Mount Epomeo, Rittmann's horst structure. At the time, the tectonic horst explanation was a reasonable one to explain the uplift, but it was made before US Geological Survey geologists Bob Smith and Roy Bailey had explained uplift of the floor of the Valles Caldera in New Mexico as being caused by a rising, buoyant body of magma following a major ignimbrite-forming eruption. Since this discovery in the 1960s, such uplift has been found to be common in calderas associated with silicic volcanism. It is thus most likely that Monte Epemeo has the same origin, with some fault directions being controlled by regional structures.

Between about 44 and 33 ka BP there were at least three major hydrovolcanic eruptions in the SW part of the island. Mainly associated with the Campotese centre, a lava dome, lavas and tephra were formed between 28 and 18 ka BP, followed by a period of volcanic quiescence for about 6000 years.

Radiometric dating of more recent volcanic products indicates that during the last 10 ka at Ischia, as at nearby Campi Flegrei, volcanic activity has been strongly episodic with periods of intense volcanism separated by long intervals of repose. Before the AD 1302 eruption there were nearly 800 years with no activity; but the centuries before and after the start of the Christian Era were particularly active (Fig. 9.2). More than ten separate eruptions took place, some of which involved considerable explosive activity. Radiometric dates suggest that eight of these occurred within 2000 years.

The AD 1302 eruption was preceded by about a year of intense seismic activity. The eruption is thought to have formed Monte Arso, a small scoria cone with a 3 km long lava flow that reached the sea at a location between the present-day towns of Ischia Porto and Ischia Ponte (Fig. 9.1). The flow destroyed the village of Geronda, and many people fled the island as a result of the eruption.

Landslides are a major problem on Ischia, where steep slopes result from continued and rapid uplift. Historically dated landslides have been cut by faults, highlighting the continued active seismicity of the island. There have been no fewer than eight large landslides in historical times and many of these were earthquake triggered. The most recent earthquakes, in 1881 and 1883, killed 129 and 2313 people, respectively. Most of the damage was centred on the northern part of the island and that of 1883 triggered a landslide. Ischia remains an unstable place!

Petrology of Ischia

The volcanic rocks of Ischia are strongly alkaline ($Na_2O + K_2O$ up to 14%) and belong to the Low-K Series of the Campanian volcanic province. The rocks are mainly trachytic but range in composition from trachybasalts to alkali trachytes and phonolites. These rocks show a trend of increasing alkalinity towards undersaturated peralkaline compositions, plausibly reflecting fractional crystallization in the magma reservoir. The alkali trachytes and phonolites contain modal sodalite, sodic pyroxenes and sometimes nepheline in addition to the standard phases of alkali feldspar, plagioclase and augite.

Eruption of the MEGT marked the onset of a new phase of activity. The ignimbrite produced by this eruption is trachytic and contains abundant lithic fragments including syenite xenoliths. The MEGT magma was less evolved than that of the preceding eruptions, and it is likely that this renewal of activity reflected a fresh influx of melt into the magma reservoir. After the MEGT, eruption activity trended towards alkali trachytes, possibly reflecting fractional crystallization in a closed system. Around 28 ka BP eruption of trachybasaltic lavas in the southern part of the island marked the arrival of new mafic magma into the volcanic system. This coincided with resurgence of the Monte Epomeo block, which may have been caused by influx of mafic melt into the magma reservoir. During the last 10 ka, eruption of alkali trachyte lavas and pyroclastic deposits reflects periodic tapping of the evolved cap of a compositionally zoned reservoir.

Ustica

The island of Ustica is about 80 km north of Palermo, off the coast of Sicily (Fig. 1.1). It is one of a pair of volcanoes; the other, to the west, has remained a submarine seamount. Ustica has a rectangular outline just over 4 km long and 2.5 wide (Fig. 9.3). The highest point is nearly 250 m. It has a generally rocky shoreline with a deep-water port in the cove of Santa Maria below the small town that is the main centre of the island. The resident population is about 1000.

Although the island was inhabited in prehistoric and Roman times it was abandoned until the eighteenth century when families came from the Eolian Islands to cultivate the land. Over time, vines, figs, prickly pears and cereals were developed. In particular, a distinctive local type of lentil became an important part of the island diet, and at one time was shipped to Naples and Palermo. However, the 1970s saw a decline in its production.

Because Ustica was used as a place to send banished criminals and political enemies of the state, a situation that remained into the 1950s, a tourist industry was slow to develop. But the clear waters are ideal for scuba diving and underwater fishing, and tourism has become an important part of the island's income. Farming and fishing have been important in sustaining the population in the past, but now much land has been abandoned. Excellent wines are made on the island from local grapes.

As on most of the islands, water is a problem. In the past, rainwater was collected and stored in vast *cisterne*, large 'tanks' carved into the soft rock of the tuff cone above Santa Maria. Today, water is ferried from Palermo by boat.

Ustica is the top of a vast submarine volcano more than 30 km across and over 2 km high. Morphologically, the island is in two parts, the main, older edifice to the south, and a lava platform, known as Tramontana, to the north. The older edifice was cut in half by a 2 km wide gravitational collapse on the north side, and following collapse, the lava platform was built.

The earliest volcanic rocks on the island are hyaloclastites and pillow lavas representing submarine eruptive activity (Fig. 9.4). These are well exposed along the SE-facing shore of the island. In many places they have been lithified by secondary minerals. The deposits have been mapped up to some tens of metres above sea level, indicating substantial post-depositional uplift. Stages in the uplift are represented round the island by wave-cut platforms at about 100, 50 and 30 m a.s.l. The age of the emergent phase of the volcanoes history was between 750 and 130 ka BP.

On top of the submarine materials, subaerial volcanism produced two main centres of activity, Monte Guardia dei Turchi (238 m) dated at 500 ka BP and Monte Costa del Fallo (230 m). Activity included production of lavas, domes, basaltic scoria and pumice lapilli deposits. There appears to have been a period of quiescence between 476 and 424 ka BP, and this was followed by a trachytic explosive event.

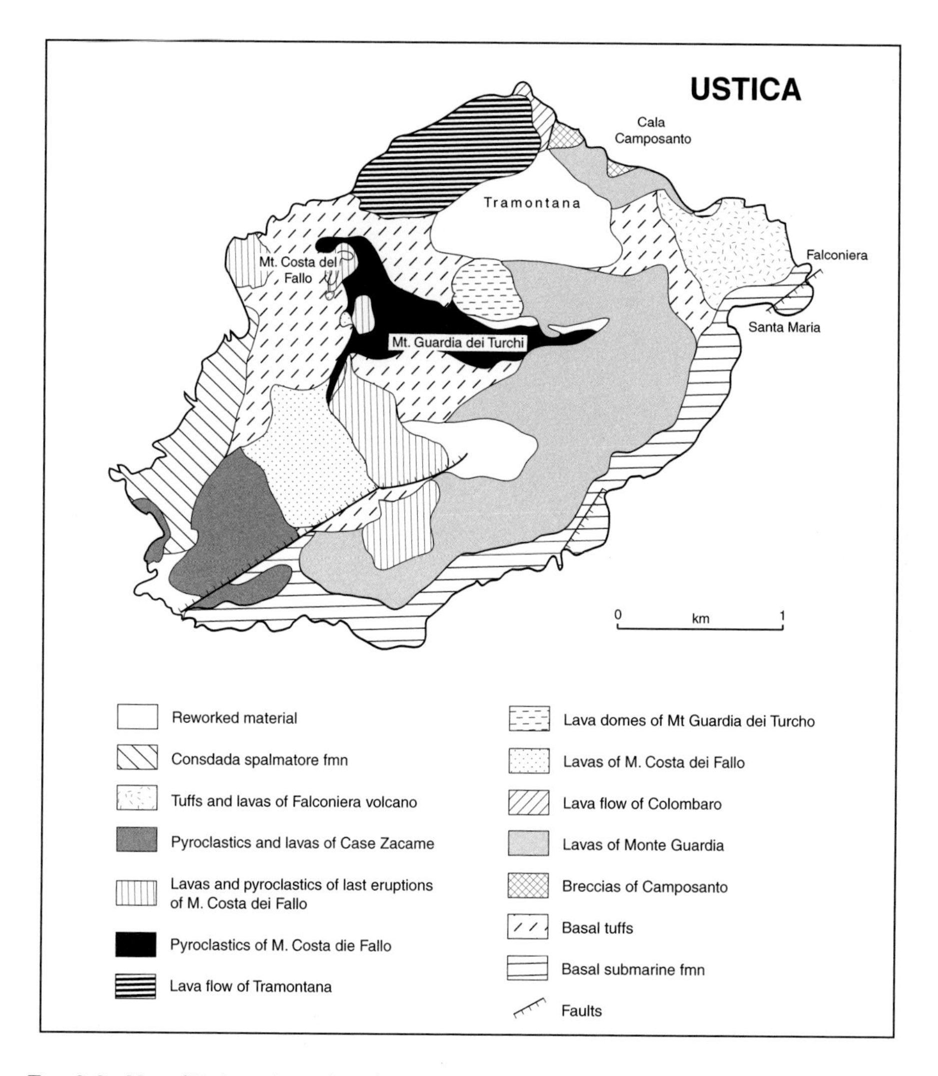

Fig. 9.3. Map of Ustica volcano (based on Romano & Sturiale 1971).

At some stage after the 100 m marine terrace had been cut at about 350 ka BP, the northern flank of the island failed, sliding into the sea and leaving a prominent scarp (Fig. 9.5). Outcrops on the north coast of a breccia containing angular blocks up to 5 m across may represent the debris avalanche deposit from this collapse (Fig. 9.6). Marine terraces at about 50 and 30 m (the latter dated at 130 ka BP) were then cut in front of the collapse scarp, and the lavas exposed in the sea cliffs erupted.

One of the youngest events in the construction of the island was a surtseyan eruption that constucted the Falconiera pyroclastic cone. The remains of the cone form a prominent 118 m high feature just north of the port of Ustica. It is built of finely bedded yellow–brown altered tuffs typical of surtseyan deposits. The eruption occurred just off the coast of the island in shallow water. Although made almost entirely of tephra,

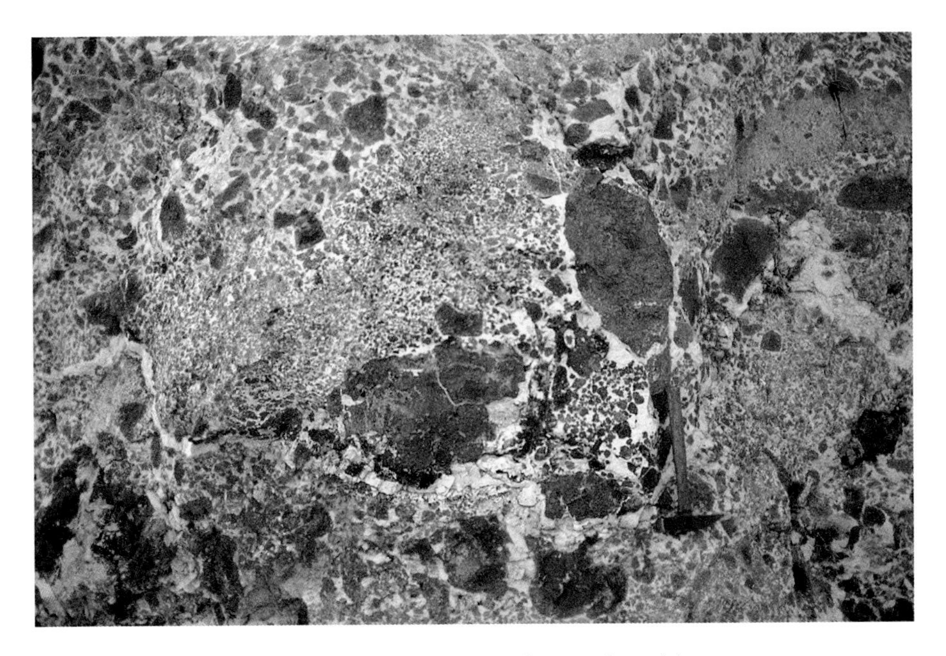

Fig. 9.4. Hyaloclastite deposits on the shore of Ustica (hammer for scale).

Fig. 9.5. Marine terrace in the fore- and middle-ground, Ustica. Behind is the scarp formed by the flank collapse of the volcano.

Fig. 9.6. Megabreccia on the SE coast of Ustica interpreted as a possible exposure of the debris avalanche associated with the collapse of the eastern side of the volcano.

exposures of lava also occur on the northern coast where a section eroded through the crater is exposed.

Another of the youngest events on the island occurred on the western coast where lava flowed into the sea and built up a subaerial lava platform.

Linosa

Together with Pantelleria and Graham Island, Linosa is associated with the Strait of Sicily graben system (Fig. 1.1), an active extensional system that began to develop in the early Pliocene by combined pull-apart and strike-slip tectonics. Extension thinned the continental crust to less than 20 km. The upper part of the crust consists of a Mesozoic–Cenozoic carbonate sequence that extends from the Iblean Mountains of Sicily to northern Africa.

Linosa lies almost midway between Sicily and Africa, about 160 km from the Sicilian coast. It is 2.5 km × 2.75 km (Fig. 9.7), and has four main cones ranging in height from just over 100 m to nearly 200 m. The coast is rocky with cliffs up to 90 m, though there are a few beaches of black sand. There is a small village with about 400 people who live by fishing, and by farming on flatter parts of the island. There is good soil over most of the island, which was occupied by both Arabs and Romans, and in 1845 was colonized by King Ferdinand II of the Two Sicilies. It has a mild climate, but may be fiercely hot

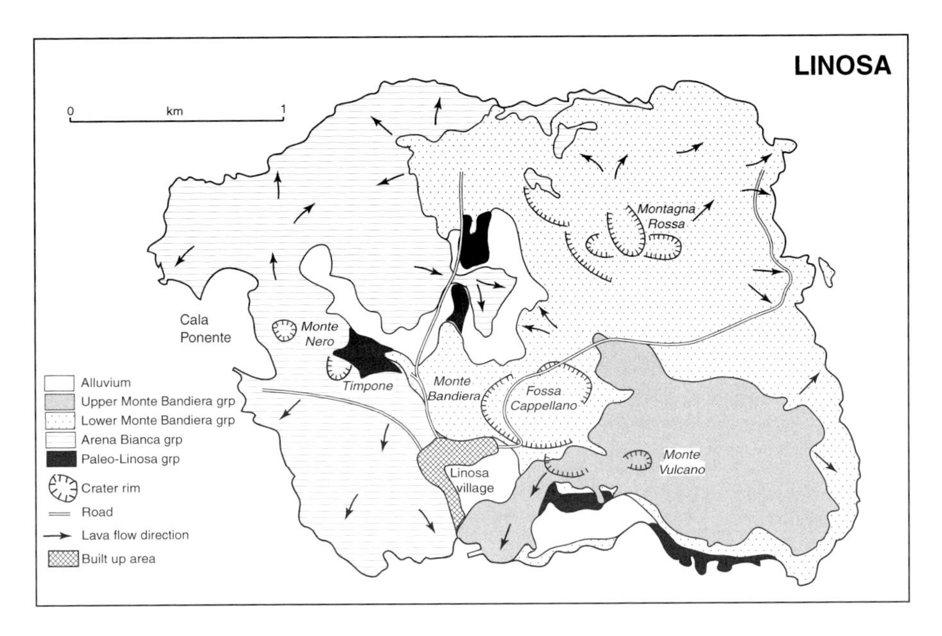

Fig. 9.7. Geological map of Linosa (based on Lanzafame *et al.* 1994).

in summer siroccos when hot air blows from Libya. It has facilities for a small number of tourists.

The products of the Linosa volcano consist of hydromagmatic tuffs, scoria and lavas. They belong to a mildly alkaline suite ranging from alkali basalt to trachyte, but are mainly alkali basalts and hawaiites.

The subaerial part of the volcano has been dated at between about 1 Ma and 500 ka BP. The sequence can be divided into four stratigraphic units by three soil horizons ranging from 20 to 70 cm in thickness. The early emergent Linosa was formed by hydromagmatic eruptions similar to that of Graham Island to be described below. Most of the early activity was hydromagmatic, but as each eruption advanced, entry of water into the crater became more restricted and basaltic scoria then was ejected.

Islands built up in this way are prey to marine erosion and can easily be destroyed. It is likely that the early Linosa was destroyed more than once before a more permanent island was established. As the island built up, eruptive craters were protected from direct entry of sea water, and magmatic eruptions produced spatter and scoria cones and lavas. Lava cover (Fig. 9.7) that forms most of the coastline limits the amount of marine erosion and gives the island a measure of permanence.

The earliest sequence exposed consists of remnants of tuff rings made up of hydromagmatic tuffs, scoria layers and thin lavas. Following a period of quiescence long enough for a soil to develop, activity resumed on the western side of the island. The remains of the first tuff ring of this second phase are exposed in Cala Ponente. Erosion is such that basaltic dykes are exposed in the cliff sections. The eruption started with hydromagmatic deposits including surges, but evolved to produce scoria falls and a thin lava. A new eruption or a later phase of the same eruption formed a scoria cone, known as Timpone, as well as a lava flow field to the south, which forms the platform west of Linosa village. Further eruptive activity produced Monte Nero NW of Timpone. This eruption started with hydromagmatic activity including surges, followed by ejection of scoria and production of a large lava flow field to the north and east. During this period, two other eruptions took place, one off the present south coast, and the other to the north of the island.

The next period of quiescence that allowed a soil to develop was followed by the eruption that formed Fossa Cappellano (Fig. 9.7), which has a 500 m wide crater. The deposits consist of brown, glassy tuff, containing scoriaceous lithic blocks of basalt and trachyte, and fossiliferous Quaternary reef sediments. The proportion of basaltic scoria again increases upward in the sequence. An eruption from a site now buried near Monte Vulcano produced lavas with channels and tubes that are exposed on the island's SE coast. The next eruption produced the largest cone on the island, Montagna Rossa, which has a summit crater open to the north, an east–west-trending line of craters south of the summit, and small cones at the base on the NW side. Lavas were erupted from fissures on the northern side near the base and to the NE. This eruption also consisted of two cycles, each involving a progression from hydromagmatic activity to lava effusion.

The third soil in the sequence is the thickest and probably represents the longest period of quiescence. The volcanic peace was finally broken by an eruption that built the Monte Vulcano cinder cone, which has a well-preserved summit crater. The eruption followed the normal trend from hydromagmatic to magmatic when lava was erupted from fissures on the lower SW.

We are currently in another period of quiescence in which a fourth soil is developing. In the mean time, marine erosion is slowly eating away at the island and its long-term survival depends on future lava-producing eruptions.

Pantelleria

The island of Pantelleria is the only other volcanic island in the Strait of Sicily to have emerged above sea level and remained as a solid piece of land. Its geology has played an important part in the interpretation of welded tuffs and ignimbrites, and in giving its name to a rock type. The island lies 70 km north of the African coast (Fig. 1.1). It has an elliptical planform 13 km × 8 km across. Its sea-floor base is some 20 km in diameter and about half its height is above sea level. The island is dominated by a 6 km diameter central caldera (Figs 9.8 and 9.9). Apart from non-volcanic Malta, it is the largest island in the Strait of Sicily.

Neolithic peoples inhabited the island and built several villages. One, at La Mursia, is surrounded by a rampart of obsidian blocks up to 7 m high. They built mysterious round or elliptical towers, known as *sesi*, made of lava blocks.

Inevitably, the Romans were there, but not this time for their own pleasure, as the island was used as a place of banishment. The Normans were there too, but for them it was a strategic position in the Strait between Africa and Europe. The Norman castle remained

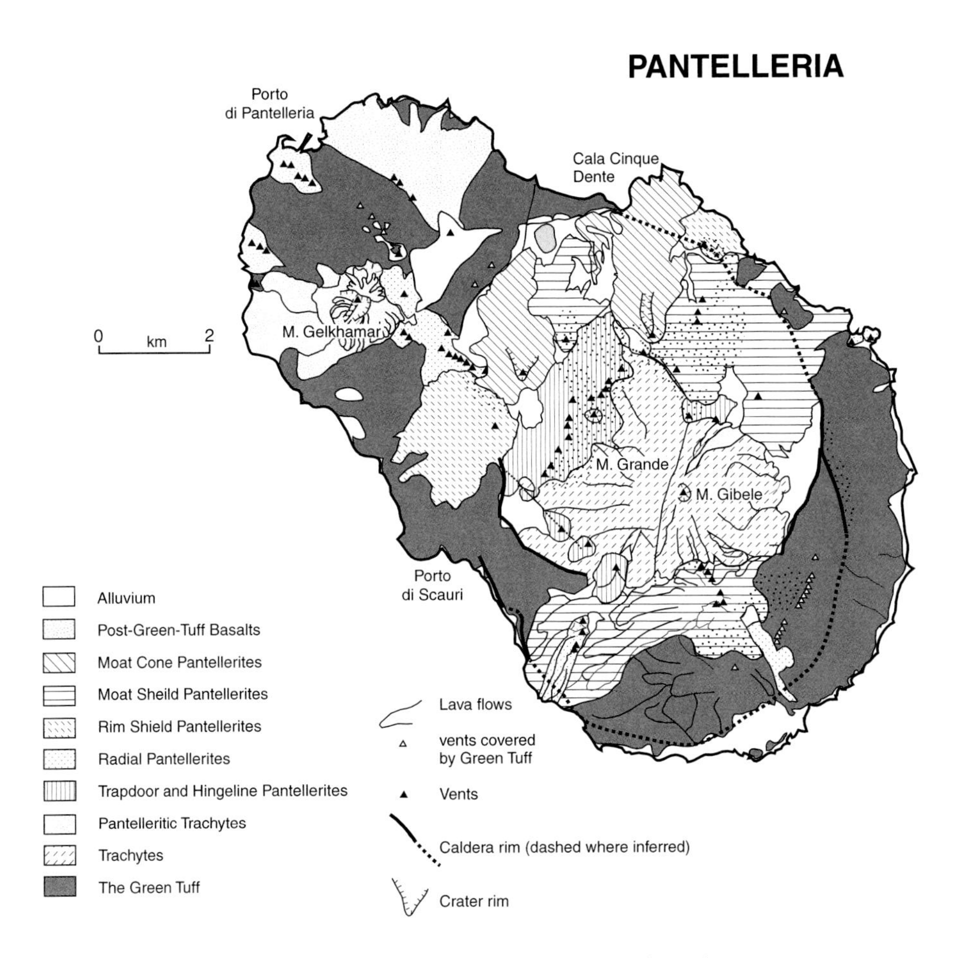

Fig. 9.8. Geological map of Pantelleria (based on Mahood & Hildreth 1986).

a prison until recent times. Only 70 km from Tunisia, the Arabic influence is strong, and this is reflected in place names.

In more recent times, Mussolini again recognized the strategic position of the island. He ringed it with gun emplacements and developed a good road network. As a result, Pantelleria was ruined by Allied bombing in 1943. The Nazis abandoned the island, which was invaded by the British, who sent its youthful defenders to Liverpool in the UK as prisoners of war, where they were set to unload US supply ships.

The soil is fertile and much of the island is under cultivation. Vines are extensive, producing, as well as wine, grapes for the table and raisins. Like grapes, capers are an important export product. Also produced are cereals, fruit and vegetables. Goats are important.

As to be expected, water is a problem. There are springs and a small intercrater lake associated with an active hydrothermal system; but these are hot and mineral rich. Rainwater is collected in cisterns and there are some wells, but water brought in by tanker

Fig. 9.9. Panoramic view towards the south and SE over the central caldera of Pantelleria. Photograph by courtesy of Wes Hildreth, US Geological Survey.

is essential to maintain a population of some 10 000. The majority of people live in the town of Pantelleria, but there are scattered homesteads and vacation *dammusi* (distinctive cottages) over much of the island. The island is ringed by cliffs, and there is only one harbour, which does not provide good protection in bad weather. There is a small airport, and the island is well served by roads including a circum-island coast road built by Mussolini.

Styles of volcanism at Pantelleria

The styles of eruptive activity on Pantelleria have some distinct differences from those elsewhere in the region. This results from the strongly peralkaline nature of the magma. Magma rheology has an important influence on volcanic behaviour, and in peralkaline melts the excess of alkalis over alumina gives the liquid a less polymerized silicate network, reducing bonding and thus decreasing the effective viscosity to a marked degree. The relatively high fluorine content of the magma also has a significant impact in lowering melt viscosity. As a result, welding of fallout tephra is common, and post-emplacement lava-like remobilization (rheomorphism) of the welded tuffs commonly produces distinctive flow structures. The low viscosity means that clasts are more likely to weld on impact. Once welded, short distance flowage may occur, giving fold textures that can be used in the field to identify such movement. In proximal locations eruptive fountains may have formed spatter-fed lava flows. The lower proportion of H_2O relative to the heavier volatile elements (F, Cl, C and S) also leads to a denser eruptive column that is more prone to collapse, increasing the possibility of the generation of pyroclastic flows.

Pantelleritic constructs on the island do not strictly meet the definitions for those formed from other silicic magmas. The lava 'domes' tend to have a distinctive graben-like split summit feature, leading to the local name of *Gelfiser* derived from an Arabic term meaning 'burst mountain'. Near the vent there can be pumice and agglutinate interbedded with lavas. The initial domes were breached by lavas up to some 3 km long, 50 m thick and with blocky crusts. The shallower lava shield volcanoes consist mainly of spatter-fed flows and welded fall deposits, some showing rheomorphic structures. It appears that some centres accumulated so fast that much of the edifice cooled as a single cooling unit.

Volcanic history of Pantelleria

The most extensive rock unit exposed on Pantelleria, the so-called Green Tuff (not to be confused with that on Ischia), is spread all over the island, covering most pre-existing rocks, which are now mainly exposed in sea cliffs. The stratigraphy is, therefore, considered quite simply in terms of pre- and post-Green Tuff. All workers agree with this, and have constructed stratigraphies based on it. There the agreement ends, and there are significant differences of opinion about the evolution of the island. We discuss some of the key disagreements between workers in the 'Notes' for this chapter.

Because outcrops of rocks that predate the Green Tuff are in the coastal cliffs, the three dimensions of the geology of this period are not clear. However, an arcuate inward-facing scarp in the southern part of the island has been interpreted as a buried caldera wall termed the La Vecchia Caldera. Outcrops in the sea cliffs show a displacement. Based on ages of rocks on either side of the caldera, the collapse can be dated at between 175 and 106 ka BP and a welded ignimbrite dated at 114 ka BP may have been formed by the eruption that caused the collapse.

The oldest exposed rocks that predate the La Vecchia caldera have an age of about 325 ka BP. The pre-La Vecchia volcanic history was one of the production of lava shields and cones, both welded and non-welded ignimbrites, and agglutinated fall deposits. These are exposed in the sea cliffs at the southern end of the island. After the La Vecchia caldera eruption there were several ignimbrite-forming eruptions as well as effusive events. Post-La Vecchia deposits can be seen banked inside the caldera wall and, in the upper part of the sequence, extending outside the depression onto the old edifice flanks.

The next major event was the eruption that gave rise to the Green Tuff and the collapse of the central caldera at about 45 ka BP. The Green Tuff eruption produced several cubic kilometres of pyroclastic material that covered the island with up to 20 m of tephra and dumped an unknown amount out to sea. The early part of the eruption was plinian, giving an extensive fall deposit and surges. This was followed by pyroclastic flows that produced edifice-mantling ignimbrites that are densely welded and show rheomorphic structures indicative of post-emplacement mass flow (Fig. 9.10). The high temperature of the tephra on emplacement implies a low eruption column in which little air was ingested to cool the magmatic particles. There were several pyroclastic flows that deposited ignimbrite, each of which had time to deform rheomorphically before the next deposit arrived. However, the time between flows was sufficiently short to allow the whole ignimbrite sequence to cool and devitrify as a single cooling unit. A distinct compositional difference between the materials at the bottom and top of the Green Tuff, starting with pantellerite and ending with trachyte, implies discharge from a compositionally zoned magma chamber.

The island's central caldera (Fig. 9.9) which was formed by the Green Tuff eruption, is elliptical in plan view with a maximum diameter of 6 km and maximum surviving relief on the walls of 90 m. However, the true depth of the caldera is at least 125 m taking into account the post-caldera fill. In places the wall is obscured by lava flows that have overflowed the rim.

The volcanic history becomes much clearer for post-Green Tuff times. Within a few thousand years, two-thirds of the caldera had been filled by trachytic lavas and associated minor ignimbrites of similar composition to the upper deposits of the Green Tuff. These are expressed in the dominant peak of Montagna Grande, the highest point of the island at 836 m, and the adjacent cone of Monte Gibele (700 m). These two peaks are part of the same trachytic edifice 5 km in diameter, the original peak of which was its vent at Monte Gibele. The two are separated by a major normal fault with an east-facing scarp. It appears that following the collapse of the caldera, instead of resurgent uplift, a huge mass of trachyte was erupted. New melt injected into the magma reservoir at about 18 ka BP caused a major inflation that resulted in uplift of part of the caldera floor, which included the western part of the original Monte Gibele edifice, by what is known as a trapdoor fault system. A block uplifted by rotation on a hingeline raised the western half some 300 m above its original position, thereby creating Montagna Grande.

Fig. 9.10. Cliff section on the SE coast of Pantelleria showing the Green Tuff filling a valley in the underlying lavas. Thickening in the valley is the result of low viscosity flow of the welded tuff into the valley. Photograph by courtesy of Wes Hildreth, US Geological Survey.

The new magma injected into the reservoir continued to erupt from fissures developed by inflation. Vents opened along the trapdoor hinge, on the caldera faults and fractures radial to the caldera generally with a NW trend. Spectacular pantelleritic flows were formed, especially that of Monte Gelkhamar near the northern end of the island.

Petrology of Pantelleria

The island of Pantelleria is the type locality of *pantellerite*, a peralkaline rhyolite-like rock that is strongly Qz-normative, Fe-rich and Al-poor. Pantellerites have abundant anorthoclase phenocrysts, but may also contain small amounts of sodic pyroxene, fayalite, aenigmatite and quartz. The trachytes have a similar mineralogy except that they do not contain aenigmatite. Washington in his early study of the volcanic rocks of Pantelleria noted the bimodal distribution of rock types with, on the one hand, alkali basalts and, on the other, silicic pantellerites and trachytes. There is a virtual lack of rocks in the range 54–62 wt% SiO_2 (Fig. 9.11). The basalts and hawaiites have phenocrysts of plagioclase, augite and olivine.

The Green Tuff shows a progressive change in composition from pantellerite through pantelleritic trachyte to trachyte. Trachyte continued to be erupted after caldera collapse. Pantelleritic lavas were not again erupted until about 20 ka later; this may reflect the time needed for the reservoir to re-generate a highly evolved fraction.

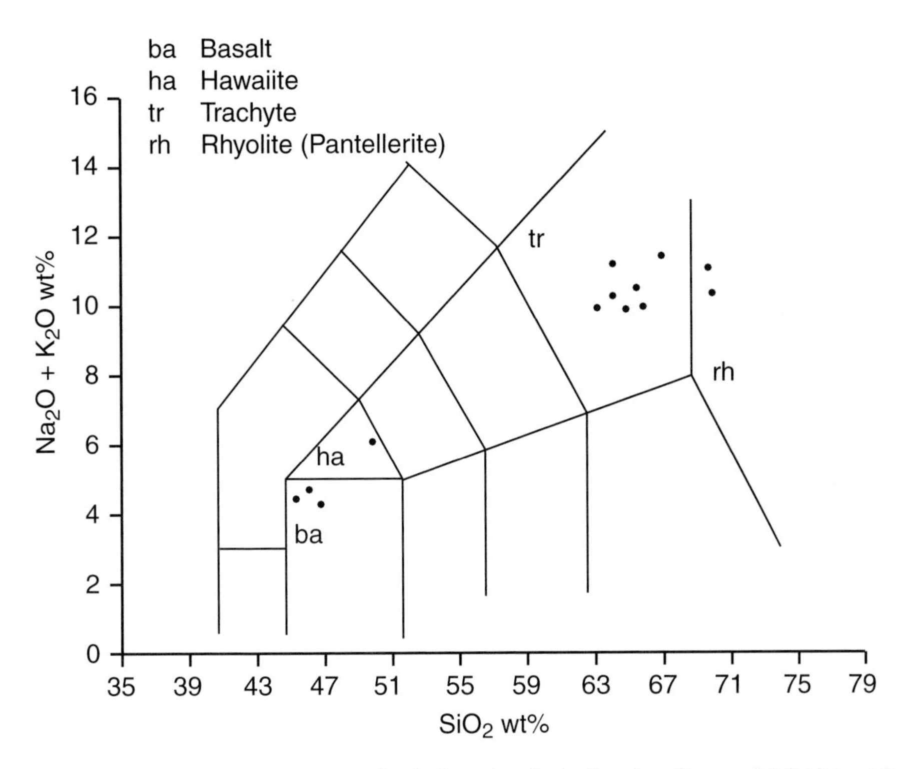

Fig. 9.11. TAS plot of the composition of rocks from Pantelleria (data from Romano 1968; Mahood & Hildreth 1986).

Subsequent to the Green Tuff eruption, there was injection of fresh basaltic magma into the reservoir. Alkali basalt eruptions are restricted to the NW of the island, including the last eruption just offshore in 1891. It is likely that the trachytic magma reservoir beneath the caldera complex acts as a 'filter', trapping ascending denser basaltic melts and preventing them from being erupted. The alkali basaltic magmas of Pantelleria are similar to those of Graham Island and Linosa, and may be considered typical of magmas in the Strait of Sicily graben system. Pantelleria differs from the other islands because a major long-term magma reservoir developed at high level, allowing the magma to fractionate to an evolved peralkaline composition. Some of the evolved melts show slightly enhanced Sr-isotope ratios, which suggest some contamination by continental crust.

Historical activity at Pantelleria

The only certain historical eruption of this volcano was that of October 1891. This was a submarine eruption of basaltic composition, which occurred on the NW slope of the volcano. The start of the eruption was preceded by fumarolic activity, earthquakes intense enough to crack water cisterns, and uplift of parts of the island. The greatest uplift was on the NE coast, where the ground rose by as much as 55 cm in 1890, and at least 25 cm in 1891. A 200 m long fracture parallel to the shoreline opened. Particularly sharp earthquakes were felt between 14 and 17 October 1891 when the eruption began on the sea floor. Once the eruption started, felt seismicity decreased.

No scientist visited the event, which only lasted a week, and our knowledge of what happened is based on the testimony of fishermen, who gave a remarkably clear account of what happened. An island was apparently not formed, but during the eruption, vast numbers of sub-spherical 'bombs' rose to the surface and floated. Some were allegedly first ejected out of the water and fell back. They were kept afloat by large gas-filled vesicles within them. The 'bombs' were hot, some incandescent, and produced columns of steam as they floated in the water. After some time, the 'bombs' tended to explode, with the sound of gun fire, and the fragments sank. The interpretation by geologists who read the reports of this phenomenon at the time was that the 'bombs' were lava pillows that were sufficiently gas rich to float to the surface rather than form beds of pillow lavas, such as those formed at Aci Castello on Etna. This type of activity is not, as far as we know, described in any modern texts, but is similar to that observed during the Azores submarine eruption in 1998–1999 off the island of Terceira (Fig. 9.12). The 'bombs' are better termed pillows or balloons.

Another submarine eruption may have taken place south of Pantelleria in December 1891.

Fig. 9.12. Floating gas-inflated lava balloons from the Serreta eruption west of Terceira island, in the Azores, 1999. This phenomenon fits exactly the description of the Pantelleria eruption of 1891. (Photograph courtesy of Nicolau Wallenstein, University of the Azores.)

Graham Island

Although Graham Island (Fig. 1.1), which formed in 1831 between Sicily and Africa, no longer exists, it is included here because the eruptive site appears to represent a new volcanic centre in the southern Italian volcanic province. There are reports of submarine eruptions in 1632, and possibly in 1701, at this site before Graham Island formed. There were further submarine eruptions in 1863 and 1999, indicating that the Graham Island eruption of 1831 was not a one-off event, and suggesting that this could be a new centre of repeated activity. Graham Island is thus an appropriate place to end our story of the volcanoes of southern Italy. It should be noted that there is also a nearby submarine site of activity, known as Pinne, which erupted in 1846, 1867 and 1911.

The formation of Graham Island (Fig. 9.13) caused considerable interest in scientific circles, and Charles Lyell gave a detailed summary of the various observations made by scientists and sailors. The arrival of a new island in the Mediterranean also attracted the attention of politicians from several of the European powers. As a result it had seven different names bestowed upon it (Nerita, Ferdinanda, Hotham, Graham, Corrao, Sciacca and Julia); the first person to land (during a lull in activity on 2 August) and raise the flag was Captain Senhouse of the British Royal Navy, and it was he who gave it the name Graham, which was eventually adopted as the formal English term.

The first signs of activity were earthquakes on 28 June 1831. These were felt both on the coast of Sicily and by a ship passing over the site. In the ship the sensation was similar to hitting a submerged sandbank. Similar movements were felt in boats close to the erupting island of Surtsey off the south coast of Iceland in the early 1960s. About a fortnight later, the captain of a Sicilian vessel reported seeing a 20 m high column of water rising into the air like a waterspout. This was followed by steam that rose to some 500 m. Similar jets occurred at about quarter of an hour intervals. Strong sulphurous smells soon reached the Sicilian coast, and the sea and shoreline there were coated with black cinders; some report that the situation was so bad that boats could hardly struggle through the water. About a week later, on 18 July, the same captain found a small island at the spot. He estimated it to be about 4 m high and observed a crater ejecting 'volcanic matter' and 'immense columns of vapour'. The sea round the island was covered with floating cinders as well as dead fish. The crater was open to the sea by a channel. At this stage, based on an earlier survey of the sea floor by the Royal Navy, the volcano must have been nearly 200 m tall.

Violent explosions continued to build up the volcanic island and by 4 August it is reported to have been about 60 m above sea level and 1½ km across. From then on, the rate of erosion of the loose tephra exceeded the rate of accumulation and the island rapidly diminished in size, developing wave-cut cliffs (Fig. 9.13). Later in the month, the existence of another submarine vent close to the surface was indicated by agitation of the sea and a rising steam column to the SW of the original island, but the subsidiary vent never reached the surface.

Carlo Gemmellaro from Catania visited the island on 12 August and Frederic Hoffmann on the 26 August. On 29 September the crater was quiet when a French party, led by Constant Prevost, landed on the island and reported that the water-filled crater was

(a)

(b)

Fig. 9.13. Two sketches of Graham Island: (**a**) 7 August 1831 (reduced from drawings by Captain Wodhouse RN), showing cliffs formed by erosion of the soft fresh tephra; (**b**) 29 September 1831; a sketch by one of the French scientific team showing more extensive erosion and the still steaming crater (from Lyell 1847).

about 50 m in diameter; the water was reddish in colour and almost boiling. Gas bubbles burst at the surface, expelling sand and cinders.

By the end of October the island had been nearly levelled to the surface of the sea. Late in 1833 there was still a dangerous reef. It was oval in planform, with a black rock some 50 m across, and just a few metres below the surface. Almost certainly this is the more resistant lava-filling of the conduit. To the SW was another shoal also consisting of lava, which was probably the site of the subsidiary vent.

From the description of the products and contemporary accounts it appears that most of the subaerial activity from the volcano was hydromagmatic (surtseyan) with cockscomb-like, or cypressoid explosions and continuous columns of generally comminuted tephra resulting from interaction between hot magma and sea water. Prevost reported cross-bedded layers, which today we would interpret as being formed by surges like those at Surtsey and Capelinhos. Reports that the interior of the eruptive columns glowed a dull red at night compare with modern observations of such surtseyan activity.

Peter Francis has pointed out that contemporary illustrations appear to show strombolian activity once the island was well established. Surtsey off Iceland (1963–1967) and the hydromagmatic eruption of Capelinhos in the Azores (1957–1958) both showed dry magmatic explosions once the sea water was excluded from the crater. Lavas were also erupted at both islands. Apparently, no subaerial lavas were erupted at Graham Island and thus no resistant layer was formed to help protect the island from erosion as occurred at Surtsey. Some say the Sicilian explanation for the rapid disappearance of the island was 'that it was in a hurry to escape the claim to it made by the English'.

Hazard and risk

Any volcanic island presents a very specific problem for civil defence authorities in terms of planning for a natural disaster. This is especially true for those with high numbers of residents (and in the summer, tourists), and for those islands far from the mainland. In the event of an eruption that is large in comparison with the size of the island, the only way to flee is by boat. For a small island, even a small magnitude eruption could leave nowhere for people to shelter.

On Ischia, there was a sustained period of seismic activity before the last eruption. Earthquakes on this island have taken a considerable toll of life already: this is clearly a tectonically unstable area and large earthquakes are to be expected again. Building standards have improved, but people on the island are vulnerable. The possibility of landslides is an additional hazard on this island. All but one of the eruptions that have occurred in the last 10 ka have taken place in the eastern sector of the island. Many of these eruptions have occurred in the northeastern sector, by far the most densely populated region of the island.

A future eruption on Linosa is likely to produce tephra that could accumulate to many metres thickness, bringing down roofs if not quickly shovelled away. Breathing ash could be a problem for both humans and animals, and grazing land could be affected. The danger of pockets of CO_2 gas collecting in low ground or hollows could also be a hazard. It should be emphasized that Linosa has had no historical eruptions; there is thus no evidence that it is still an active centre. The possibility of future activity should not, however, be ignored.

Pantelleria has to be considered as still active. It has hot springs with temperatures up to nearly boiling, indicating that a hydrothermal system exists. Based on the volcano's previous history, a range of possibilities exists for future activity. The most likely event is a small basaltic eruption either on land or as a surtseyan eruption off the coast.

Places to visit

Ischia

Ischia port, where the ferries and *aliscafi* dock was, until 1854, a complete crater and tuff ring. The low outer wall was excavated to create a harbour. The structure is thought to have been formed by an eruption in the third century BC.

The historical Arso lava flow is covered with pine trees. The crater associated with the eruption occurs east of Fiaiano and is surrounded by scoriaceous deposits formed during the eruption.

At Baia di Sorgeto on the west coast of the island, products of the Citarra Formation are well exposed; deposits consist of alternating coarse pumice breccias and laminated fine ash layers, some of which have an unequivocal surge origin.

To the east is the Castello d'Ischia lava dome, which is clearly visible with the prominent castle built on its top.

Particularly lithic-rich Monte Epomeo Green Tuff can be observed at Mt. St. Angelo on top of the older lava domes that form the base of the peninsula.

Examples of fumarole fields and thermal springs, include the beach at Maronti, and those at Olmitello and Cava Scura have temperatures of 65 °C and 72 °C respectively.

A climb to the top of Monte Epomeo provides good views of the island and outcrops of the Epomeo Green Tuff.

Ustica

Ustica is so small that the whole island is within walking range. Close to the town is the Falconiera surtseyan cone, which displays fine sections of wet, hydromagmatic deposits. On the coast south of the town are good examples of the hyaloclastites with secondary zeolites.

The road along the north coast allows access to coastal sections, including a breccia at Cala del Camposanto that may be a remnant of an avalanche deposit related to the collapse of the northern flank of the volcano. The volcanic centres in the middle of the island are easily accessible by roads and tracks.

Linosa

Like Ustica, the island of Linosa is small and easily accessible on foot. All the main centres can be visited with ease.

Pantelleria

As this island is somewhat larger, a car is of help here, although there are buses. The top of Montagna Grande provides an overall view of much of the geology of the island. The perimeter road that encircles the island provides access to many aspects of the geology. Pre-Green Tuff rocks can be seen in the cliffs at Cala Cinque Dente. The Green Tuff is seen overlying a cinder cone at Cala dell'Alca. It is also exposed on the perimeter road on the SE slopes, and at the southernmost tip of the island. Views of the caldera can be had from the roads that cut the outer wall. Monte Gelkhamar, south of Pantelleria town, provides an accessible and relatively fresh example of a dome with associated flows. A natural fumarolic sauna can be had in a small cave, known as Bagno Asciutto, south of Siba. A boat trip round the island provides views of the geology exposed in the sea cliffs, including sections through volcanic centres.

Notes

Ischia

Charles Lyell (1881) was one of the first to recognize marine molluscs high on the summit of Ischia. Rittmann (1930) first recognized the main structure of the island as being a horst and not a central volcano as was suggested by earlier workers such as Fonseca (1847) and Fuchs (1873). Gillot *et al.* (1982) used K/Ar dating to establish that the age of the Ischia horst was <30 ka BP and that the MEGT eruption was around 56 ka BP. The major ignimbrite formation of the island, the Monte Epomeo Green Tuff, was first described by Rittmann (1930) and subsequently by Vezzoli (1988), who also published a 1:10 000 geological map of the island.

Orsi *et al.* (1991*a*) compared the Ischia horst with the Pantelleria caldera and related both to simple shearing block resurgence. The space problem associated with such caldera resurgence at Ischia was highlighted by Tibaldi & Vezzoli (1998), who proposed that contemporaneous regional extension along normal faults allowed space for the resurgence without deformation. Fusi *et al.* (1990) discuss the resurgence and relations with regional tectonics.

Acocella & Funiciello (1999) showed that the resurgence of the Ischia horst is octagonal in shape, following regional tectonic trends, and was tilted about a NE–SW axis. Buchner *et al.* (1996) dated fossils and demonstrated that the Ischia horst has undergone 70 m uplift in the last 8500 years.

^{14}C dating of the volcanic products of the last 5000 years (Orsi *et al.* 1996*b*) has shown that eruptions were not evenly spaced and that periods of intense volcanic activity alternated with long quiescence.

The volcanic history of the island has been given by Capaldi *et al.* (1976–1977).

Ustica

The island was geologically mapped by Romano & Sturiale (1971) with an accompanying memoir. Cinque *et al.* (1988) more recently described the geology and geochemistry of the island, and De Vita *et al.* (1998) have dated rocks from the island. Calanchi *et al.* (1984) describe the submarine part of the volcano.

Linosa

Early study of the stratigraphy of Linosa was by Di Paola (1973). This was followed by more detailed studies by Lantini *et al.* (1988) and Grasso *et al.* (1998), and a map (Lanzafame *et al.* 1994).

Pantelleria

One of the first works on the geology of Pantelleria is that of Foerstner (1881). Washington (1914) gave an early account, largely accurate, of the volcanology and petrology of the island. Rittmann set up a project to investigate the geology of the island, resulting in a geological map and memoir (Rittmann 1967) and a number of papers on general geology (Villari 1974), domes (Villari 1968), the ignimbrites (Villari 1969) and the caldera (Villari 1970).

Cornette *et al.* (1983) reinterpreted some aspects of the geology. They were followed by Mahood & Hildreth (1986), who produced a highly detailed description of the geology of the island. There are differences in interpretation between the authors of these last two papers, and with Villari, mainly about the central caldera structure, and the origin of Montagna Grande. An old, mainly buried caldera mapped by Mahood & Hildreth (1986), was described by previous researchers as several unrelated faults.

Washington considered what we now interpret as dense welded tuffs to be lavas. Detailed textural examination by subsequent workers from the group of Rittmann recognized that they were pyroclastic rocks, and Villari identified some as ignimbrites. Wright (1980), who undertook a major study of the geology of Pantelleria, considered that most of the welded tuffs were of fall origin. The Green Tuff is the best exposed of the welded tuffs and has been subjected to most study. Mahood (1984), in her classic work on the volcanology of strongly peralkaline eruptions, argued that the mantling Green Tuff was largely emplaced by pyroclastic flows. She cited as evidence to support this interpretation the lack of deposition on the lee side of major topographic obstacles and the presence of lithic breccias. Recent work by Orsi *et al.* (1991*b*) also supported the proposition that the Green Tuff consists of pyroclastic flow, surge and fall deposits.

An English-language account of the 1891 eruption was given by Washington (1909), based mainly on an account by A. Ricco.

Graham Island

Useful reviews of the history of this ephemeral island have been given by Lyell (1847), Washington (1909) and more recently by Francis (1995).

Chapter 10. **The future**

The world of volcanoes is continually changing. We have tried to make this book as timeless as possible, but we have to recognize that some things may have changed by the time this book is published. Etna and Stromboli are in a state of continuous activity and any one of the others may burst into life or show signs of unrest. There is also the rather remote possibility of a brand new volcano making an appearance somewhere in the region!

There have been considerable advances in volcano forecasting and prediction during the last few decades, but even so the possibility of unexpected activity still lurks. This uncertainty adds to the vital need for forward planning by government to cope with an eruptive event. The size of the task of civil protection increases yearly as the number of people, together with the associated economic infrastructure, expands in areas likely to be affected by even the smallest of eruptions.

There are three key questions that volcanologists are asked by authorities when considering civil defence: When will the eruption start? Where will it be? What will happen? These are not always easy questions to answer except in hindsight! Guidelines can be established once there are precursory events or an eruption is under way. These may be based on previous experience, repeated events, and inferred possibilities. For example, an upwardly migrating seismic swarm should sound alarm bells that precautions need to be taken. Indeed, any change in a volcano's state needs careful attention.

All is not gloom. Volcanology has a lot to offer the public by way of warning and understanding of volcanic eruptions. If those who live in volcanic areas understand the phenomena in a general way before events happen they are better able to make decisions for themselves, and authorities are able to make realistic plans. The splendid video produced by the late Maurice and Katia Krafft, French volcanologists killed during an eruption on Unzen in Japan, has been instrumental in showing the nature of the problem to civil authorities. In Naples a start has been made to explain volcanoes to children as part of their school curriculum, and this should go a long way in preparing this city and its environs for the next eruption, whether from Vesuvius, Campi Flegrei, or even Ischia. Such educational programmes should be encouraged throughout the area and include the effects of earthquakes and other hazards as well.

Monitoring of Italian volcanoes is increasing, thus improving the ability to predict, or at least to advise on possible eventualities when a volcano does show signs of unrest. The 'how big' question is still elusive. The relationship between magnitude of eruptions and their frequencies tends to follow a power law so that there are statistically far more small eruptions than large ones. Planning must, therefore, concentrate on small to moderate magnitude eruptions, but not neglect the possibility of a 'big one'.

There has recently been much talk of *super volcanoes*, referring to those that have had very large magnitude eruptions. Perhaps super *eruptions* would be a better term, as most so-called super volcanoes spend much of their life giving rise to relatively small eruptions. The Campanian Ignimbrite is probably the only one that would fall in the *super* category. There have, however, been several relatively large ignimbrite-forming eruptions such as the Neapolitan Yellow Tuff eruption of Campi Flegrei and the Monte Epomeo Green Tuff eruption of Ischia. An eruption of even this scale in southern Italy could have profound effects on the whole of Europe, the Middle East and North Africa, certainly from an economic point of view.

We can consider several possibilities, of varying likelihood, for, say, the next 50 years, the normal span for long-term planning. It could be that:

(1) currently erupting volcanoes will continue their activity at much the same rate as today, and volcanoes in repose will stay in that state;

(2) one or more of the volcanoes currently erupting will change their eruptive style, requiring new forecasting;

(3) one of the volcanoes at present in repose will erupt;

(4) an unexpected event will occur (e.g. a sector collapse, a volcano will be born at a new site, a volcano considered extinct will become active);

(5) a major ignimbrite eruption will take place.

Most of these possibilities are likely to take place at some stage given a sufficiently long period of time, but could occur with differing probabilities during the next half-century. Option (1) is probably the most likely; this is the *status quo*.

Option (5), the possibility of a large ignimbrite-forming eruption, is the least likely, but cannot be ruled out; planning for such a mega-event may not be appropriate unless there are indicative precursory signs. Whether these would be recognized as such is another matter. Evidence from Santorini suggests that one or more strong earthquakes, which destroyed buildings, occurred on the island at least some months before the Minoan eruption. The effects may have been felt as far away as Crete. It is thought the inhabitants abandoned the island, taking with them their valuables. In this case evacuation meant leaving the island altogether, thus increasing the chance of survival whatever the size of the eruption.

The situation may not be so clear in the case of such precursors taking place on a mainland or near-coastal island. Modern monitoring techniques may give a better picture of what is happening during a state of unrest than was available to our Bronze Age forebears, but it is not clear that the magnitude of impending activity would be obvious. Thus evacuation of an area of radius 10 km may appear adequate, whereas for a large ignimbrite-forming eruption a 100 km radius (depending on topography) may be more appropriate.

Volcanoes can change their style of eruption. For example, some thousands of years ago, Mount Etna erupted more silicic magmas than at present, and gave rise to violent eruptions and caldera collapse over a high-level magma reservoir. Such changes may relate to new tectonic conditions, changes in the stress field induced by changing sea level, wetter or drier conditions affecting the water table, new batches of magma of different composition, or changes in rate of magma generation and residence times. Such changes would probably be recognized only when they start to happen, and in terms of hazard would require the volcano to be reassessed.

It is not always easy to distinguish between a volcano in repose and one that is now extinct. In either case a state of unrest is likely to herald new activity. However, what type of activity may not be clear, and precursors can start years or decades before an eruption. The same conditions probably apply to the birth of a new volcano. Volcanoes that have not erupted for a long time (i.e. for thousands of years) tend not to be monitored, available resources being funnelled towards those centres perceived to be more in need.

The degree of unexpectedness of an event to some extent depends on the amount of monitoring and vigilance, and the scale of the event. A volcanologist used to working close to eruptive activity is keenly aware that it is the unexpected that is the biggest danger. By unexpected we mean a deviation from a recognized pattern. An example of this might be mild and persistent strombolian explosions changing to vigorous fire fountaining.

However, from the point of view of public safety it is the bigger, rare events that are of particular concern because they can be unexpected. It is true that they need not necessarily be so. For example, careful monitoring of ground deformation giving the rate of extension can detect the possibility and timing of sector collapse. Nevertheless, an earthquake can cause instability leading to collapse, and earthquakes are not normally predictable.

Monitoring

It is clear from the above discussion that monitoring of volcanoes is of prime importance: first, in an attempt to predict future activity; and, second, to develop a bank of 'hindsight' data, where the significance of an observation is realized only after the event but may be used predictively in the future. In areas like those round the volcanoes of southern Italy, where there are high densities of populations of vulnerable people, monitoring is particularly important. Monitoring also provides data that can be used to further understand a volcano and volcanic processes.

The amount of monitoring of Italian volcanoes has increased consistently over the last few decades and especially since 1970. Not all the volcanoes are monitored to the same extent, nor do they all have the same techniques applied to them. Monitoring includes both geophysical and geochemical techniques. Most of the techniques available have been applied at one or more volcanoes in this area.

Seismic arrays are a critical part of any monitoring programme and one of the most useful tools. Seismic unrest at a volcano is often an important precursor of activity, and can be used to track magma movement. During an eruption, increased seismic activity may precede or accompany changes in rate or style of activity. Tremor often accompanies high-level magma movement usually starting before an eruption. Patterns in seismic energy release can sometimes be identified during an eruption, a given pattern foretelling a specific type of event.

Monitoring of ground deformation, both vertical and horizontal, can also be a valuable tool. The ground surface responds to movements of magma to and from high-level reservoirs and magma emplacement in dykes. In addition, flank instability can be monitored and used to predict forthcoming slope failures. However, the meticulous measurement of small movements that is required has always restricted the use of this technique. The availability of GPS (Global Positioning System) in recent years is changing this, and more widespread observations of ground movements are to be expected. The use of remote-sensing radar techniques such as interferometry may also revolutionize monitoring of Earth movements at volcanoes. Repeated microgravity measurements can also indicate changes in the distribution of high-level magma.

Changes in gas and water geochemistry can indicate changes in the state of a volcano. This includes not only composition but also temperature and, in the case of gases, rate of output. Increased output of SO_2 has been observed in the vapour plume of Etna just before eruptions, and variations in radon release may also be an important indicator.

Finally, an important part of monitoring is surveillance of the actual activity. Interpretation of the activity as it happens leads to prediction of what may happen in the near future. Again, repeating patterns may develop although these may not be the same for all eruptions even at the same volcano. In addition, physical modelling of volcanic processes is becoming an important tool with which to understand the way a volcano works. To be modelled successfully, the phenomenon being investigated must be properly defined and this can only be done by detailed observation including the measurement of physical properties of the materials being erupted. Such measurements include rate of eruption, heat flux, rheology, rate of crust development on lavas, explosion column heights, etc. These are often, because of the nature of the activity and inherent dangers, not easy to measure.

A postscript

We cannot promise any visitor to southern Italy the sight of incandescent red lava: volcanoes are singularly fickle and do not perform to order. For those who see one of these volcanoes in action, it will be memorable: for those who do not, we offer the following from Sir William Hamilton as a substitute:

'I warned my family not to be alarmed, as I expected there would be an earthquake at the moment of the lava's bursting out; but before eight of the clock in the morning I perceived that the mountain had opened a mouth, without noise, about a hundred yards lower than the ancient crater, on the side towards the Monte di Somma, and I plainly perceived, by a white smoak, which always accompanies the lava, that it had forced its way out: as soon as it had vent, the smoak no longer came out with violence from the top. As I imagined that there would be no danger in approaching the mountain when the lava had vent, I went up immediately, accompanied by one peasant only. I passed the hermitage, and proceeded far in the valley between the mountain of Somma and that of Vesuvius, which is called Atrio di Cavallo. I was making observations upon the lava, which had already, from the spot where it first broke out, reached the valley; when on a sudden, about noon, I heard a violent noise within the mountain, and at about a quarter of a mile off the place where I stood, the mountain split and with much noise, from this new mouth a fountain of liquid fire shot up many feet high, and then like a torrent, rolled on directly towards us. The earth shook at the same time that a volley of pumice stones fell thick upon us; in an instant clouds of black smoak and ashes caused almost a total darkness; the explosions from the top of the mountain were much louder than any thunder I have ever heard, and the smell of sulphur was very offensive. My guide alarmed took to his heals; and I must confess that I was not at my ease. I followed close, and we ran near three miles without stopping; as the earth continued to shake under our feet, I was apprehensive of the opening of a fresh mouth, which might have cut off our retreat. I also feared that the violent explosions would detach rocks from the mountain of the Somma, under which we were obliged to pass; besides the pumice-stones, falling upon us like hail, were such a size as to cause a disagreable sensation upon the part where they fell. After having taken breath, as the earth still trembled greatly, I thought it most prudent to leave the mountain, and return to my Villa, where I found my family in a great alarm, at the continual and violent explosions of the volcano, which shook our house to its very foundation, the doors and windows swinging upon their hinges. About two of the clock in the afternoon another lava forced its way out . . .

The noise and smell of sulphur increasing, we removed from our Villa to Naples; and I thought proper, as I passed by Portici, to inform the Court of what I had seen; and I humbly offered it as my opinion, that his Sicilian Majesty should leave the neighbourhood of the threatening mountain. However, the Court did not leave Portici till about twelve of the clock, when the lava was very near. I observed on my way to Naples, which was less than two hours after I had left the mountain, that the lava had actually covered three miles of the very road through which we had retreated.'

Notes

Two recent books on monitoring volcanoes are those by McGuire *et al.* (1995) and Scarpa & Tilling (1996). The effect on society by volcanoes has been discussed in detail by Chester (1993).

One serious problem encountered by scientists in advising civil defence authorities is that of explaining the nature of the hazard. Words are often inadequate in doing this. The late Maurice and Katia Krafft left a vast collection of film footage of erupting volcanoes showing a wide range of types of activity. Before they died they had started to make a video about volcanic activity to illustrate hazard. This was completed after their death (Krafft *et al.* 1991) and is available through UNESCO. It makes exciting viewing even to a volcanologist and certainly does a good job of showing the problems that could be faced by an eruption.

The quotation describing the 1767 eruption of Vesuvius is from Hamilton (1776).

Appendix. **Chemical compositions for a selection of rocks from the volcanoes of southern Italy**

	Vesuvius		Campi Flegrei			Roccamonfina				Vulture		
	1	2	3	4	5	6	7	8	9	10	11	12
SiO_2	51.9	47.9	62.3	59.33	59.99	46.4	53.85	63.21	49	44.34	54.67	37.0
TiO_2	0.49	0.95	0.46	0.38	0.43	0.94	0.52	0.22	0.88	1.13	0.14	1.22
Al_2O_3	19.1	16.4	18.98	18.19	19.17	15.7	19.22	17.43	16.1	15.81	21.1	10.7
Fe_2O_3	4.3	8.3	1.77	3.41	2.35	5.3	2.3	2.04	3.1	6.09	1.26	5.47
FeO			1.65		0.72	3.4	2.16		5.4	3.34	0.61	2.18
MnO	0.13	0.15	0.25	0.15	0.22	0.15	0.11	0.21	0.16	0.2	0.12	0.19
MgO	1.83	5.26	0.35	0.51	0.21	6	1.78	bdl	7.5	5.32	0.24	3.30
CaO	5.7	10.8	1.62	2.28	1.71	11.6	4.77	1.14	11.6	12.83	1.92	20.5
Na_2O	4.29	2.27	5.51	4.57	7.47	1.6	3.81	4.97	1.9	3.17	5.37	1.46
K_2O	8.72	6.36	7.03	7.92	6.89	6.6	8.07	6.75	2.5	3.2	6.91	1.77
P_2O_5	0.24	0.83	0.08	0.12	0.02	0.58	0.2	0.09	0.32	1.22	0.02	0.59
CO_2	0.4	bdl										9.79
H_2O	1.99	0.13			0.82	0.94			1.02	1.89	7.65	
LOI				3.31			3.62	3.54				5.27
Total	99.09	99.35	100	100.17	100	99.21	100.41	99.6	99.48	98.54	100.01	99.5

	Vulcano				Stromboli			Ischia		Etna			
	13	14	15	16	17	18	19	20	21	22	23	24	25
SiO_2	52.7	51.79	73	67.2	53.33	57.34	49.89	52.6	62.92	51.47	47.14	47.21	60.95
TiO_2	0.82	0.66	0.1	0.26	0.8	0.84	0.98	1.36	0.57	1.45	1.79	1.62	1.44
Al_2O_3	16.31	14.96	13.6	14.3	16.1	17.28	18.05	18.69	19.53	14.92	17.58	16.5	17.62
Fe_2O_3	9.35	9.03	1.15	2.2	3.18	3.68	3.86	5.9	0.92	0.94	3.25	4.43	3.07
FeO			1.05	1.7	4.58	3.22	4.9	2.76	1.77	9.07	7.1	6.45	1.93
MnO	0.16	0.17	0.08	0.06	0.15	0.14	0.16	0.14	0.15	0.18	0.17	0.21	0.14
MgO	4.35	4.78	0.15	1.2	6.74	3.62	5.97	3.25	0.3	9.6	5.54	6.23	1.19
CaO	8.51	8.6	1	2.4	10.54	7.32	10.78	7.52	1.16	9.1	11.47	11.06	3.92
Na_2O	2.72	3.51	4.5	3.9	2.52	3.28	2.6	3.61	6.29	3.1	3.96	3.2	5.66
K_2O	2.93	4.53	5.15	5.2	1.21	2.57	2.07	3.89	6.62	0.25	1.08	1.76	2.77
P_2O_5	0.33	0.44	0.05		0.19	0.27	0.45	0.62		0.2	0.74	0.51	0.41
CO_2										0.19	0.3	0.14	0.12
H_2O			0.6	1.8	0.47	0.28		0.43	0.66	0.37	0.61	0.31	0.23
LOI	1.03	1.2					0.28						
Total	99.21	99.67	100.43	100.22	99.81	99.84	99.99	100.77	100.89	100.84	100.73	99.63	99.45

	Linosa		Ustica		Pantelleria	
	26	27	28	29	30	31
SiO_2	46.55	49.6	51.62	53.1	46.22	69.5
TiO_2	2.33	2.05	1.45	1.18	5.68	0.5
Al_2O_3	15.23	16.31	17.28	18.22	12.23	8.7
Fe_2O_3	2.78	0.71	4.2	4.86	4.91	
FeO	8.05	8.87	4.81	3.45	7.71	7.8
MnO	0.17	0.17	0.15	0.18		0.32
MgO	8.77	5.61	4.64	3.33	6.74	0.13
CaO	9.04	8.87	8.83	5.75	9.86	0.39
Na_2O	3.87	4.44	4.96	5.9	3.39	5.9
K_2O	1.5	1.55	1.18	2.2	1.13	4.5
P_2O_5		0.6	0.41	0.91	1.46	0.05
CO_2	0.66					
H_2O	0.95	1.15	0.12	0.15	0.22	
LOI						
Total	99.9	99.93	99.65	99.23	99.55	97.79

1, Tephriphonolite pumice from Vesuvius AD 79 eruption (Ayuso *et al.* 1998).
2, Phonotephrite scoria from Vesuvius 1631? eruption (Ayuso *et al.* 1998).
3, Trachyte, the Campanian Ignimbrite, Campi Flegrei (Armienti *et al.* 1983).
4, Trachyte, the Neapolitan Yellow Tuff, Campi Flegrei (Scarpati *et al.* 1993).
5, Phonolite, Monte Nuovo, Campi Flegrei (Armienti *et al.* 1983).
6, Tephrite–basanite lava, HKS, Roccamonfina (Appleton 1972).
7, Tephriphonolite, Brown Leucitic Tuff, HKS, Roccamonfina (Luhr & Giannetti 1987).
8, Trachyte, Lower Galluccio Tuff, White Trachytic Tuff, Roccamonfina (Cole *et al.* 1992).
9, Tephrite–basanite lava, LKS, Roccamonfina (Appleton 1972).
10, Tephrite/basanite, foidite lava, Vulture (De Fino *et al.* 1986).
11, Tephriphonolitic trachytic ignimbrite, Vulture (De Fino *et al.* 1986).
12, Carbonatite-bearing tuff, Vulture (Stoppa & Principe 1998).
13, Shoshonite lava, 'Older Series', Vulcano (Ellam *et al.* 1988).
14, Shoshonite lava, 'Younger Series', Vulcano (Ellam *et al.* 1988).
15, Rhyolite, obsidian lava from Fossa Cone, Vulcano (Keller 1980*a*).
16, Trachyte, breadcrust bomb, Fossa eruption 1888–1890, Vulcano (Keller 1980*b*).
17, Basaltic andesite, CA Series, Strombolicchio, Stromboli (Hornig-Kjarsgaard *et al.* 1993).
18, Andesite, HKCA Series, Palaeostromboli, Stromboli (Hornig-Kjarsgaard *et al.* 1993).
19, Shoshonitic basalt, scoria 1998 explosion, Stromboli (Rosi *et al.* 2000).
20, Basaltic trachyandesite lava, Grotta di Terra, Phase 3, Ischia (Poli *et al.* 1987).
21, Trachytic obsidian, Scarrupo di Panza, Phase 3, Ischia (Poli *et al.* 1987).
22, Olivine tholeiite basalt, Adrano, Mount Etna (Chester *et al.* 1985).
23, Hawaiite, Simeto Valley, Mount Etna (Duncan 1978).
24, Hawaiite, 1974 eruption, Mount Etna (Chester *et al.* 1985).
25, Benmoreite, ignimbrite at Biancavilla, Mount Etna (Duncan 1976).
26, Alkali basalt, M. Biancarella, Linosa (Di Paola 1973).
27, Hawaiite, Scalo Vecchio, Linosa (Di Paola 1973).
28, Hawaiite, M. Guardia dei Turchi, Ustica (Romano & Sturiale 1971).
29, Mugearite, dyke Passo della Madonna, Ustica (Romano & Sturiale 1971).
30, Basalt, M. Sant' Elmo, Pantelleria (Washington 1914).
31, Pantellerite (peralkaline rhyolite), Green Tuff, Pantelleria (Mahood 1984).

Plate 1. A painting of the 1760 eruption of Vesuvius (see Fig. 2.1) viewed from the south by Pietro Fabris, based on a field sketch by the artist (from Hamilton 1776). The flow has cut the main road between Torre del Greco and Torre Annunziata. The hill to the left of the picture is the cinder cone of Camaldoli della Torre with a convent on top.

Plate 2. Vesuvius seen from the centre of Naples some 17 km distant. Note the buildings encroaching the slopes of the volcano.

Plate 3. Aerial photograph of the summit of Vesuvius (Courtesy Jet Propulsion Laboratory, California). Note avalanche deposits formed in the 1944 eruption (A) and the 1944 lava flow (L) in the Atrio de Cavallo.

Plate 4. Vulture volcano seen from the SE. Note the truncated summit region caused by sector collapse. The collapse structure the Valle dei Grigi is open to the west, away from the camera.

Plate 5. The Fossa cone, Vulcano as seen from the Acquacalda beach to the north. Fumaroles rise through the Acquacalda beach in the foreground. The Forgia Vecchia (FV) a small crater formed by a historical eruption in the 18th century.

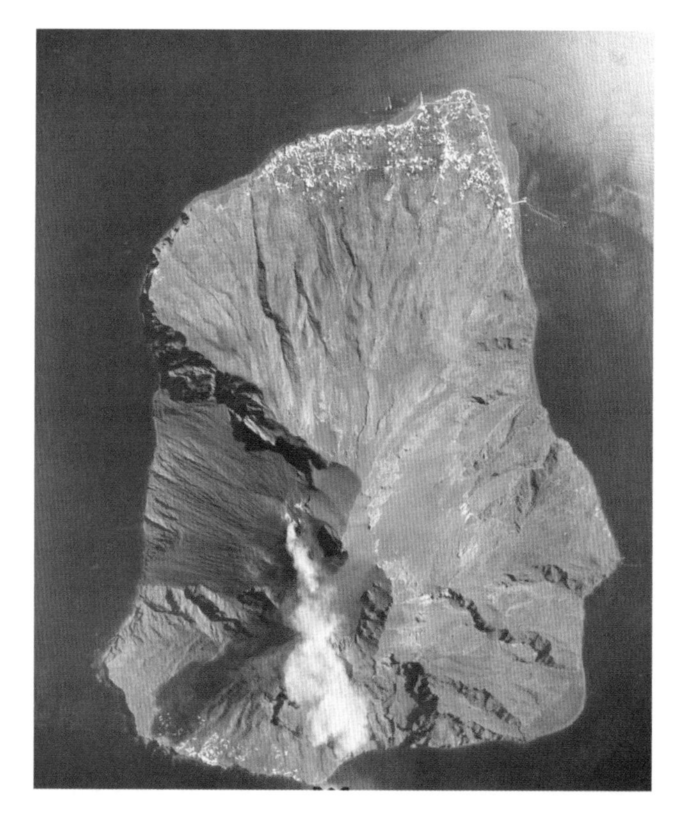

Plate 6. Aerial photograph of the island of Stromboli (courtesy of the Jet Propulsion Laboratory, California). The active craters to the west of the summit at the head of the Sciara del Fuoco can be located by the source of the steam plume.

Plate 7. Strombolian explosion from one of the craters at the crater terrace viewed from Pizzo Sopra la Fossa, Stromboli. The height of the bomb trajectories is about 250 m.

Plate 8. Pumice quarries cut into the eastern flanks of Monte Pilato, Lipari. Monte Pilato overlies the Pomiciazzo obsidian flow (P) that provided the source for Neolithic obsidian.

Plate 9. Etna seen from the NW. The ridge extending towards the left from the summit is the NE Rift. The town of Randazzo is in the foreground.

Plate 10. Active aa lava during the 2001 eruption of Etna.

Plate 11. Active pahoehoe lava from the SE Crater, Etna, in 1999.

Plate 12. Cinder cone formation during the first phase of the west flank eruption of Etna in 1974.

Plate 13. A strombolian explosion seen at dusk from the NE Crater in 1969.

Plate 14. Fire fountaining at night from the SE Crater, Etna, June 2000.

Plate 15. The main upper vent of the 2001 eruption of Etna during a phase of phreatomagmatic activity. Heavy tephra fall is occurring to the right of the picture.

Plate 16. The lower vent of the 2001 eruption of Etna. This was the main source of lava, but explosive activity occurred from several vents.

Glossary

In geology, terms are not always used by everyone in precisely the same way. The purpose of this glossary is first to provide a thumbnail sketch of the meaning of terms we have used in the book; we hope this will be useful particularly to students. Second, where usage varies, *we* give the meaning *we* ascribe to the terms. Names in bold within the definitions refer to other entries.

aa lava: lava that has a rough surface made up of materials including **clinker**, **scoria**, and **block**-sized lava fragments. Name derived from the onomatopoeic Hawaiian word *a'ā* implying 'hard to walk on'

accretionary lapilli: spherical or nearly spherical masses of indurated **ash**, ranging from a few millimetres to several centimetres in diameter. These form as moist aggregates of ash in eruption clouds and can result from, for example, rain falling through an eruption cloud, or occur in wet **hydromagmatic eruptions**

aenigmatite: a rare titanium-bearing silicate mineral that occurs in some alkaline volcanic rocks, normally a constituent of the groundmass. It has a composition of $Na_2Fe_5^{2+}TiSi_6O_{20}$ and in thin section shows a characteristic deep red to black pleochroism

agglutinate: **spatter** that has welded together, normally close to the **vent**, owing to its high-temperature/low-viscosity condition.

alkali basalt: a **basalt** in which the alkali/SiO_2 ratio is relatively high. Normally contains crystals of **plagioclase**, **pyroxene** (**augite**) and **olivine** (compare **tholeiite**)

alkalic rock series: an evolutionary sequence of volcanic rocks with compositions ranging from **alkali basalt**, through **hawaiite**, **mugearite** and **benmoreite** to **trachyte**. Formed by low-pressure fractionation in a high-level **magma reservoir**

amphiboles: a group of hydrous ferromagnesian silicate minerals. One of the most common is hornblende

andesite: an intermediate volcanic rock between **basalt** and **rhyolite** in composition. It has 53–63% SiO_2 and typically contains **phenocrysts** of **plagioclase**, **augite** and usually **hornblende**. **Biotite** may also be present

analcime: a **feldspathoid** mineral with composition $NaAlSi_2O_6H_2O$

aphanitic (aphyric) texture: texture of an igneous rock (usually **lava**) with a microcrystalline groundmass and few or no **phenocrysts**

ash: fine-grained **tephra** with a grain size of <2 mm

augite: see **pyroxenes**

basalt: a dark volcanic rock, rich in Fe and Mg, containing *c.* 45–52 wt% SiO_2. It is the most common lava composition and makes up the floors of the terrestrial oceans.

Typically contains crystals of calcic **plagioclase**, **augite** and **olivine**. (See **alkali basalt** and **tholeiite**)

basanite: an alkali basaltic rock that has a low SiO_2 content. In these rocks **feldspathoids** occur alongside **feldspar**, and they are typically rich in **olivine**

benmoreite: an intermediate member of the **alkalic rock series** with a typical range of 59–62 wt% SiO_2. A pale, sometimes pinkish rock, in which **plagioclase** is the main **phenocryst** phase. Tends to have a platy cleavage (see **trachyte**)

biotite: a dark, platy silicate mineral of the mica group, with a complex composition ($K(Mg,Fe)_3(AlSi_3O_{10})(OH)_2$)

block: an angular fragment of rock with a diameter greater than 64 mm (compare **boulder**)

block and ash flow: a **pyroclastic flow** formed by collapse of a volcanic **dome** or a lava flow on a steep slope. The deposit consists of poorly sorted **blocks** and **ash**

block lava: lava that has a surface consisting of angular, **block**-sized fragments

bocca: the mouth of a volcanic **vent** (literally 'mouth' in Italian). The term is not in general use outside Italy; but the equivalent Spanish word, *boca*, is used in Spanish-speaking countries as a volcanological term

bomb (volcanic): a **tephra** fragment greater than 64 mm in diameter. If formed from liquid **magma**, it may have a variety of forms including spindle shapes formed by rotation during flight, so-called cow-pats from blobs of liquid **lava**, or irregular forms from shreds of vesicular **lava**. Bombs formed from poorly vesicular lava or consisting of **lithic fragments** are commonly blocky

bomb sag: deformation of strata caused when a bomb strikes the ground. The strata below the bomb are depressed downwards. Most commonly formed in wet deposits such as those formed by a **hydromagmatic eruption**

boulder: a block of rock greater than 256 mm across that has a subrounded form (compare **block**)

bradyseism: ground movements on the floor of a **caldera** usually accompanied by seismic swarms. The term was originally coined to describe events at Campi Flegrei. Such events are more generally referred to outside Italy as *caldera unrest*

breadcrust bombs: volcanic bombs that develop a congealed crust during flight, but in which continued **exsolution** of gases in the interior causes expansion, so cracking the crust to a bread-like form

breccia: a rock composed mainly of broken, angular rock fragments. There may be a fine-grained matrix

calcite: calcium carbonate ($CaCO_3$). The most common carbonate mineral

calc-alkaline rock series: an evolutionary sequence of sub-alkaline rocks from **basalt** through **andesite** to **rhyolite** typical of volcanism at subductional plate boundaries

caldera: a large volcanic depression, roughly circular to elliptical in planform with a diameter normally greater than 1.5 km. Interpreted to be the result of collapse (or multiple collapses) into a partly emptied magma reservoir. A nested caldera shows different generations of smaller calderas within a larger caldera. The prefix resurgent is used to designate a caldera whose floor initially subsided, but was later uplifted on one or more occasions. Word is the Spanish for *cauldron*, also used to describe topographic depressions in the Canary Islands

carbonatite: an igneous (both intrusive and extrusive) rock that contains more than 50% primary carbonate minerals such as **calcite**

cinder: general term for coarse volcanic ash and lapilli

cinder cone: a volcanic cone with summit crater and mainly built of **ash**, **scoria** and **bombs**. Typically formed by **strombolian explosions** or **fire fountains**

clinker: a jagged, vesicular fragment of lava

columnar jointing: a joint pattern perpendicular to the cooling surface in a volcanic rock. It is formed by cooling contraction of the rock, and forms roughly six-sided columns

composite volcano: a volcanic cone built by alternating layers of **lava** and **tephra**. Synonymous with 'stratovolcano'

crater: a roughly circular volcanic depression normally less than 1.5 km across. It may have the form of an inverted cone, or have a flat floor. Normally formed by explosive activity over the feeding conduit, but there may also be enlargement by collapse (compare **pit**)

cross-bedding: sedimentary structure in which the bedding planes are oblique to the top and bottom of the unit. Sets of beds form a broken chevron pattern. In **pyroclastic rocks** they are characteristic of surge deposits, but also occur in reworked **tephra**

crystal fractionation: a mechanism by which magmas evolve from one liquid composition to another by separation of crystals as they form. This takes place by a number of processes including the sinking or floating of crystals depending on whether they are more or less dense than the surrounding melt; or by *in situ* crystallization with crystals growing from the reservoir walls. As a result, the composition of the remaining liquid changes to one that is more **silicic**. The term *fractional crystallization* is subtly different in that it involves isolation of the growing crystals without necessarily their removal from the melt

dagala: a local term for an inlier of older rock formed by being surrounded by younger lava. The term is synonymous with *kipuka*, widely used for the same landform especially in the USA and derived from a Hawaiian word

debris avalanche (volcanic): a large mass of material moving rapidly under the force of gravity as a result of **sector collapse** on the flanks of a volcano. The deposit so formed consists of angular blocks with associated smaller fragments. The surface of the deposit is characteristically hummocky when fresh

debris flow: movement of fragmental material as a gravity flow involving water. In volcanic terrains the sediment is usually **tephra**, sometimes including blocks of lava. The flow is usually initiated by rainfall, or overflow from a crater lake. Debris flow deposits are usually poorly sorted (see **lahar**)

diorite: the intrusive equivalent of **andesite**

dolerite: an intrusive equivalent of **basalt**. It has a fine- to medium-grained texture

dome (volcanic): a steep-sided mass of lava accumulated directly above the vent. The lava is erupted slowly and, rather than flow far from the vent, tends to increase in thickness as the volume increases. Such eruptions are of **magma** that has a high effective **viscosity**

dyke (US **dike**): a vertical, or near-vertical, sheet of intrusive igneous rock formed by **magma** moving along a fracture either vertically or horizontally. Generally discordant with the surrounding rocks. Most eruptions result from magma rising to the surface as dykes

ephemeral vent: (also called ephemeral **bocca**): a **rootless vent** that emits lava for only a short time, usually a matter of hours

epicentre: the point on the Earth's surface directly above the **focus** of an earthquake

exsolution: the release of volatiles from solution in a magma or lava to produce gases

fault: a dislocation of rocks along a plane. Movements on faults cause earthquakes

feldspars: quantitatively the most important igneous rock-forming silicates. They consist of a group of aluminosilicates of sodium, potassium and calcium. The plagioclase minerals form a solid solution series between the end-members albite ($NaAlSi_3O_8$) and anorthite ($CaAl_2Si_2O_8$). The potassic form is orthoclase ($KAlSi_3O_8$)

feldspathoids: a group of aluminosilicate minerals similar to **feldspars**, but containing less silica

fire fountain: an explosive event in which there is a continuous jet of fragmenting lava rising up to several hundred metres above a vent. Fine particles can be carried by convection in the atmosphere to higher levels than the main jet. Normally associated with basalt eruptions (compare **strombolian explosion**)

fissure: a vertical or subvertical crack, formed by extension or at the tip of a penetrating **dyke**

focus: position of the source of an earthquake (see **epicentre**)

foidite: general name for an igneous rock rich in **feldspathoid** minerals

fractionation: see **crystal fractionation**

fumarole: a vent emitting volcanic **gas**

gas: volatiles are an important constituent of **magma**. The main gases to be released at a volcano are water, carbon dioxide, sulphur dioxide and hydrogen sulphide

graben: a trough or valley bounded by approximately parallel-trending faults formed under tension. These can be of tectonic origin, but may also be the surface expression of an underlying **dyke**

haüyne: a sodic **feldspathoid** with a composition $(Na,Ca)_{4-8}(Al_6Si_6O_{24})(SO_4,S)_{1-2}$

hawaiite: a basic member of the **alkalic rock series** with a **typical** range of 47–52 wt% SiO_2. Formally defined as a sodic variety of trachybasalt. Contains phenocrysts of **plagioclase, augite** and **olivine**

hazard: refers to a potentially dangerous phenomenon or activity and its effects (compare **risk** and **vulnerability**)

hornblende: see **amphiboles**

hornito: see **spatter cone**

horst: elevated, linear block of land bounded by approximately parallel-trending faults. (compare **graben**)

hyaloclastite: a volcanic rock consisting mainly of generally poorly sorted fragments formed during a submarine (or subglacial) eruption by lava–water interaction. The fragments, initially glassy, are often altered to a clay mineral, palagonite, which takes its name from the village of Palagonia on the edge of the Iblean Plateau, Sicily (compare **pillow lavas**)

hydromagmatic eruption: any eruption involving explosions caused by the fragmentation of magma by contact with water. The water may be in the form of lakes, sea water or ground water. The products are often highly comminuted (compare **phreatomagmatic eruption**)

hydrothermal: relating to naturally heated water, its activity and products from it

ignimbrite: a normally poorly sorted **tephra** deposit consisting of **shards** and **pumice** emplaced from a **pyroclastic flow**

intensity: a subjective measure of the strength of an earthquake at a given distance from the **epicentre**, based on effects such as building damage. Expressed as a 12-point scale known as the Mercalli scale

interferometry (RADAR): a technique for determining ground deformation using airborne or satellite Radar Synthetic Aperture data

isopach: a line on a map joining points of equal thickness of a stratum or group of strata

isopleth: a line on a map joining points of equal value such as the mean or maximum diameter of **pumice** or **lithic fragments** in a **tephra** deposit

kaersutite: an amphibole characterized chemically by a high titanium content

lahar: a flow of volcanic materials and water caused by slope instability often triggered by heavy rainfall. This is a specifically volcanic form of **debris flow** and the word is of Indonesian origin

lapilli: fragments of **tephra** between 2 and 64 mm in diameter

latite: an extrusive igneous rock containing roughly equal amounts of alkali **feldspar** and sodic **plagioclase**

lava: rock either in the molten or solid form, consisting of erupted **magma**

lava channel: a channel developed on a lava flow field by lava constrained laterally by margins of congealed lava known as **levees**. When active they may be bank full or partly drained allowing the inner walls of the channel to be visible

lava tube: a lava tunnel formed by the roofing over of a **lava channel** by a congealed crust. Visible in congealed lava if the active lava has drained out

leucite: a pale **feldspathoid** mineral with the composition $KAlSiO_6$. Normally found in K-rich, SiO_2-poor volcanic rocks

leucitite: a volcanic rock containing **leucite** (30–50%) and calcium **pyroxenes**. A variety of **foidite**

levee: bank of congealed lava and scoria on the margin of a **lava channel**. Levees can build up with time by overflows of lava from the channel. Levees can also form on the margins of **pyroclastic flows** and **debris flows**

lithic fragment: a fragment of older rock incorporated in either lava or tephra deposits. The fragment may have been torn from the walls of the volcanic conduit, or picked up from the ground during flow; it may be older volcanic rock, or basement material

lithostatic pressure: the vertical stress caused by the weight of overlying rocks

maar: similar to a **tuff ring**, but with crater floor below ground level. Ejected products are in some cases entirely **lithic fragments**

mafic: description of rocks that have a high content of magnesium and iron, and a low content of silica. They are normally dark coloured

magma: molten rock below the surface where it may remain and cool as an intrusion, or rise to produce an eruption (compare **lava**)

magma reservoir: a magma storage area beneath a volcano. Sometimes referred to as a *magma chamber* but this is misleading because it is often a complex of igneous intrusions

magnitude: a standard measure of the energy released by an earthquake. It is usually expressed by the Richter scale, which is logarithmic

melilite: a group of complex silicates of calcium, aluminium and magnesium minerals ranging in composition from $Ca_2MgSi_2O_7$ to $Ca_2Al_2SiO_7$. Commonly found in **feldspathoidal** rocks in particular where there has been reaction between basaltic magma and carbonate sediments

monzodiorite: a felsic plutonic rock that lies between **monzonite** and **diorite** in mineralogical composition

monzonite: the intrusive form of **latite**

mugearite: an intermediate member of the **alkalic rock series** with a range of 53–57 wt% SiO_2. Formally defined as a sodic variety of trachybasalt. A pale rock with **plagioclase** the main **phenocryst** phase

nepheline: a common **feldspathoid** mineral of composition $(Na,K)AlSiO_4$

Newtonian fluid: one in which the rate of shearing is directly proportional to the applied shear stress. Lavas only rarely have Newtonian properties (see **non-Newtonian fluid**)

non-Newtonian fluid: one in which the rate of shearing is not proportional to the applied shear stress. This may take a number of forms, but in lava there appears to be a minimum applied shear stress required to cause shear. In other words, the lava has a **yield strength** that must be exceeded for flow to occur

ogives: concentric pressure ridges on the surface of a lava flow. Term borrowed from glaciology

olivines: a group of ferromagnesian silicate minerals forming solid solution series from Mg_2SiO_4 to Fe_2SiO_4

orthoclase: see **feldspars**

pahoehoe lava: lava that has a smooth (glassy when fresh) crust. The surface is often contorted into waves and rope-like forms. Flow advance may be as a sheet, or by growth of sub-metre-sized toes of lava. Term derived from an onomatopoeic Hawaiian word implying that it is easy to walk on

pantellerite: a **peralkaline rhyolite**, often with a green colour reflecting the presence of alkali **pyroxenes** and **amphiboles**

peralkaline: an igneous rock in which the molecular amount of alkali oxides (Na_2O + K_2O) exceeds molecular alumina (Al_2O_3)

phenocrysts: larger crystals set in a fine-grained or glassy matrix of an igneous rock. In lavas they have normally grown in the magma before eruption

phreatomagmatic eruption: a form of **hydromagmatic eruption** in which the water component is ground water. Often used synonymously with **hydromagmatic eruption**

phreatic explosion: a form of explosion in which the products are entirely **lithic fragments** derived from the wall rocks

pigeonite: see **pyroxenes**

pillow lava: a characteristic product of underwater eruption consisting of discrete sub-spherical, pillow-like masses of lava with a glassy rind

piperno: a pyroclastic **agglutinate** formed of poorly vesicular fragments of lava that are welded together. Type locality is Campi Flegrei

pit: steep-sided volcanic depression less than about 1.5 km with a sub-circular planform formed by collapse (see **crater** and **caldera**)

plinian eruption: a sustained explosive event that may continue for up to several days, but is usually shorter. The eruption column may rise as high as 50 km and penetrate the tropopause. Normally associated with more **silicic** magmas. Named after Pliny the Younger, who first described such an eruption at Vesuvius in AD 79

plagioclase: see **feldspars**

pumice: a pale-coloured, highly vesicular volcanic rock normally of silicic composition. (compare **Scoria**)

pyroclastic fall deposits: tephra deposited from ballistic trajectories directly from the vent, or by falling from a laterally spreading column or plume

pyroclastic flow: a dense, gravity-driven flow of hot volcanic fragments supported by hot gas. They are generated by collapse of an explosive eruption column (to form an **ignimbrite**), by collapse of the side of a lava **dome** (see **block and ash flow**), or by **sector collapse** (compare **pyroclastic surge**)

pyroclastic rock: a collective term for rock formed of consolidated **tephra**

pyroclastic surge: a dilute, turbulent gravity-driven flow of volcanic particles and gas. They may be hot or cold. Typical of **hydromagmatic eruptions**, but also frequently associated with purely magmatic activity

pyroxenes: a group of ferromagnesian silicate minerals (some calcium bearing). One of the most common is **augite**, a calcium-poor variety. **Pigeonite** is a calcium-rich variety

quartz: a silicate mineral with the composition SiO_2

rheology: the study of the deformation and rate of flow of materials under stress. Hence, rheological properties, or the rheology of a substance

rhyolite: a silicic volcanic rock with more than 69% SiO_2. Has a relatively high effective **viscosity** when molten. Crystals, when present, include alkali **feldspar**, **plagioclase** and **quartz**. When almost entirely glassy it is referred to as obsidian

rift zone: a linear concentration of fissures caused by tension. It is a preferred pathway for the rise of magma, and thus often marked at the surface by concentrations of vent structures such as **cinder cones**

risk: probability of a hazard causing loss of life or damage to property

rootless vent: a vent not connected to a deep-seated feeding conduit, but resulting from lava erupting through the crust of a lava flow from its molten interior (see **ephemeral vent**). This commonly forms small lava flows. Explosive rootless vents can form by lava flowing over water, snow or ice and causing it to flash into steam

ropy lava: (see **pahoehoe**)

sandwave structures: a form of **cross-bedding**

scoria: coarsely vesicular and irregular-shaped fragments of lava, usually dark in colour and of low to intermediate silica content

seamount: a submarine volcanic edifice whose top has not emerged above sea level

sector collapse: gravitational collapse of a huge part of the flank of a volcano. Such collapses can be triggered by a number of processes including explosions, loss of rock strength by hydrothermal activity and oversteepening. The result is a generally amphitheatre-shaped scar (see **debris avalanche**)

shard: a spicule-like fragment of volcanic glass formed by extreme vesiculation and fragmentation of a magma. Often has a 'Y' shape where parts of more than one bubble wall have been preserved

shield volcano: a mainly lava construct with radiating flows of **basalt** or other fairly fluid lava forming a shallow profile with slopes generally less than 8°. The summit usually has a **crater** or **caldera**

shoshonite: a K-rich intermediate rock formally defined as a potassic variety of basaltic trachyandesite. Characteristic of mature island-arc environments

silicic: description of rocks that have a high content of silica and alkalis, and low iron and magnesium (compare **mafic**)

sill: a sheet-like, horizontal to subhorizontal intrusive igneous body, generally concordant with the surrounding rocks

slab lava: lava that has a surface composed of upturned slabs of crust

sorting: a measure of the uniformity of grain size in a clastic deposit. Poorly sorted deposits have a wide range of grain sizes, whereas those that are well sorted consist of similar-sized grains

spatter: ejected blebs of lava that, owing to their fluid condition, tend to **agglutinate** together on landing round a vent

spatter cone: a small, steep-sided cone built up of agglutinated **spatter** over a vent. Also referred to as a **hornito** from the Spanish word *horno* meaning 'oven'

strombolian explosion: discrete explosion caused by bubble coalescence at the top of a magma column forming a giant bubble below a crust, and then bursting. Normally associated with more **mafic** magmas. Named after the characteristic activity at Stromboli

syenite: a plutonic rock rich in alkali **feldspar**; the intrusive equivalent of **trachyte**

tephra: a collective term used for all fragmental materials, regardless of size, produced by explosive volcanic eruptions

tephrite: an **alkali basalt**-like volcanic rock with a low SiO_2 content. **Feldspathoids** occur alongside **feldspar**, and they have a low **olivine** content

tholeiite: a type of **basalt** in which the alkali/SiO_2 ratio is relatively low, and plots in the sub-alkali field of the total alkalis v. silica diagram. Some tholeiitic basalts are oversaturated with respect to silica (compare **alkali basalt**)

timpa: local term for a large escarpment on Etna (fault controlled). Corresponds to the Hawaiian term *Pali* for the same type of landform

trachyandesite: an alkali-rich intermediate volcanic rock. Sodic-rich varieties are termed **benmoreites** and more potassic varieties **latites**

trachybasalt: an alkali-rich basaltic volcanic rock. Sodic-rich varieties are termed **hawaiites**

trachyte: a member of the **alkalic rock series** with an SiO_2 content typically greater than 62 wt%. Normally a pale, fine-grained rock containing crystals of alkali **feldspar**. Commonly shows a trachytic texture, which is a fabric formed by the alignment of feldspar crystals in the matrix, often giving the rock a platy cleavage

tuff: a general term for consolidated ash

tuff cone: formed by **hydromagmatic eruptions** and having outer slopes normally greater than 25° and a summit crater (compare **tuff ring**)

tuff ring: formed by **hydromagmatic eruptions** similar to **tuff cone**, but less steep, and having a lower height-to-width ratio and wider crater

tumulus: an upturned boat-shaped feature on a lava surface. Consists of tilted slabs of crust lifted by lava pressure from below. They normally have a fracture along the crest, and are typically several metres high, ranging in length from a few metres to tens of metres

ultravulcanian explosion: one in which only solid fragments of older rock are expelled. The driving force may be magmatic gases or vaporized ground water. Such explosive activity normally accompanies 'throat clearing' activity in a vent before a magmatic eruption starts

vent: orifice through which eruptions occur (see **bocca**)

vesicle: gas-filled cavity in a volcanic rock

viscosity: a measure of the rate at which a material will shear for a given applied stress (compare **yield strength**)

vulcanian explosion: discrete, cannon-like explosions of relatively viscous magma. The products typically include **breadcrust bombs**. Term coined from the eruption on the island of Vulcano in 1888–1890

vulnerability: susceptibility to loss from volcanic or earthquake activity (compare **risk** and **hazard**)

welded tuff: a **pyroclastic rock** in which the **shards** (and **pumice** where present) have welded together to form a dense rock. These can form in **ignimbrites** when the shards have a low viscosity on emplacement, or from fall of fluid tephra fragments (compare **agglutinate** and **piperno**)

xenocryst: a phenocryst-like mineral that is not related to the rock in which it occurs

xenolith: fragment of foreign rock brought from depth by a magma. Of particular interest are those derived from the mantle or a magma reservoir below the volcano

yield strength: see **non-Newtonian fluid**

References

ACOCELLA, V. & FUNICIELLO, R. 1999. The interaction between regional and local tectonics during resurgent doming: the case of the island of Ischia, Italy. *Journal of Volcanology and Geothermal Research*, **88**, 109–123.

ADAMS, J. 1995. *Risk*. UCL Press, London.

ADMIRALTY 1944. *Italy*. BR 517C, Vol. I. Naval Intelligence Division, Admiralty, London.

ADMIRALTY 1945. *Italy*. BR 517C, Vol. IV. Naval Intelligence Division, Admiralty, London.

ALESSIO, M., BELLA, F., *et al.* 1971. Datazione con il metodo del C-14 di carboni e livelli humificati (paleosuoli) intercalati nelle formazioni piroclastiche dei Campi Flegrei (Napoli). *Rendiconti della Societa Italiana di Mineralogia e Petrologia*, **27**(II), 305–308.

ALESSIO, M., BELLA, F., IMPROTA, S., BELLUOMINI, G., CALDERONI, G., CORTESI, C. & TURI, F. 1973. University of Rome C-14 dates X. *Radiocarbon*, **15**(1), 165–178.

ALESSIO, M., BELLA, F., IMPROTA, S., BELLUOMINI, G., CALDERONI, G., CORTESI, C. & TURI, F. 1974. University of Rome C-14 dates XII. *Radiocarbon*, **16**(1), 358–367.

ALLARD, P. 1997. Endogenous magma degassing and storage at Mount Etna. *Geophysical Research Letters*, **24**, 2219–2222.

ALLARD, P., MAIORANI, A., TEDESCO, D., CORTECCI, G. & TURI, B. 1991. Isotopic study of the origins of sulfur and carbon at Solfatara fumaroles, Campi Flegrei Caldera. *Journal of Volcanology and Geothermal Research*, **48**, 139–159.

ANDREWS, R. & BROWN, J. 1999. *Sicily: The Rough Guide*, 3rd edn. Rough Guides, London.

ANON. 1867. *Volcanoes and their Phenomena*. Nelson, Edinburgh.

ANON. 1980. *Map of Campi Flegrei*. Touring Club Italiano, Rome.

ANON. 1993. *Parco dell'Etna, Carta Touristica* (1:50 000). Touring Club Italiano, Milan.

ANON. 1995. *Pianificazione Nazionale D'Emergenza Dell'Area Vesuviana*. Dipartimento della Protezione Civile, Rome.

APPLETON, J. D. 1972. Petrogenesis of potassium-rich lavas from the Roccamonfina Volcano, Roman Region, Italy. *Journal of Petrology*, **13**, 425–456.

ARMIENTI, P., BARBERI, *et al.* 1983. The Phlegraean Fields: magma evolution within a shallow chamber. *Journal of Volcanology and Geothermal Research*, **17**, 289–311.

ARMIENTI, P., BARBERI, F., INNOCENTI, F., POMPILIO, M., ROMANO, R. & VILLARI, L. 1984. Compositional variation in the 1983 and other recent Etnean lavas: insights on the shallow feeding system. *Bulletin Volcanologique*, **47**, 995–1007.

ARMIENTI, P., CLOCHIATTI, R., *et al.* 1994. The longstanding 1991–1993 Mount Etna eruption: petrography and geochemistry of lavas. *Acta Vulcanologica*, **4**, 15–28.

ARRIGHI, S., PRINCIPE, C. & ROSI, M. 2001. Violent Strombolian and subplinian eruptions at Vesuvius during post 1631 activity. *Bulletin of Volcanology*, **63**, 126–150.

ASTER, R. C. & MEYER, R. P. 1988. Three-dimensional velocity structure and hypocenter distribution in the Campi Flegrei caldera, Italy. *Tectonophysics*, **149**, 195–218.

AYUSO, R. A., De VIVO, B., ROLANDI, G., SEAL, R. R., II & Paone, A. 1998. Geochemical and isotopic (Nd–Pb–Sr–O) variations bearing on the genesis of volcanic rocks from Vesuvius, Italy. *Journal of Volcanology and Geothermal Research*, **82**, 53–78.

AZZARO, R. & BARBANO, M. S. 1996. Relationship between seismicity and eruptive activity at Mt. Etna volcano (Italy) as inferred from historical record analysis: the 1883 and 1971 case histories. *Annali di Geofisica*, **39**, 445–461.

BARBERI, F., CIVETTA, L., GASPARINI, P., INNOCENTI, P., SCANDONE, R. & VILLARI, L. 1974. Evolution of a section of the Africa–Europe plate boundary: palaeomagnetic and volcanological evidences from Sicily. *Earth and Planetary Science Letters*, **22**, 123–132.

BARBERI, F., INNOCENTI, F., LIRER, L., MUNNO, R. & PESCATORE, P. 1978. The Campanian ignimbrite: a major prehistoric eruption in the Neopolitan area (Italy). *Bulletin Volcanologique*, **41**, 1–22.

BARBERI, F., CORRADO, G., INNOCENTI, F. & Luongo, G. 1984. Phlegraean Fields 1982–1984: brief chronicle of a volcanic emergency in a densely populated area. *Bulletin Volcanologique*, **47**(2), 175–185.

BARBERI, F., CASSANO, E., LA TORRE, P. & SBRANA, A. 1991. Structural evolution of Campi Flegrei caldera in light of volcanological and geophysical data. *Journal of Volcanology and Geothermal Research*, **48**, 33–49.

BARBERI, F., ROSI, M. & SODI, A. 1993*b*. Volcanic hazard assessment at Stromboli based on a review of historical data. *Acta Vulcanologica*, **3**, 173–187.

BARBERI, F., CARAPEZZA, M. L., VALENZA, M. & VILLARI, L. 1993*a*. The control of lava flow during the 1991–1992 eruption of Mt. Etna. *Journal of Volcanology and Geothermal Research*, **56**, 1–35.

BARBERI, F., CIONI, R., ROSI, M., SANTACROCE, R., SBRANA, R. & VECCI, R. 1989. Magmatic and phreatomagmatic phases in explosive eruption of Vesuvius as deduced by grain-size and component analysis of the pyroclastic deposits. *Journal of Volcanology and Geothermal Research*, **38**, 287–307.

BARCA, D. & VENTURA, G. 1991. Evoluzione vulcano-tettonica dell'isola di Salina (Arcipelago delle Eolie). *Memorie della Società a Geologica Italiana*, **47**, 401–415.

BECCALUVA, L., DI GIROLAMO, P. & SERRI, G. 1991. Petrogenesis and tectonic setting of the Roman Volcanic Province, Italy. *Lithos*, **26**, 191–221.

BELKIN, H. E. & DE VIVO, B. 1993. Fluid inclusion studies of ejected nodules from plinian eruptions of Mt. Somma–Vesuvius. *Journal of Volcanology and Geothermal Research*, **58**, 89–100.

BELKIN, H. E., KILBURN, C. R. J. & DE VIVO, B. 1993. Sampling and major element chemistry of the recent (A.D. 1631–1944) Vesuvius activity. *Journal of Volcanology and Geothermal Research*, **58**, 273–290.

BEN-AVRAHAM, Z. & GRASSO, M. 1990. Collisional zone segmentation in Sicily and surrounding areas in the Central Mediterranean. *Annales Tectonicae*, **4**, 131–139.

BERGEAT, A. 1899. *Die aolischen Inseln (Stromboli, Panaria, Salina, Lipari, Vulcano, Filicudi and Alicudi*. Abhandlungen Akademie Der Wissenschaften München, **20**(I).

BERNABÒ BREA, L. & CAVALIER, M. 1992. *Isole Eolie. Vulcanologica. Archeologica*. Oreste, Ragusi.

BERNABÒ BREA, L. 1998. *Le Isole Eolie dal tardo antico ai Normani*, 2nd edn. M. Lapucci Edizioni del Girasole, Ravenna.

BERRINO, G. 1994. Gravity changes induced by height–mass variations at Campi Flegrei caldera. *Journal of Volcanology and Geothermal Research*, **61**, 293–309.

BERRINO, G., CORRADO, G. & RICCARDI, U. 1998. Sea gravity data in the Gulf of Naples: a contribution to delineating the structural pattern of the Vesuvian area. *Journal of Volcanology & Geothermal Research*, **82**, 139–150.

BERTAGNINI, A. & LANDI, P. 1996. The Secche di Lazzaro pyroclastics of Stromboli volcano: a phreatomagmatic eruption related to the Sciara del Fuoco sector collapse. *Bulletin of Volcanology*, **58**, 239–245.

BERTAGNINI, A., LANDI, P., ROSI, M. & VIGLIARGIO, A. 1998. The Pomici di Base plinian eruption of Somma–Vesuvius. *Journal of Volcanology and Geothermal Research*, **83**, 219–239.

BERTAGNINI, A., LANDI, P., SANTACROCE, R. & SBRANA, A. 1991. The 1906 eruption of Vesuvius: from magmatic activity through the flashing of a shallow depth hydrothermal system. *Bulletin of Volcanology*, **53**, 517–532.

BIANCA, F., CASTELLANO, M., MILANO, G., VENTURA, G. & VILARDO, G. 1998. The Somma–Vesuvius stress field induced by regional tectonics: evidences from seismological and mesostructural data. *Journal of Volcanology and Geothermal Research*, **82**, 199–218.

BIANCHI, R., CORADINI, A., *et al.* 1987. Modeling of surface deformation in volcanic areas, the 1970–1972 and 1982–1984 crises of Campi Flegrei, Italy. *Journal of Geophysical Research*, **92**, 14139–14150.

BIJU-DUVAL, B., DERCOURT, J. & LE PICHON, X. 1977. From Tethys Ocean to the Mediterranean Seas: a plate tectonics model of the evolution of the Western Alpine System. *In*: BIJU-DUVAL, B. & MONTADENT, L. (eds) *Structural History of the Mediterranean Basin*. Technip, Paris, 143–164.

BLACKBURN, E., WILSON, L. & SPARKS, R. S. J. 1976. Mechanisms and dynamics of strombolian activity. *Journal of the Geological Society, London*, **132**, 429–440.

BLANCHARD, P. 2000. *Blue Guide. Southern Italy: from Rome to Calabria*. Black, London.

BLONG, R. J. 1984. *Volcanic Hazards*. Academic Press, Sydney.

BOTTARI, A., LO GIUDICE, E., PATANE, G., ROMANO, R. & STURIALE, C. 1975. L'Eruzione Etnea del gennaio–marzo 1974. *Rivista Mineraria Siciliana*, **144/145**, 175–198.

BRIVIO, P. A., Lo Giudice, E. & Zilioli, E. 1989. Thermal infrared surveys at Volcano Island: an experimental approach to the thermal monitoring of volcanoes. *In*: LATTER, J. H. (ed.) *Volcanic Hazards: Assessment and Monitoring*. IAVCEI Proceedings in Volcanology, **1**, 357–372.

BROCCHINI, D., PRINCIPE, C., CASTRADORI, D., LAURENZI, M. A. & GORLA, Z. 2001. Quaternary evolution of the southern sector of the Campanian Plain and the early Somma–Vesuvius activity: insights from the Trecace 1 well. *Mineralogy and Petrology*, **73**, 67–91.

BRUNO, P. P. G. & RAPOLLA, A. 1999. Study of the sub-surface structure of Somma–Vesuvius (Italy) by seismic reflection data. *Journal of Volcanology and Geothermal Research*, **92**, 373–387.

BRUNO, P. P. G., CIPPITELLI, G. & RAPOLLA, A. 1998. Seismic study of the Mesozoic carbonate basement around Mt. Somma–Vesuvius, Italy. *Journal of Volcanology and Geothermal Research*, **84**, 311–322.

BUCHNER, G., ITALIANO, A. & VITA-FINZI, C. 1996. Recent uplift at Ischia, Southern Italy. *In*: MCGUIRE, W. J., JONES, A. P. & NEUBERG, J. (eds) *Volcano Instability on the Earth and Planets*. Geological Society, London, Special Publications **110**, 000–000.

BULLARD, F. M. 1954. Activity of Stromboli in June and December 1952. *Bulletin Vulcanologique*, Série 2, **15**, 91–98.

CALANCHI, N., COLANTONI, G., GABBIANELLI, G., ROSSI, P. L. & SERRI, G. 1984. Physiography of Anchise Seamount and of the submarine part of Ustica Island (south Tyrrhenian): petrochemistry of dredged volcanic rocks and geochemical characteristics of their mantle sources. *Mineralogia Petrologia Acta*, **28**, 215–241.

CALANCHI, N., DE ROSA, R., MAZZUOLI, R., RICCI LUCCHI, F., ROSSI, P. L. & SANTACROCE, R. 1987. *L'attivita del centro di Pollara (Salina, Isole Eolie)*. Bollettino Gruppo Nazionale per La Vulcanologia (GNV), Roma, 187–213.

CALANCHI, N., DE ROSA, R., MAZZUOLI, R., ROSSI, P., SANTACROCE, R. & VENTURA, G. 1993. Silicic magma entering a basaltic magma chamber: eruptive dynamics and magma mixing—an example from Salina (Aeolian Islands, Southern Tyrrhenian Sea). *Bulletin of Volcanology*, **55**, 504–522.

CALANCHI, N., ROSSI, P. L., SANMARCHI, F. & TRANNE, C. A. 1996. *Guida Eolie: Escursionistico vulcanologica delle Isole*. Union, Viterbo.

CALANCHI, N., TRANNE, C. A., LUCCHINI, F., ROSSI, P. L. & VILLA, I. M. 1999. Explanatory notes to the geological map, 1:10,000, of Panarea and Basiluzzo, Aeolian Islands, Italy. *Acta Vulcanologia*, **11**, 223–243.

CALVARI, S. & GROPPELLI, G. 1996. Relevance of the Chiancone volcaniclastic deposit in the recent history of Etna Volcano (Italy). *Journal of Volcanology and Geothermal Research*, **72**, 239–258.

CALVARI, S. & PINKERTON, H. 1998. Formation of lava tubes and extensive flow field during the 1991–1993 eruption. *Journal of Geophysical Research*, **103**, 27291–27301.

CALVARI, S. & PINKERTON, H. 1999. Lava tube morphology and evidence for lava flow emplacement mechanisms. *Journal of Volcanology and Geothermal Research*, **90**, 263–280.

CALVARI, S., COLTELLI, M., NERI, M., POMPILIO, M. & SCRIBANO, V. 1994*a*. The 1991–1993 Etna eruption: chronology and lava flow-field evolution. *Acta Vulcanologica*, **4**, 1–14.

CALVARI, S., GROPELLI, G. & PASQUARÈ, G. 1994*b*. Preliminary geological data on the southwestern wall of the Valle del Bove, Mt. Etna, Sicily. *Acta Vulcanologica*, **5**, 15–30.

CAPALDI, L. & GILLOT, P. Y. 1985. Geochronology and Plio-Pleistocene volcanic rocks from southern Italy. *Rendiconti della Societa Italiana di Mineralogia e Petrologia*, **40**, 25–44.

CAPALDI, G., CIVETTA, L., DI GIROLAMO, P., LANZARA, R., ORSI, G. & SCARPATI, C. 1987. Volcanological and geochemical contraints on the deposits of yellow tuff in the Neopolitan–Phlegrean area. *Rendiconti dell' Accademia di Scienza Fisiche e Matematiche* (special issue), 25–40.

CAPALDI, G., CIVETTA, L. & GASPARINI, P. 1976–1977. Volcanic history of the island of Ischia (South Italy). *Bulletin Volcanologique*, **40**, 11–22.

CAPUANA, P., CONTINISIO, R. & GASPARINI, P. 1992. Structural setting of a typical alkali–potassic volcano: Roccamonfina, southern Italy. *Journal of Volcanology and Geothermal Research*, **53**, 355–369.

CARDACI, C., COVIELLO, M., LOMBARDO, G., PATANÈ, G. & SCARPA, R. 1993. Seismic tomography of Etna volcano. *Journal of Volcanology and Geothermal Research*, **56**, 357–368.

CAREY, S. N. & SPARKS, R. S. J. 1986. Quantitative models of the fallout and dispersal of tephra from volcanic columns. *Bulletin of Volcanology*, **48**, 109–125.

CARNIEL, R & IACOP, F. 1996. On the persistency of crater assignment criteria for Stromboli explosion-quakes. *Annali di Geofisica*, **39**, 327–345.

CARTER, S. R. & CIVETTA, L. 1977. Genetic implications of the isotope and trace element variations in the eastern Sicilian volcanics. *Earth and Planetary Science Letters*, **36**, 168–180.

CARTER, S. R., EVENSEN, N. M., HAMILTON, P. J. & O'NIONS, R. K. 1978. Continental volcanics derived from enriched and depleted source regions: Nd- and Sr-isotope evidence. *Earth and Planetary Science Letters*, **37**, 401–408.

CELLO, G. 1987. Structure and deformation processes in the Strait of Sicily 'rift zone'. *Tectonophysics*, **141**, 237–247.

CHESTER, D. K. 1993. *Volcanoes and Society*. Edward Arnold, London.

CHESTER, D. K. & DUNCAN, A. M. 1979. Interrelationships between volcanic and alluvial sequences in the Simeto River Valley, Mount Etna, Sicily. *Catena*, **6**, 293–315.

CHESTER, D. K., DUNCAN, A. M. & GUEST, J. E. 1987. The pyroclastic deposits of Mount Etna, Sicily. *Geological Journal*, **22**(3), 225–245.

CHESTER, D. K., DUNCAN, A. M., GUEST, J. E., JOHNSTON, P. A. & SMOLENAARS, J. J. L. 2000. Human response to Etna Volcano during the Classical Period. *In*: MCGUIRE, B., GRIFFITHS, D. & STEWART, I. (eds) *The Archaeology of Geological Catastrophes*. Geological Society, London, Special Publications, **171**, 179–188.

CHESTER, D. K., DUNCAN, A. M., GUEST, J. E. & KILBURN, C. R. J. 1985. *Mount Etna: The Anatomy of a Volcano*. Chapman and Hall, London.

CINQUE, A., CIVETTA, L., ORSI, G. & PECCERILLO, A. 1988. Geology and geochemistry of the island Ustica. *Rendiconti della Societa Italiana di Mineralogia e Petrologia*, **43**, 987–1002.

CIONI, R., CIVETTA, L., MARIANELLI, P., METRICH, N., SANTACROCE, R. & SBRANA, A. 1995. Compositional layering and syn-eruptive mixing of a periodically refilled shallow magma chamber: the AD 79 plinian eruption of Vesuvius. *Journal of Petrology*, **36**, 739–776.

CIONI, R., MARIANELLI, P. & SANTACROCE, R. 1998. Thermal and compositional evolution of the shallow magma chambers of Vesuvius: evidence from pyroxene phenocrysts and melt inclusions. *Journal of Geophysical Research*, **103**, 18277–18294.

CIONI, R., SANTACROCE, R. & SBRANA, A. 1999. Pyroclastic deposits as a guide for reconstructing the multi-stage evolution of the Somma–Vesuvius Caldera. *Bulletin* of *Volcanology*, **60**, 207–222.

CLOCCHIATTI, R. DEL MORO, A., GIONCADA, A., JORON, J. L., MOSBAH, M., PINARELLI, L. & SBRANA, A. 1994. Assessment of a shallow magmatic system—the 1888–90 eruption, Vulcano island, Italy. *Bulletin of Volcanology*, **56**, 466–486.

COLE, P. D. 1991. Migration direction of sand-wave structures in pyroclastic surge deposits: implications for depositional processes. *Geology*, **19**, 1108–1111.

COLE, P. D. & SCARPATI, C. 1993. A facies interpretation of eruption and emplacement mechanisms of the upper part of the Neopolitan Yellow Tuff, Campi Flegrei, Southern Italy. *Bulletin of Volcanology*, **55**, 311–326.

COLE, P. D., GUEST, J. E. & DUNCAN, A. M. 1993. The emplacement of intermediate volume ignimbrite: a case study of Roccamonfina volcano, Southern Italy. *Bulletin of Volcanology*, **55**, 467–480.

COLE, P. D., GUEST, J. E., DUNCAN, A. M., CHESTER, D. K. & BIANCHI, T. 1992. Post-collapse volcanic history of calderas on a composite volcano: an example from Roccamonfina, southern Italy. *Bulletin of Volcanology*, **54**, 253–266.

COLE, P. D., PERROTTA, A. & SCARPATI, C. 1994. The volcanic history of the southwestern part of the city of Naples. *Geological Magazine*, **131**, 785–799.

COLLELLA, A. & HISCOTT, R. N. 1997. Pyroclastic surges of the Pleistocene Monte Guardia sequence (Lipari island, Italy): Depositional processes. *Sedimentology*, **44**, 47–66.

COLTELLI, M., DEL CARLO, P. & VEZZOLI, L. 1995*a*. A plinian eruption of basaltic composition in the historical activity of Mt Etna. *Periodico di Mineralogia Roma*, **64**, 145–146.

COLTELLI, M., DEL CARLO, P. & VEZZOLI, L. 1995*b*. Stratigraphy of the Holocene Mt. Etna explosive eruptions. *Periodico di Mineralogia Roma*, **64**, 141–143.

COLTELLI, M., GARDUNO, V. H., NERI, M., PASQUARÈ, G. & POMPILIO, M. 1994. Geology of the northern wall of Valle del Bove, Mt. Etna (Sicily). *Acta Vulcanologica*, **5**, 55–68.

CONDOMINES, M., TANGUY, J. C., KIEFFER, G. & ALLÈGRE, C. J. 1982. Magmatic evolution of a volcano studied by ^{230}Th–^{238}U disequilibrium and trace element systematics: the Etna case. *Geochimica et Cosmochimica Acta*, **46**, 1397–1416.

CONDOMINES, M., TANGUY, J.-C. & MICHAUD, V. 1995. Magma dynamics at Mt Etna: constraints from U–Th-–a–Pb radioactive disequilibria and Sr isotopes in historical lavas. *Earth and Planetary Science Letters*, **132**, 25–41.

CORNETTE, Y., CRISCI, G. M., GILLOt, P. Y. & ORSI, G. 1983. Recent volcanic history of Pantelleria: a new interpretation. *Journal of Volcanology and Geothermal Research*, **17**, 361–373.

CORSARO, R. A. & CRISTOFOLINI, R. 1996. Origin and differentiation of recent basaltic magmas from Mount Etna. *Mineralogy and Petrology*, **57**, 1–21.

CORSARO, R. A., CRISTOFOLINI, R. & PATANÈ, L. 1996. The 1669 eruption at Mount Etna: chronology, petrology and geochemistry, with inferences on the magma sources and ascent mechanism. *Bulletin of Volcanology*, **58**, 348–358.

CORTESE, E. & SABATINI, V. 1892. *Descrizione geologico-petrografica delle Isole Eolie*. Memorie Carta Geologica d' Italia, Roma.

CORTESE, M., FRAZZETTA, G. & La Volpe, L. 1986. Volcanic history of Lipari (Aeolian Islands, Italy) during the last 10,000 years. *Journal of Volcanology and Geothermal Research*, **27**, 117–133.

COSENTINO, M., CRISTOFOLINI, R., *et al.* 1981. L'eruzione dell'Etna del 17–23 marzo 1981. *Rendiconti della Società Geologica Italiana*, **4**, 249–252.

CRISCI, G. M., DE ROSA, R., ESPERANCA, S., MAZZUOLI, R. & SONNINO, M. 1991. Temporal evolution of a three component system: the island of Lipari (Aeolian Arc, southern Italy). *Bulletin of Volcanology*, **53**, 207–221.

CRISCI, G. M., DELIBRIAS, G., DE ROSA, R., MAZZUOLI, R. & SHERIDAN, M. F. 1983. Age and petrology of the Late Pleistocene Brown Tuffs on Lipari, Italy. *Bulletin Volcanologique*, **46**(4), 381–391.

CRISCI, G. M., DE ROSA, R., LANZAFAME, G., MAZZUOLI, R., SHERIDAN, M. F. & ZUFFA, G. G. 1981. Monte Guardia Sequence: a Late-Pleistocene eruptive cycle on Lipari (Italy). *Bulletin of Volcanology*, **44**, 241–255.

CRISTOFOLINI, R. & LO GIUDICE, A. 1969. Le latitande—siti di un complesso intermedio tra Trifoglietto e Mongibello affiorante tra la Valle del Bove ed Adrano–Biancavilla (Etna). *Rendiconti della Società Italiana di Mineralogia e Petrologia*, **25**, 227–261.

CRISTOFOLINI, R. & ROMANO, R. 1982. Petrologic features of Etnean rocks. *In*: ROMANO, R. (ed.) *Mount Etna Volcano, a Review of Recent Earth Science Studies*. Memorie della Società Geologica Italiana, **23**, 99–115.

CRISTOFOLINI, R., MENZIES, M. A., BECCALUVA, L. & TINDLE, A. 1987. Petrological notes on the 1983 lavas at Mount Etna, Sicily, with reference to their REE and Sr–Nd isotope composition. *Bulletin of Volcanology*, **49**, 599–607.

D'ANTONIO, L., CIVETTA, L., *et al.* 1999. The present state of the magmatic system of the Campi Flegrei caldera based on a reconstruction of its behavior in the past 12 ka. *Journal of Volcanology and Geothermal Research*, **91**, 247–268.

DE ASTIS, G., DELLINO, P., DE ROSA, R. & LA VOLPE, L. 1997*a*. Eruptive and emplacement mechanisms of widespread fine-grained pyroclastic deposits on Vulcano Island (Italy). *Bulletin of Volcanology*, **59**, 87–102.

DE ASTIS, G., LA VOLPE, L., PECCERILLO, A. & CIVETTA, L. 1997*b*. Volcanological and petrological evolution of Vulcano island (Aeolian Arc, southern Tyrrhenian Sea). *Journal of Geophysical Research*, **102**, 8021–8050.

DE FINO, M., LA VOLPE, L., *et al.* 1988. The Stromboli eruption of December 6, 1985–April 15, 1986: volcanological, petrological and seismological data. *Rendiconti della Società Italiana di Mineralogia e Petrologia*, **43**, 1021–1038.

DE FINO, M., LA VOLPE, L., PECCERILLO, A., PICCARRETA, G. & POLI, G. 1986. Petrogenesis of Monte Vulture volcano (Italy): inferences from mineral chemistry, major and trace element data. *Contributions to Mineralogy and Petrology*, **92**, 135–145.

DE FINO, M., LA VOLPE, L. & PICCARRETA, G. 1991. Role of magma mixing during the recent activity of La Fossa di Vulcano (Aeolian Islands, Italy). *Journal of Volcanology and Geothermal Research*, **48**, 385–398.

DE FIORE, O. 1922. Vulcano (Isole Eolie). *Zeitschrift für Vulkanologie Bund*, **IIIS**.

DE FIORE, O. 1925. Il Massiccio Riolitico di Monte Lentia. *Zeitschrift für Vulkanologie*, **3**, 178–182.

DE FIORE, O. 1926. Le Neoformazioni di Monte Saraceno. *Zeitschrift für Vulkanologie*, **3**, 207–214.

DELLINO, P. & LA VOLPE, L. 1995. Fragmentation versus transportation mechanisms in the pyroclastic sequence of Monte Pilato–Rocche Rosse (Lipari, Italy). *Journal of Volcanology and Geothermal Research*, **64**, 211–231.

DELLINO, P. & LA VOLPE, L. 1996. Image processing analysis in reconstructing fragmentation and transportation mechanisms of pyroclastic deposits. The case of Monte Pilato–Rocche Rosse eruptions, Lipari (Aeolian Islands, Italy). *Journal of Volcanology and Geothermal Research*, **71**, 13–29.

DELLINO, P. & LA VOLPE, L. 2000. Structures and grain size distribution in surge deposits as a tool for modelling the dynamics of dilute pyroclastic density currents at La Fossa di Vulcano (Aeolian Islands, Italy). *Journal of Volcanology and Geothermal Research*, **96**, 57–78

DE LORENZO, G. 1904. The history of volcanic action in the Phlegrean Fields. *Quarterly Journal of the Geological Society of London*, **60**, 296–315.

DE NATALE, G. & PINGUE, F. 1993. Ground deformations in collapsed caldera structures. *Journal of Volcanology and Geothermal Research*, **57**, 19–38.

DE NATALE, G., CAPUANO, P., TROISE, C. & ZOLLO, A. 1998. Seismicity at Somma–Vesuvius and its implications for the 3D tomography of the volcano. *Journal of Volcanology and Geothermal Research*, **82**, 175–197.

De Natale, G., Pingue, F., Allard, P. & Zollo, A. 1991. Geophysical and geochemical modelling of the 1982–1984 unrest phenomena at Campi Flegrei Caldera (southern Italy). *Journal of Volcanology and Geothermal Research*, **48**, 199–222.

De Rita, D. & Giordano, G. 1996. Volcanological evolution of Roccamonfina volcano (Italy): origin of the summit caldera. *In*: McGuire, W. J., Jones, A. P. & Neuberg, J. (eds) *Volcano Instability on the Earth and Other Planets*. Geological Society, London, Special Publications, **110**, 209–224.

De Rita, D., Giordano, G. & Milli, S. 1997 Forestepping–backstepping stacking pattern of volcaniclastic successions: Roccamonfina volcano, Italy. *Journal of Volcanology and Geothermal Research*, **78**, 267–288.

De Rosa, R., Gillot, P. Y., Lanzafame, G. & Mazzuoli, R. 1985. *The Island of Lipari. IAVCEI Field Guide*. G. Costanzo, Catania.

De Vita, S., Laurenzi, M. A., Orsi, G. & Voltaggio, M. 1978. Application of $^{40}Ar/^{39}Ar$ and ^{230}Th dating methods to the chronostratigraphy of Quaternary basaltic volcanic areas: the Ustica Island case history. *Quaternary International*, **47/48**, 117–127.

De Vita, S., Orsi, G., *et al.* 1999. The Agnano–Monte Spina eruption (4100 years BP) in the restless Campi Flegrei caldera (Italy). *Journal of Volcanology and Geothermal Research*, **91**, 269–301.

De Vivo, B. & Rolandi, G. (eds) 2001. Special issue: Mt. Somma–Vesuvius and volcanism of the Campanian Plain. *Mineralogy and Petrology*, **73**(1–3).

De Vivo, B., Rolandi, G., Gans, P. B., Calvert, A., Bohrson, W. A., Spera, F. J. & Belkin, H. E. 2001. New constraints on the pyroclastic eruptive history of the Campanian volcanic Plain (Italy). *Mineralogy and Petrology*, **73**, 47–65.

Dewey, J. F., Pitman, W. C., Ryan, W. B. F. & Bonnin, J. 1973. Plate tectonics and the evolution of the Alpine System. *Geological Society of America Bulletin*, **84**, 3137–3180.

Di Girolamo, P., Ghiara, M. R., Lirer, L., Munno, R., Rolandi, G. & Stanzione, D. 1984. Vulcanologia e petrolologia dei Campi Flegrei. *Bollettino della Società Geologica Italiana*, **103**, 349–413.

Di Paola, G. M. 1973. The island of Linosa (Sicily Channel). *Bulletin Volcanologique*, **37**, 1–26.

Di Vito, M., Lirer, L., Mastrolorenzo, G. & Rolandi, G. 1987. The 1538 Monte Nuovo eruption (Campi Flegrei, Italy). *Bulletin of Volcanology*, **49**, 608–615.

Di Vito, M., Lirer, L., Mastrolorenzo, G., Rolandi, G. & Scandone, R. 1985. *Volcanological Map of Campi Flegrei*. University of Naples.

Di Vito, M. A., Isaia, R., *et al.* 1999. Volcanism and deformation since 12,000 years at the Campi Flegrei caldera (Italy). *Journal of Volcanology and Geothermal Research*, **91**(2–4), 221–246.

Dreier, R., Widmer, R., Schick, R. & Zurn, W. 1994. Stacking of broadband seismograms of shocks at Stromboli. *Acta Vulcanologia*, **5**, 173–178.

Duggan, C. 1994. *A Concise History of Italy*. Cambridge University Press, Cambridge.

Duncan, A. M. 1976. Pyroclastic flow deposits in the Adrano area of Mount Etna, Sicily. *Geological Magazine*, **113**, 357–363.

Duncan, A. M. 1978. The trachybasaltic volcanics of the Adrano area, Mount Etna, Sicily. *Geological Magazine*, **115**, 273–285.

Duncan, A. M. & Guest, J. E. 1982. Mount Etna: variations in its internal plumbing. *Geophysical Surveys*, **5**, 213–227.

Duncan, A. M., Chester, D. K. & Guest, J. E. 1984. The Quaternary stratigraphy of Mount Etna, Sicily: the effects of differing palaeoenvironments on styles of volcanism. *Bulletin Volcanologique*, **47**, 497–516.

Duncan, A. M., Cole, P. D., Guest, J. E. & Chester, D. K. 1996. Transport and emplacement mechanisms of mass-flow deposits on Monte Vulture volcano, Basilicata, southern Italy. *In*: McGuire, W. J., Jones, A. P. & Neuberg, J. (eds) *Volcano Instability on the Earth and Other Planets*. Geological Society, London, Special Publications, **110**, 237–247.

DVORAK, J. J. & BERRINO, G. 1991. Recent ground movement and seismic activity in Campi Flegrei, southern Italy, episodic growth of a resurgent dome. *Journal of Geophysical Research*, **96**, 2309–2323.

DVORAK, J. J. & MASTROLORENZO, G. 1991. *The Mechanisms of Recent Vertical Crustal Movements in Campi Flegrei Caldera, Southern Italy*. Geological Society of America, Special Paper, **263**.

ELLAM, R. M., HAWKESWORTH, C. J., MENZIES, M. A. & ROGERS, N. W. 1989. The volcanism of southern Italy: role of subduction and the relationship between potassic and sodic alkaline magmatism. *Journal of Geophysical Research*, **94**, 4589–4601.

ELLAM, R. M., MENZIES, M. A., HAWKESWORTH, C. J., LEEMAN, W. P., ROSI, M. & SERRI, G. 1988. The transition from calc-alkaline to potassic magmatism in the Aeolian Islands, Southern Italy. *Bulletin of Volcanology*, **50**, 386–398.

ESPERANÇA, S. & CRISCI, G. M. 1995. The island of Pantelleria: a case study for the development of DMM–HIMU isotopic compositions in a long-lived extensional setting. *Earth and Planetary Science Letters*, **136**, 167–182.

ETIENNE, R. 1992. *Pompeii: the Day a City Died*. New Horizons, London.

FALSAPERLA, S. & SCHICK, R. 1993. Geophysical studies on Stromboli volcano—a review. *Acta Vulcanologica*, **3**, 153–162.

FALSAPERLA, S., LANGER, H., MONTALTO, A. & SPAMPINATO, S. 1994. Seismic investigations of volcanic tremor at Stromboli (Italy). *Acta Vulcanologica*, **60**, 75–88.

FALSAPERLA, S., LANGER, H. & SPAMPINATO, S. 1998. Statistical analyses and characteristics of volcanic tremor on Stromboli Volcano (Italy). *Bulletin of Volcanology*, **60**, 75–88.

FERRARI, L. & MANETTI, P. 1993. Geodynamic framework of the Tyrrhenian volcanism: a review. *Acta Vulcanologica*, **3**, 1–9.

FERRUCCI, F. & PATANE, D. 1993. Seismic activity accompanying the outbreak of the 1991–1993 eruption of Mt. Etna (Italy). *Journal of Volcanology and Geothermal Research*, **57**, 125–135.

FERRUCCI, F., HIRN, A., De NATALE, G., VIRIEUX, J. & MIRABILE, L. 1992. P–SV conversions at a shallow boundary beneath Campi Flegrei Caldera (Italy), evidence for the magma chamber. *Journal of Geophysical Research*, **97**, 15351–15359.

FINLEY, M. I. & MACK-SMITH, D. 1968. *A History of Sicily*. Chatto and Windus, London (3 vols).

FINLEY, M. I., MACK-SMITH, D. & DUGGAN, C. 1986. *A History of Sicily*. Chatto & Windus, London.

FISHER, R. V. & SCHMINCKE, H.-V. 1984. *Pyroclastic Rocks*. Springer, Berlin.

FISHER, R. V., ORSI, G., ORT, M. H. & HEIKEN, G. 1993. Mobility of large-volume pyroclastic flow emplacement of the Campanian ignimbrite, Italy. *Journal of Volcanology and Geothermal Research*, **56**, 205–220.

FLEMMING, N. C. 1969. *Archaeological Evidence for Eustatic Change of Sea Level and Earth Movements in the Western Mediterranean during the last 2,000 years*. Geological Society of America, Special Paper, **109**.

FOERSTNER, H. 1881. Nota preliminare sulla geologia dell'isola di Pantelleria, secundo gli studi fatti negli anni 1874 e 1881. *Bolletino de Reale Comitato Geologico d'Italia*, **12**, 523–556.

FONSECA, G. 1847. *Descrizione e carta geologica dell'isola d'Ischia*. Annali Accademia. Aspiranti Naturalisti Napoli, **2a/1**.

FOTHERGILL, B. 1969. *Sir William Hamilton, Envoy Extraordinary*. Faber, London.

FRANCALANCI, L. & SANTO, A. P. 1993. Magmatological evolution of Filicudi volcanoes, Aeolian Islands, Italy: constraints from mineralogical, geochemical and isotopic data. *Acta Vulcanologica*, **3**, 203–227.

FRANCALANCI, L., MANETTI, P., PECCERILLO, A. & KELLER, J. 1993. Magmatological evolution of the Stromboli volcano (Aeolian Arc, Italy): inferences from major and trace element and Sr isotopic composition of lavas and pyroclastic rocks. *Acta Vulcanologica*, **3**, 127–151.

FRANCIS, P. 1993. *Volcanoes*. Oxford University Press, Oxford.

FRANCIS, P. 1995. Fire and water. *Geology Today*, Jan.–Feb., 27–31.

FRAZZETTA, G. 1998. Lipari and Vulcano (Aeolian Islands, Italy) during the last 10 kyr. Inferences from volcanological and human data. *In*: MORELLO, N. (ed.) *International Commission on the History of Geological Sciences, Proceedings of the 20th Symposium*, 171–207.

FRAZZETTA, G. & ROMANO, R. 1984. The 1983 eruption: event chronology and morphological evolution of lava flows. *Bulletin of Volcanology*, **47**, 1079–1096.

FRAZZETTA, G., LA VOLPE, L. & SHERIDAN, M. F. 1989. Interpretation of emplacement units in recent surge deposits on Lipari, Italy. *Journal of Volcanology and Geothermal* Research, **37**, 339–350.

FUCHS, C. W. C. 1873. *Monografia geologica dell'isola d'Ischia con carta geologica 1:25,000*. Memorie per Servire alla descrizione carta geologica d'Italia, Roma, **2/11**.

FUSI, N., TIBALDI, A. & VEZZOLI, L. 1990. Vulcanismo, risorgenza calderica e relazioni con la tettonica regionale nell'isola d'Ischia. *Memorie della Società Geologica Italiana*, **45**, 971–980 (published in 1992).

GABBIANELLI, G., GILLOT, P. Y., LANZAFAME, G., ROMAGNOLI, C. & ROSSI, P. L. 1990. Tectonic and volcanic evolution of Panarea (Aeolian Islands, Italy). *Marine Geology*, **92**, 313–326.

GABBIANELLI, G., ROMAGNOLI, C., ROSSI, P. L. & CALANCHI, N. 1993. Marine geology of the Panarea–Stromboli area (Aeolian Archipelago, Southern Tyrrhenian Sea). *Acta Vulcanologica*, **3**, 11–20.

GAMLIN, H. (1891). *Emma, Lady Hamilton*. Howell, Liverpool.

GIANNETTI, B. 1979*a*. The geology of the Roccamonfina caldera. *Giornale Geologia (series 2)*, **43**, 187–206.

GIANNETTI, B. 1979*b*. Studio geologico–petrographico della caldera del vulcano di Roccamonfina (Italia centro-meridionale). *Bollettino della Società Geologica Italiana*, **100**, 311–374.

GIANNETTI, B. 1994*a*. Comments on Cole *et al.* (1992*a*) I The extracaldera 'Galluccio Tuff' Roccamonfina Volcano, Italy. *Atti delle Accademia Nazionale dei Lincei Classe di Scienze Fisiche, Matematiche e Naturali*, **5**, 125–133.

GIANNETTI, B. 1994*b*. Comments on Cole *et al.* (1992*b*) II The intracaldera 'Galluccio Tuff' and 'Garofali Formation' Roccamonfina Volcano, Italy. *Atti delle Accademia Nazionale dei Lincei Classe di Scienze Fisiche, Matematiche e Naturali*, **5**, 211–221.

GIANNETTI, B. 1994*c*. Comments on Cole *et al.* (1992*c*) III The stratigraphy of Roccamonfina Volcano, Italy. *Atti delle Accademia Nazionale dei Lincei Classe di Scienze Fisiche, Matematiche e Naturali*, **5**, 341–324.

GIANNETTI, B. 2001. Origin of the calderas and evolution of Roccamonfina volcano (Roman region, Italy). *Journal of Volcanology and Geothermal Research*, **106**, 301–319.

GIANNETTI, B. & CASA, G. 2000. Stratigraphy, chronology and sedimentology of the White Trachytic Tuff, Roccamonfina volcano, Italy. *Journal of Volcanology and Geothermal Research*, **96**, 243–295.

GIANNETTI, B. & LUHR, J. F. 1983. The White Trachytic Tuff of Roccamonfina volcano (Roman Region, Italy). *Contributions to Mineralogy and Petrology*, **84**, 235–252.

GIBERTI, G., JAUPART, C. & SARTORIS, G. 1992. Steady state operation of Stromboli volcano, Italy: constraints on the feeding system. *Bulletin of Volcanology*, **54**, 535–541.

GILLOT, P. Y. & KELLER, J. 1993. Radiochronological dating of Stromboli. *Acta Vulcanologica*, **3**, 69–77.

GILLOT, P. Y., CHIESA, S., PASQUARÈ, G. & VEZZOLI, L. 1982. 33,000 yr K/Ar dating of the volcanic–tectonic horst of the isle of Ischia, Gulf of Naples. *Nature*, **229**, 242–245.

GILLOT, P. Y., FRAZZETTA, G. & LA VOLPE, L. 1990. Volcano-tectonic evolution (Aeolian Islands, Southern Italy) from geochronological (K–Ar) study. *In*: *International Volcanological Congress, Mainz, Germany, 3–8 September 1990 (abstracts)*.

GILLOT, P.-Y., KIEFFER, G. & ROMANO, R. 1994. The evolution of Mount Etna in the light of potassium–argon dating. *Acta Vulcanologica*, **5**, 81–87.

GIONCADA, A. & SBRANA, A. 1991. La Fossa Caldera, Vulcano: inferences from deep drilling. *Acta Vulcanologica*, **1**, 115–125.

GIORDANO, G. 1998*a*. Facies characteristics and magma–water interaction of the White Trachytic Tuffs (Roccamonfina Volcano, Southern Italy). *Bulletin of Volcanology*, **60**, 10–26.

GIORDANO, G. 1998*b*. The effect of paleotopography on lithic distribution and facies associations of small volume ignimbrites: the WTT Cupa (Roccamonfina volcano, Italy). *Journal of Volcanology and Geothermal Research*, **87**, 255–273.

GRESTA, S., LONGO, V. & VIAVATTENE, A. 1990. Geodynamic behaviour of eastern and western sides of Mount Etna. *Tectonophysics*, **179**, 81–92.

GRINDLEY, G. W. 1973. Structural control of volcanism of Mount Etna. *Philosophical Transactions of the Royal Society of London, Series A*, **274**, 165–175.

GUEST, J. E. 1973. The summit of Mount Etna prior to the 1971 eruptions. *Philosophical Transactions of the Royal Society of London, Series A*, **274**, 63–78.

GUEST, J. E. 1982. Styles of eruption and flow morphology on Mt. Etna. *In*: ROMANO, R. (ed.) *Mount Etna Volcano, a Review of Recent Earth Science Studies*. Memorie della Società Geologica Italiana, **23**, 49–73.

GUEST, J. E. & DUNCAN, A. M. 1981. Internal plumbing of Mount Etna. *Nature*, **290**, 584–586.

GUEST, J. E. & MURRAY, J. B. 1979. An analysis of hazard from Mount Etna Volcano. *Journal of the Geological Society, London*, **136**, 347–354.

GUEST, J. E. & SKELHORN, R. R. (eds) 1973. Mount Etna and the 1971 eruption. *Philosophical Transactions of the Royal Society of London, Series A*, **274**.

GUEST, J. E., CHESTER, D. K. & DUNCAN, A. M. 1984*a*. The Valle del Bove, Mount Etna: its origin and relations to the stratigraphy and structure of the volcano. *Journal of Volcanology and Geothermal Research*, **21**, 1–23.

GUEST, J. E., DUNCAN, A. M. & CHESTER, D. K. 1988. Monte Vulture Volcano (Basilicata, Italy): an analysis of morphology and volcaniclastic facies. *Bulletin of Volcanology*, **50**, 244–257.

GUEST, J. E., HUNTINGDON, A. T., WADGE, G., BRANDER, J. L., BOOTH, B., CARTER, S. & DUNCAN, A. 1974. Recent eruption of Mount Etna. *Nature*, **250**, 385–387.

GUEST, J. E., KILBURN, C. R. J., PINKERTON, H. & DUNCAN, J. E. 1987. The evolution of lava flow-fields: observations of the 1981 and 1983 eruptions of Mount Etna, Sicily. *Bulletin of Volcanology*, **49**, 527–540.

GUEST, J. E., UNDERWOOD, J. R. & GREELEY, R. 1980. The role of lava tubes in flows from the Observatory vent, 1971 eruption on Mount Etna. *Geological Magazine*, **117**, 601–606.

GUEST, J. E., WOOD, C. & GREELEY, R. 1984*b*. Lava tubes, terraces and megatumuli on the 1614–24 pahoehoe lava flowfield, Mount Etna, Sicily. *Bulletin Volcanologique*, **47**, 635–648.

GVIRTZMAN, Z. & NUR, A. 1999*a*. Plate detachment, asthenosphere upwelling, and topography across subduction zones. *Nature*, **27**, 563–566.

GVIRTZMAN, Z. & NUR, A. 1999*b*. The formation of Mount Etna as the consequence of slab rollback. *Nature*, **401**, 782–785.

HAMILTON, Sir W. 1776. *Campi Phlegraei. Observations on the Volcanoes of the Two Sicilies*. Private publication, Naples.

HAWKESWORTH, C. J. & VOLLMER, R. 1979. Crustal contamination versus enriched mantle: $^{143}Nd/^{144}Nd$ and $^{87}Sr/^{86}Sr$ evidence from the Italian volcanics. *Contributions to Mineralogy and Petrology*, **69**, 151–165.

HIEKE MERLIN, O. 1967. I prodotti vulcanici del Monte Vulture (Lucania). *Memorie degli Istituti di Geologia et Mineralogia, Università di Padova*, **26**, 3–67.

HIRN, A., NERCESSIAN, A., SAPIN, M., FERRUCCI, F. & WITTLINGER, G. 1991. Seismic heterogeneity of Mt Etna: structure and activity. *Geophysical Journal International*, **105**, 139–153.

HOFFER, W. 1982. *Volcano: The Search for Vesuvius*. Summit Books, New York.

HORNIG-KJARSGAARD, I., KELLER, J., KOBERSKI, U., STADLBAUER, E., FRANCALANCI, L. & LENHART, R. 1993. Geology, stratigraphy and volcanological evolution of the island of Stromboli, Aeolian Arc, Italy. *Acta Vulcanologica*, **3**, 21–68.

HUGHES, J. W., GUEST, J. E. & DUNCAN, A. M. 1990. Changing styles of effusive eruption on Mount Etna since AD 1600. *In*: RYAN, M. P. (ed.) *Magma Storage and Transport*. Wiley, Chichester, 385–406.

IMBO, G. 1928. Parossismo di Stromboli nel settembre 1930. *Bulletin Vulcanologique*, **15/18**, 177–185.

IMBO, G. 1951. Attivita eruttiva vesuviana e relative osservasioni dell'intervallo intereruttivo 1906–1944 ed in particolare del parossismo del Marzo 1944. *Annali Osservatorio Vesuviano Napoli (unico celebrativo del centenario dell'Osservatorio Vesuviano)*, **5**, 185–380.

JENKINS, I. D. & SLOAN, K. 1996. *Vases and Volcanoes: Sir William Hamilton and his Collection*. British Museum Press, London.

JOHNSTON-LAVIS, H. J. 1888. Futher notes on the late eruption of Vulcano Island. *Nature*, **39**, 109–111.

JOHNSTON-LAVIS, H. J. 1889*a*. *Report to the Committee Appointed for the Investigation of the Volcanic Phenomena of Vesuvius and its Neighbourhood*. British Association, London, 320–326.

JOHNSTON-LAVIS, H. J. 1889*b*. On a remarkable sodalite trachyte discovered in Naples, Italy. *Geological Magazine*, **140**, 939–944.

JOHNSTON-LAVIS, H. J. 1890. The eruption of Vulcano Island. *Nature*, **42**, 78–79.

JOHNSTON-LAVIS, H. J. 1909. The eruption of Vesuvius in April 1906. *Scientific Transactions of the Royal Dublin Society*, **9**(2), 139–200.

JOHNSTON-LAVIS, H. J. 1918. *Bibliography of the Geology and Eruptive Phenomena of the More Important Volcanoes of Southern Italy*. University of London Press, London.

JORON, J. L., METRICH, N., ROSI, M., SANTACROCE, R. & SBRANA, A. 1987. Chemistry and petrography. *In*: SANTACROCE, R. (ed.) *Somma Vesuvius*. CNR Quaderni de La Ricerca Scientifica, **114**, 105–174.

JUDD, J. W. 1888. *Volcanoes: What they Are and What they Teach*. Kegan Paul & Trench, London.

KAMENETSKY, V. & CLOCCHIATTI, R. 1996. Primitive magmatism of Mt. Etna: insights from mineralogy and melt inclusions. *Earth and Planetary Science Letters*, **142**, 553–572.

KELLER, J. 1980*a*. The Island of Vulcano. *Rendiconti Società Italiana di Mineralogia e Petrologia*, **36**, 369–414.

KELLER, J. 1980*b*. The island of Salina. *Rendiconti della Società Italiana die Mineralogia e Petrologia*, **36**, 489–524.

KELLER, J. 1981. Alkali basalts from the Tyrrhenian Sea Basin: magmatic and geodynamic significance. *Bulletin Volcanologique*, **44**, 327–337.

KELLER, J., Hornig-Kjarsgaard, I., Koberski, U., Stradlbauer, E. & Lenhart, R. 1993. *Geological Map of Stromboli*. CNR Gruppo Nazionale per la Vulcanologia, Pisa.

KIEFFER, G. 1973. Une éruption à caractères Katamaiens à l'origine de coulées ponceuses et al coulées responsable de la formation de la caldeira du Cratère Elliptique de l'Etna (Sicile). *Comptes rendus de l'Académie des Sciences*, **277D**, 2321–2324.

KIEFFER, G. 1977. Données nouvelles sur l'origine de la Valle del Bove et sa place dans l'histoire volcanologique de l'Etna. *Comptes rendus de l'Académie des Sciences*, **285**, 1391–1393.

KIEFFER, G. 1979. L'activité de L'Etna pendant les derniers 20 000 ans. *Comptes rendus de l'Académie des Sciences*, **288**, 1023–1026.

KIEFFER, G. & TANGUY, J. C. 1993. L'Etna: évolution structurale, magmatique et dynamique d'un volcan 'polygenique'. *Memoires de la Société Géologique de France*, **163**, 253–271.

KILBURN, C. R. J. & GUEST, J. E. 1993. Aa lavas of Mount Etna, Sicily. *In*: KILBURN, C. R. J. & LUONGO, G. (eds) *Active Lavas: Monitoring and Modelling*. UCL Press, London, 73–106.

KILBURN, C. J. & MCGUIRE, W. J. 2001. *Italian Volcanoes*. Terra, Harpenden.

KING, R. 1973. *Sicily*. David & Charles, Newton Abbot.

KING, R. 1987. *Italy*. Harper and Row, London.

KIRCHER, A. 1664. *Mundus Subterraneus*. Amsterdam.

KIRK, W. L., SIDDAL, R. & STEAD, S. 2000. The Johnston-Lavis collection: a unique record of Italian volcanism. *In*: McGuire, W. J., Griffiths, D. R., Hancock, P. L. & Stewart, I. S. (eds) *The Archaeology of Geological Catastrophes*. Geological Society, London, Special Publications, **171**, 189–194.

Klerkx, J. 1970. La caldera de la Valle del Bove: sa signification dans l'évolution de l'Etna (Sicile). *Bulletin Volcanologique*, **34**, 726–737.

Kokelaar, P. & Romagnoli, C. 1995. Sector collapse, sedimentation and clast population evolution at an active island-arc volcano: Stromboli, Italy. *Bulletin of Volcanology*, **57**, 240–262.

Krafft, M. 1993. *Volcanoes: Fire from the Earth*. Thames and Hudson, London.

Krafft, M. (with Bradley, S. & Newhall, C. G.) 1991. *Understanding Volcanic Hazards*. Northwest Interpretive Association, Castle Rock, WA (video).

Lantini, E., Lanzafame, G., Rossi, P. L., Tranne, C. A. & Calanchi, N. 1988. Vulcanesimo e tettonica nel Canale di Sicilia: l'isola di Linosa. *Mineralogische und Petrographische Acta*, **XXI**, 69–93.

Lanzafame, G., Rossi, G., Tranne, C. A & Lanti, E. 1994. *Carta geologica del'Isola di Linosa, 1:5000*. SELCA, Florence.

La Volpe, L. & Rapisardi, L. 1977. Osservazione geologiche sul versante meridionale del M Vulture: genesi ed evoluzione del bacino lacustre de Atella. *Bollettino della Societa Geologica Italiana*, **96**, 181–197.

La Volpe, L., Patella, D., Rapisardi, L. & Tramacere, A. 1984. The evolution of the Monte Vulture volcano (Southern Italy): inferences from volcanological, geological and deep dipole electrical soundings data. *Journal of Volcanology and Geothermal Research*, **22**, 147–162.

Le Maitre, R. W. (ed.) 1989. *A Classification of Igneous Rocks and Glossary of Terms. Recommendations of the IUGS Subcommission on the Systematics of Igneous Rocks*. Blackwell, Oxford.

Lentini, F. 1982. The geology of Mt. Etna basement. *In*: Romano, R. (ed.) *Mount Etna Volcano, a Review of Recent Earth Science Studies*. Memorie della Società Geologica Italiana, **23**, 7–26.

Lewis, N. 1978. *Naples '44*. Collins, London.

Lirer, L., Di Vito, M., Giacomelli, L., Scandone, R. & Vica, A. 1990. Contributo delle analisi granulometriche alla ricostruzione della dinamica dell'eruzione di Averno (Campi Flegrei). *Bollettino della Società Geologica Italiana*, **109**, 583–597.

Lirer, L., Luongo, G. & Scandone, R. 1987. On the volcanological evolution of Campi Flegrei. *EOS Transactions, American Geophysical Union*, **68**, 226–234.

Lirer, L., Munno, R., Petrosino, P. & Vinci, A. 1993. Tephrostratigraphy af the AD 79 pyroclastic deposits in perivolcanic areas of Mt. Vesuvio (Italy). *Journal of Volcanology and Geothermal Research*, **58**, 133–149.

Lirer, L., Munno, R., Petrosino, P. & Vinci, A. 1995. Tephrostratigraphy of the AD 79 pyroclastic deposits in perivolcanic areas of Mt. Vesuvio (Italy). *Journal of Volcanology and Geothermal Research*, **65**, 157–159.

Lirer, L., Munno, R., Postiglione, I., Vinci, A. & Vitelli, L. 1997. The AD 79 eruption as a future explosive scenario in the Vesuvian area: evaluation of associated risk. *Bulletin of Volcanology*, **59**, 112–124.

Lirer, L., Pescatore, T., Booth, B. & Walker, G. P. L. 1973. Two Plinian pumice fall deposits from Somma–Vesuvius, Italy. *Geological Society of America Bulletin*, **84**, 759–772.

Lirer, L., Rolandi, G. & Rubin, M. 1991. ^{14}C age of the 'Museum Breccia' (Campi Flegrei) and its relevance for the origin of the Campanian ignimbrite. *Journal of Volcanology and Geothermal Research*, **48**, 223–227.

Luhr, J. F. & Giannetti, B. 1987. The Brown Leucitic Tuff of Roccamonfina volcano (Roman region, Italy). *Contributions to Mineralogy and Petrology*, **95**, 420–436.

Lyell, Sir C. 1847. *Principles of Geology*, 7th edn. John Murray, London.

Lyell, Sir C. 1858. On the structure of lavas which have consolidated on steep slopes; with remarks on the mode of origin of Mount Etna, and on the theory of 'Craters-of Elevation'. *Philosophical Transactions of the Royal Society of London*, **148**, 703–786.

LYELL, Sir C. 1881. *Life, Letters and Journals of Charles Lyell, Bart.* John Murray, London (2 vols).

MACDONALD, G. A. 1972. *Volcanoes*. Prentice Hall, Englewood Cliffs, NJ.

MAHOOD, G. 1984. Pyroclastic rocks and calderas associated with strongly peralkaline magmatism. *Journal of Geophysical Research*, **89**, 8540–8552.

MAHOOD, G. & HILDRETH, W. 1986. Geology of the peralkaline volcano at Pantelleria, Strait of Sicily. *Bulletin of Volcanology*, **48**, 143–172.

MALINVERNO, A. & RYAN, W. B. F. 1986. Extension in the Tyrrhenian Sea and shortening in the Apennines as a result of arc migration driven by sinking of the lithosphere. *Tectonics*, **5**, 227–245.

MANETTI, P., PASQUARE, G., TIBALDI, A. & TSEGAYE, A. 1995*a*. Geology, structure and evolution of the island of Alicudi, AeolianVolcanic Arc, Italy. *Acta Vulcanologica*, **7**, 7–12.

MANETTI, P., PASQUARE, G., TIBALDI, A. & TSEGAYE, A. 1995*b*. *Carta Geologica delle Isole di Alicudi e Filicudi (Isole Eolie)*. CNR Gruppo Nazionale per La Vulcanologia, Pisa.

MANETTI, P., PASQUARE, G. & TSEGAYE, A. 1995*c*. A new geo-volcanological map of Filicudi Island (Aeolian Arc, Italy). *Acta Vulcanologica*, **7**, 1–5 (includes 1:10 000 map).

MASTROLORENZO, G. 1994. Averno tuff rings in Campi Flegrei (South Italy). *Bulletin of Volcanology*, **56**, 561–572.

MASTROLORENZO, G., MUNNO, R. & ROLANDI, G. 1993. Vesuvius 1906: a case study of a paroxysmal eruption and its relation to eruption cycles. *Journal of Volcanology and Geothermal Research*, **58**, 217–237.

MAZZUOLI, R., TORTORICI, L. & VENTURA, G. 1995. Oblique rifting in Salina, Lipari and Vulcano islands (Aeolian islands, southern Italy). *Terra Nova*, **7**, 444–452.

MCGUIRE, W. J. 1982. Evolution of the Etna volcano: information from the southern wall of the Valle del Bove Caldera. *Journal of Volcanology and Geothermal Research*, **13**, 241–271.

MCGUIRE, W. J. & PULLEN, A. 1989. Location and orientation of eruptive fissures and feeder dykes at Mount Etna: influence of gravitational and regional stress regime. *Journal of Volcanology and Geothermal Research*, **38**, 325–344.

MCGUIRE, W. J., KILBURN, C. R. J. & MURRAY, J. B. (eds) 1995. *Monitoring Active Volcanoes*. University College Press, London.

MCKENZIE, D. P. 1970. Plate tectonics of the Mediterranean region. *Nature*, **226**, 239–243.

MCKENZIE, D. 1977. Can plate tectonics describe continental deformation? *In*: BIJU-DUVAL, B. & MONTADENT, L. (eds) *Structural History of the Mediterranean Basins*. Technip, Paris, 189–197.

MERCALLI, G. & SILVESTRI, O. 1891. Le eruzioni dell'Isole di Vulcano, incominciate il 3 Agosto 1888 e terminate il 22 Marzo 1890. Relazione scientifica. *Annali Dell'Ufficio Centrale Meteorologico e Geodinamico Italiano*, **10**, 1–213.

MIDDLEMOST, E. A. K. 1997. *Magmas, Rocks and Planetary Development*. Longman, Harlow.

MILANO, G., VILARDO, G. & LUONGO, G. 1994. Continental collision and basin opening in southern Italy: a new plate subduction in the Tyrrhenian Sea. *Tectonophysics*, **230**, 249–264.

MIRABILE, L. 1998. An image of Mt. Vesuvius obtained by 2D seismic tomography. *Journal of Volcanology and Geothermal Research*, **82**, 161–173.

MORELLO, N. (ed.) 1998 *Volcanoes and History: Proceedings of the 20th INHIGEO Symposium, 19–25 September 1995*. Brigati, Genoa.

MURRAY, J. B. & GUEST, J. E. 1982. Vertical ground deformation on Mount Etna, 1975–1980. *Geological Society of America Bulletin*, **93**, 1160–1175.

MURRAY, J. B. & VOIGHT, B. 1996. Slope stability and eruption prediction on the eastern flank of Mount Etna. *In*: MCGUIRE, W. J., JONES, A. P. & NEUBERG (eds) *Volcano Instability on the Earth and other Planets*. Geological Society, London, Special Publications, **110**, 111–123.

NATALE, M. T. 1997. *Stromboli: the Abode of Aeolus*. Veant, Stromboli.

NEUBERG, J., LUCKETT, R., RIPEPE, M. & BRAUN, T. 1994. Highlights from a seismic broad-band array on Stromboli Volcano. *Geophysical Research Letters*, **21**, 749–752.

NEWHALL, C. G. & DZURISIN, D. 1988. *Historical Unrest at Large Calderas of the World.* US Geological Survey Bulletin, **1855**.

ORSI, G., D'ANTONIO, M., DE VITA, S. & GALLO, G. 1992*a*. The Neopolitan Yellow Tuff, a large magnitude trachyte phreatoplinian eruption: eruptive dynamics, magma withdrawal and caldera collapse. *Journal of Volcanology and Geothermal Research*, **53**, 275–287.

ORSI, G., DE VITA, S. & DI VITO, M. 1996*a*. The restless, resurgent Campi Flegrei nested caldera (Italy): constraints on its evolution and configuration. *Journal of Volcanology and Geothermal Research*, **74**, 179–214.

ORSI, G., GALLO, G. & ZANCHI, A. 1991*a*. Simple-shearing block resurgence in caldera depressions. A model from Pantelleria and Ischia. *Journal of Volcanology and Geothermal Research*, **47**, 1–11.

ORSI, G., GALLO, G., HEIKEN, G., WOHLETZ, K., YU, E. & BONANI, G. 1992*b*. A comprehensive study of the Cretaio Tephra of Ischia (Italy). *Journal of Volcanology and Geothermal Research*, **53**, 329–354.

ORSI, G., PIOCHI, M., CAMPAJOLA, L., D'ONOFRIO, A., GIALANELLA, L. & TERRASI, F. 1996*b*. ^{14}C geochronological constraints for the volcanic history of the island of Ischia (Italy) over the last 5000 years. *Journal of Volcanology and Geothermal Research*, **71**, 249–257.

ORSI, G., RUVO, L. & SCARPATI, C. 1991*b*. The recent explosive volcanism at Pantelleria. *Geologische Rundschau*, **80**, 187–200.

PASQUARE, G., FRANCALANCI, L., GARDUNO, V. H. & TIBALDI, A. 1993 Structure and geologic evolution of the Stromboli volcano. *Acta Volcanologica*, **3**, 79–89.

PATANÈ, D., PRIVITERA, E., FERRUCCI, F. & GRESTA, S. 1994. Seismic activity leading to the 1991–1993 eruption of Mt. Etna and its tectonic implications. *Acta Vulcanologica*, **4**, 47–55.

PECCERILLO, A. & WU, T. W. 1992. Evolution of calc-alkaline magmas in continental arc volcanoes: evidence from Alicudi, Aeolian Arc (southern Tyrrhenian Sea, Italy). *Journal of Petrology*, **33**, 1295–1315.

PECCERILLO, A., GUERRIERI, S., CARNESECCHI, F. & FRANCALANCHI, L. 1988. Genesi ed evoluzione dei magmi eoliani: nuovi dati sul vulcano di Alicudi. *Bollettino Gruppo Nazionale per La Vulcanologia (GNV)*, 443–456.

PECCERILLO, A., KEMPTON, P. D., HARMON, R. S., WU, T. W., SANTO, A. P., BOYCE, A. J. & TRIPODO, A. 1993. Petrological and geochemical characteristics of the Alicudi volcano, Aeolian islands, Italy: implications for magma genesis and evolution. *Acta Vulcanologica*, **3**, 235–249.

PERRET, F. A. 1916. The lava eruption of Stromboli, summer–autumn 1915. *American Journal of Science*, **192**, 443–463.

PERRET, F. A. 1924. *The Vesuvius Eruption of 1906: Study of a Volcanic Cycle*. Carnegie Institution Washington, **339**.

PERROTTA, A. 1992. *Evoluzione vulcanologia dei Campi Flegrei e dinamica dell'eruzione della Breccia Museo*. PhD thesis, University of Naples.

PERROTTA, A. & SCARPATI, C. 1994. The dynamics of the Breccia Museo eruption (Campi Flegrei, Italy) and the significance of spatter clasts associated with lithic breccias. *Journal of Volcanology and Geothermal Research*, **59**, 335–355.

PICHLER, H. 1980*a*. Geological map of the Island of Lipari. *Rendiconti della Società Italiana di Mineralogia e Petrologia*, **36** (inset map).

PICHLER, H. 1980*b*. The Island of Lipari. *Rendiconti della Società Italiana di Mineralogia e Petrologia*, **36**, 415–440.

PINKERTON, H. & SPARKS, R. S. J. 1976. The 1975 sub-terminal lavas, Mount Etna: a case history of the formation of compound lava field. *Journal of Volcanology and Geothermal Research*, **1**, 167–182.

PINKERTON, H. & SPARKS, R. S. J. 1978. Field measurements of the rheology of lava. *Nature*, **276**, 383–384.

POLI, S., CHIESA, S., GILOT, P.-Y., GUCHARD, F. & VEZZOLI, L. 1989. Time dimension in the geochemical approach and hazard estimates of a volcanic area: the isle of Ischia case. *Journal of Volcanology and Geothermal Research*, **36**, 327–335.

RADICE, B. 1963. *The Letters of the Younger Pliny*. Penguin, Harmondsworth.

RAMAGNOLI, C., KOKELAAR, P. & ROSSI, P. L. 1993. The submarine extension of Sciara del Fuoco feature (Stromboli Island): morphological classification. *Acta Vulcanologica*, **3**, 91–98.

RASA, R., AZZARO, R. & LEONARDI, O. 1996. Aseismic creep on faults and flank instability at Mount Etna volcano, Sicily. *In*: MCGUIRE, W.J, JONES, A. P. & NEUBERG, J. (eds) *Volcano Instability on the Earth and Other Planets*. Geological Society, London, Special Publications, **110**, 179–192.

RITTMANN, A. 1930. Geologie der Insel Ischia. *Zeitschrift für Vulkanologie*, **6**.

RITTMANN, A. 1931. Der Ausbruch des Stromboli am 11 September 1930. *Zeitschrift für Vulkanologie*, **14**, 47–77.

RITTMANN, A. 1950*a*. Sintesi geologica dei Campi Flegrei. *Bollettino della Società Geologica Italiana*, **69**, 117–128.

RITTMANN, A. 1950*b*. Rilevamento geologico della collina di Camaldoli nei Campi Flegrei. *Bollettino della Società Geologica Italiana*, **69**, 1–129.

RITTMANN, A. 1962. *Volcanoes and their Activity* (translated from the 2nd German edition by E. A. Vincent). Wiley, New York.

RITTMANN, A. 1967. Studio geovulcanologico e magmatalogico dell'Isola di Pantelleria. *Rivista Mineraria Siciliana*, **106/108**, 147–182.

RITTMANN, A. 1973. Structure and evolution of Mount Etna. *Philosophical Transactions of the Royal Society of London, Series A*, **274**, 5–16.

RITTMANN, A., ROMANO, R. & STURIALE, C. 1971. L'eruzione etnea dell'aprile–giugno 1971. *Atti dell'Accademia Gioenia di Scienze Naturali Catania*, **7**, 1–28.

ROBERTSON, A. H. F. & GRASSO, M. 1995. Overview of the late Tertiary–Recent tectonic and palaeo-environmental development of the Mediterranean region. *Terra Nova*, **7**, 114–127.

ROBSON, G. R. 1967. Thickness of Etnean lavas. *Nature*, **216**, 251–252.

ROLANDI, G., BARRELLA, A. M. & BORRELLI, A. 1993*a*. The 1631 AD eruption of Vesuvio. *Journal of Volcanology and Geothermal Research*, **58**, 183–201.

ROLANDI, G., MASTROLORENZO, G., BARRELLA, A. M. & BORRELLI, A. 1993*b*. The Avellino Plinian eruption of Somma–Vesuvius (3760 y BP): the progressive evolution from magmatic to hydromagmatic style. *Journal of Volcanology and Geothermal Research*, **58**, 43–65.

ROLANDI, G., PETROSINO, P. & MCGEEHIN, J. 1998. The interplinian activity at Somma–Vesuvius in the last 3500 years. *Journal of Volcanology and Geothermal Research*, **82**, 19–52.

ROMAGNOLI, C., KOKELAAR, P., ROSSI, P. L. & SODI, A. 1993. The submarine extension of Sciara del Fuoco feature (Stromboli isl.): morphologic characterization. *Acta Vulcanologica*, **3**, 91–98.

ROMANO, R. 1968. New petrochemical data of volcanites from the island of Pantelleria (Channel of Sicily). *Geologische Rundschau*, **57**, 773–783.

ROMANO, R. 1973. Le Isole di Panarea e Basiluzzo. Contributo alla conoscenza geo-vulcanologica e magmatologica delle Isole Eolie. *Rivista Minerario Sicilia*, **24**(139–141), 3–39.

ROMANO, R. (ed.) 1982. *Mount Etna Volcano, a Review of Recent Earth Science Studies*. Memorie della Società Geologica Italiana, **23**.

ROMANO, R. 1991. *Mt. Etna: carta naturalistica e turistica, 1:60,000*. Club Alpino Italiano. Società Elaborazioni Cartografiche, Florence.

ROMANO, R. & GUEST, J. E. 1979. Volcanic geology of the summit and northern flank of Mount Etna, Sicily. *Bolletino della Società Geologica Italiana*, **98**, 189–215.

ROMANO, R. & STURIALE, C. 1971. L'Isola di Ustica. *Rivista Mineraria Siciliana*, **XXII**, 3–61.

ROMANO, R. & STURIALE, C. 1975. Geologia della Tavoletta 'Monte Etna Sud' (F. 262–IIISO). *Bolletino della Società Geologica Italiana*, **98**, 189–215.

ROMANO, R. & STURIALE, C. 1982. The historical eruptions of Mt. Etna (volcanological data). *In*: ROMANO, R. (ed.) *Mount Etna Volcano, a Review of Recent Earth Science Studies*. Memorie della Società Geologica Italiana, **23**, 75–97.

ROMANO, R., STURIALE, C. & LENTINI, F. 1979. *Carta Geologica del Monte Etna: 1:50,000*. Consiglio Nazionale Delle Ricerche (CNR), Progetto Finalizzato Geodinamica, Catania.

ROSI, M. 1980. The island of Stromboli. *Rendiconti della Società Italiana di Mineralogia e Petrologia*, **36**, 1–24.

ROSI, M. & SANTACROCE, R. 1983. The AD 472 'Pollena' eruption: volcanological and petrological data for this poorly known plinian-type event at Vesuvius. *Journal of Volcanology and Geothermal Research*, **17**, 249–271.

ROSI, M. & SBRANA, A. (eds) 1987. *Phlegraean Fields*. Consiglio Nazionale delle Ricerche, Quaderni de La Ricerca Scientifica, **114**(9) (includes a geological map).

ROSI, M., BERTAGNINI, A. & LANDI, P. 2000. Onset of the persistent activity at Stromboli Volcano (Italy). *Bulletin of Volcanology*, **62**, 294–300.

ROSI, M., PRINCIPE, C. & VECCI, R. 1993. The 1631 eruption of Vesuvius reconstructed from the review of chronicles and study of deposits. *Journal of Volcanology and Geothermal Research*, **58**, 151–182.

ROSI, M., SBRANA, A. & PRICIPE, C. 1983. The Phlegraean Field: structural evolution, volcanic history and eruptive mechanisms. *Journal of Volcanology and Geothermal Research*, **17**, 273–288.

ROSI, M., VEZZOLI, L., CASTEL'MENZANO, A. & GRIECO, G. 1999. Plinian pumice fall deposits of the Campanian ignimbrite eruption (Phlegrean Fields, Italy) *Journal of Volcanology and Geothermal Research*, **91**, 179–198.

ROURE, F., HOWELL, D. G., MÜLLER, C. & MORETTI, I. 1990. Late Cenozoic subduction complex of Sicily. *Journal of Structural Geology*, **12**, 259–266.

RYMER, H., CASSIDY, J., LOCKE, C. A. & MURRAY, J. B. 1995. Magma movements in Etna volcano associated with the major 1991–1993 lava eruption: evidence from gravity and deformation. *Bulletin of Volcanology*, **57**, 451–461.

SANTACROCE, R. (ed.) 1987. Somma–Vesuvius. Consiglio Nazionale delle Ricerche, Quaderni de 'La Ricerca Scientifica', Roma, **114**(8) (includes a geological map).

SANTACROCE. R. 1996. Preparing Naples for Vesuvius. *IAVCEI News*, **1**(2), 5–7.

SANTO, A. P. 2000. Volcanological and geochemical evolution of Filicudi (Aeolian Islands, south Tyrrhenian Sea, Italy). *Journal of Volcanology and Geothermal Research*, **96**, 79–101.

SANTO, A. P., CHEN, Y., CLARK, A. H., FARRAR, E. & TSEGAYE, A. 1995. 40Ar/39Ar ages of the Filicudi volcanics: implications for the volcanological history of the Aeolian Arc, Italy. *Acta Vulcanologica*, **7**, 13–18.

SARTORIUS VON WALTERSHAUSEN, W. 1880. *Der Aetna. Nach den Manuskripten des Verstorbenen herausgegeben von A. von Lasaulx*. W. Engelmann, Leipzig (2 vols).

SCANDONE, R., BELLUCCI, F., LIRER, L. & ROLANDI, G. 1991. The structure of the Campanian Plain and the activity of the Neopolitan volcanoes (Italy). *Journal of Volcanology and Geothermal Research*, **48**, 1–31.

SCARPA, R. & TILLING, R. I. (eds) 1996. *Monitoring and Mitigation of Volcanic Hazards*. Springer, Berlin.

SCARPATI, C. 1990. *Stratigrafia, geochimica e dinamica errruttiva del Tufo Giallo Napoletano*. PhD thesis, University of Naples.

SCARPATI, C., COLE, P. D. & PERROTTA, A. 1993. The Neopolitan Yellow Tuff—a large volume multiphase eruption from Campi Flegrei, Southern Italy. *Bulletin of Volcanology*, **55**, 343–356.

SCARTH, A. 1994. *Volcanoes*. UCL Press, London.

SCARTH, A. 1999. *Vulcan's Fury: Man against the Volcano*. Yale University Press, New Haven, CT.

SCARTH, A. & TANGUY, J.-C. 2001. *Volcanoes of Europe*. Terra, Harpenden.

SERRI, G. 1990. Neogene–Quaternary magmatism of the Tyrrhenian region: characterization of the magma sources and geodynamic implications. *Memorie della Società Geologica Italiana*, **41**, 219–242.

SHARP, A. D. L., DAVIS, P. M. & GRAY, F. 1980. A low velocity zone beneath Mount Etna and magma storage. *Nature*, **287**, 587–591.

SHERIDAN, M. F., FRAZZETA, G. & LA VOLPE, L. 1987. Eruptive histories of Lipari and Vulcano, Italy, during the past 22,000 years. *In*: FINK, J. H. (ed.) *The Emplacement of Silicic Domes and Lava Flows*. Geological Society of America, Special Paper, **272**, 29–33.

SIGURDSSON, H. 1999. *Melting the Earth: The History of Ideas on Volcanic Eruptions*. Oxford University Press, New York.

SIGURDSSON, H., CAREY, S., CORNELL, W. & PESCATORE, T. 1985. The eruption of Vesuvius in AD 79. *National Geographic Research*, **1**(3), 332–387.

SIGURDSSON, H., HOUGHTON, B., MCNUTT, S. R., RYMER, H. & STIX, J. 2000. *Encyclopedia of Volcanoes*. Academic Press, San Diego, CA.

STOPPA, F. & PRINCIPE, C. 1998. Eruption style and petrology of a new carbonatitic suite from the Mt. Vulture (Southern Italy): the Monticchio Lakes Formation. *Journal of Volcanology and Geothermal Research*, **80**, 137–153.

TAMBURELLI, C., BABBUCCI, D. & MANTOVANI, E. 2000. Geodynamic implications of 'subduction related' magmatism: insights from the Tyrrhenian–Apennines region. *Journal of Volcanology and Geothermal Research*, **104**, 33–43.

TANGUY, J.-C. 1978. Tholeiitic basalt magmatism at Mount Etna and its relations with the alkaline series. *Contributions to Mineralogy and Petrology*, **66**, 51–67.

TANGUY, J.-C. 1981. Les éruptions historiques de l'Etna: chronologie et localisation. *Bulletin Volcanologique*, **44**, 585–640.

TANGUY, J.-C., CONDOMINES, M. & KIEFFER, G. 1997. Evolution of the Mount Etna magma: constraints on the present feeding system and eruptive mechanism. *Journal of Volcanology and Geothermal Research*, **75**, 221–250.

TAYLOR, H. P., GIANNETTI, B. & TURI, B. 1979. Oxygen isotope geochemistry of the potassic igneous rocks from the Roccamonfina volcano, Roman comagmatic region, Italy. *Earth and Planetary Science Letters*, **46**, 81–106.

TEDESCO, D., ALLARD, P., SANO, Y., WAKITA, H. & PECE, A. 1990. Helium-3 in subaerial and submarine fumaroles of Campi Flegrei Caldera, Italy. *Geochimica et Cosmochimica Acta*, **54**, 1105–1116.

TIBALDI, A. 2001. Multiple sector collapses at Stromboli volcano, Italy: how they work. *Bulletin of Volcanology*, **63**,112–125.

TIBALDI, A. & VEZZOLI, L. 1998. The space problem of caldera resurgence: an example from Ischia Island, Italy. *Geologische Rundschau*, **87**, 53–66.

TINTI, S., BORTOLUCCI, E. & ROMAGNOLI, C. 2000. Computer simulations of tsunamis due to sector collapse at Stromboli, Italy. *Journal of Volcanology and Geothermal Research*, **96**, 103–128.

TONARINI, S., ARMIENTI, P., D'ORAZIO, M., INNOCENTI, F., POMPILIO, M. & PETRINI, R. 1995. Geochemical and isotopic monitoring of Mt. Etna 1989–1993 eruptive activity: bearing on the shallow feeding system. *Journal of Volcanology and Geothermal Research*, **64**, 95–115.

TREVELYAN, R. 1976. *The Shadow of Vesuvius: Pompeii AD 79*. Folio Society, London.

TURCO, E. & ZUPPETTA, A. 1998. A kinematic model for the Plio-Quaternary evolution of the Tyrrhenian–Apenninic system: implications for rifting processes and volcanism. *Journal of Volcanology and Geothermal Research*, **82**, 1–18.

VENTURA, G. 1994. Tectonics, structural evolution and caldera formation on Vulcano island (Aeolian Archipelago, southern Tyrrhenian Sea). *Journal of Volcanology and Geothermal Research*, **60**, 207–224.

VEZZOLI, L. (ed.). 1988. *The Island of Ischia*. Consiglio Nationale delle Ricerche, Quaderni de 'La Ricerca Scientifica' Roma, **114**(10).

VILLARI, L. 1968. On the geovolcanological and morphological evolution of an endogenous dome (Pantelleria, Mt. Gelkhamar). *Geologische Rundschau*, **57**, 784–795.

VILLARI, L. 1969. On particular ignimbrites of the Island of Pantelleria (Channel of Sicily). *Bulletin Volcanologique*, **33**, 1–12.

VILLARI, L. 1970. The caldera of Pantelleria. *Bulletin Volcanologique*, **34**(3), 1–9.

VILLARI, L. 1974. The island of Pantelleria. *Bulletin Volcanologique*, **38**, 680–724.

VILLARI, L. 1980*a*. The island of Alicudi. *Rendiconti della Società Italiana di Mineralogia e Petrologia*, **36**, 441–446.

VILLARI, L. 1980*b*. Carta geologica dell'Isola di Filicudi. *Rendiconti della Società Italiana di Mineralogia e Petrologia*, **36**.

VILLARI, L. 1980*c*. The island of Filicudi. *Rendiconti della Società Italiana di Mineralogia e Petrologia*, **36**, 467–488.

VILLARI, L. & NAPPI, G. 1975. *Carta Geologica dell'Isola di Alicudi (Isole Eolie)*. Istituto Internazionale di Vulcanologia, CNR Catania.

VINCIGUERRA, S., LATORA, V., BICCIATO, S. & KANIMURA, R. T. 2001. Identifying and discriminating seismic patterns leading flank eruptions at Mt. Etna Volcano during 1981–1996. *Journal of Volcanology and Geothermal Research*, **106**, 211–228.

VOLLMER, R. & HAWKESWORTH, C. J. 1980. Lead isotope composition of potassic rocks from Roccamonfina (south Italy). *Earth and Planetary Science Letters*, **47**, 91–101.

WADGE, G. 1977. The storage and release of magma on Mount Etna. *Journal of Volcanology and Geothermal Research*, **2**, 361–384.

WALKER, G. P. L. 1967. Thickness and viscosity of Etnean lavas. *Nature*, **213**, 484–485.

WALKER, G. P. L. 1973. Lengths of lava flows. *Philosphical Transactions of the Royal Society of London, Series A*, **274**, 107–118.

WASHINGTON, H. S. 1906. *The Roman Comagmatic Region*. Publications of the Carnegie Institution, **57**.

WASHINGTON, H. S. 1909. The submarine eruptions of 1831 and 1891 near Pantelleria. *American Journal of Science*, **27**, 131–150.

WASHINGTON, H. S. 1913. The volcanoes and rocks of Pantelleria. *Journal of Geology*, **21**, 683–713.

WASHINGTON, H. S. 1914. The volcanoes and rocks of Pantelleria. *Journal of Geology*, **22**, 16–27.

WASHINGTON, H. S., AUROUSSEAU, M. & KEYES, M. G. 1926. The lavas of Etna. *American Journal of Science*, **12**, 371–408.

WILLIAMS, H. 1941. Calderas and their origin. University of California Publications, Bulletin of the Department of Geological Sciences, **25**, 239–346.

WILSON, L. & WALKER, G. P. L. 1987. Explosive volcanic eruptions. IV: Ejecta dispersal in plinian eruptions: the control of eruption conditions of atmospheric properties. *Geophysical Journal of the Royal Astronomical Society*, **89**, 651–678.

WRIGHT, J. V. 1980. Stratigraphy and geology of the welded air-fall tuffs of Pantelleria, Italy. *Geologische Rundschau*, **69**, 263–291.

ZOLLO, A., GASPARINI, P., *et al.* 1998. An image of Mt. Vesuvius obtained by 2D seismic tomography. *Journal of Volcanology and Geothermal Research*, **82**, 161–174.

Index

Numbers in **bold** refer to plates. Page numbers in *italic* refer to figures